The Late Liz

THE
LATE LIZ

The Autobiography of an Ex-Pagan

by
Elizabeth Burns

Appleton-Century-Crofts
New York

Third Printing, March, 1962

Library of Congress Card Number: 57-7207

PRINTED IN THE UNITED STATES OF AMERICA

For my two sons

The Late Liz

CHAPTER ONE

This is the story of me, Liz Burns; what I used to be like, what happened, and what I am like now. It would be a vast relief to skip what I used to be like and start with today but there's no point telling what happened unless you give some picture of the person it happened to.

Suppose it got rumored about that a woman had died and then risen from the dead, would you believe it? I think not. Look at the trouble Jesus Christ had. You'd want proof. You'd have to hear how she died and what of, and above all you'd have to be convinced she actually did die, before you could hope to get set for the resurrection.

Death isn't so cut and dried as it sounds. In looking back I see now that life is a series of small deaths. For example, some of me died when, very young, I accepted the fact that my father hated my mother. Some of me died each time I sat on the sidelines wondering what secrets you had to know to get boys to dance with you. And then a great chunk of me died the first night of my first marriage. After that, it was death after death. There is only one resurrection but a lot of inch-by-inch dying.

Right now, at the beginning, I might as well state that this trip is to Skid Row and gone. The Skid Row with silk sheets. If you're the Holy Joe type, it could shock you straight out of your halo. On the other hand, if you belong to the Don't Give A Damn Society, bored with God and suchlike, you'd better know that sooner or later you're going to meet God too because He's here both ways—blasphemously, and in all His might and splendor. There's God and sex. He Who made us and we who make a mess of ourselves.

That's how this trip goes and that's how I plan to tell it. Facts, for once. Liz Burns is sick and tired of fuzz, fuzz about sin and more fuzz about God. As someone put it, you finally get sick and tired of being sick and tired.

Like the average female I was born with one head, two ears, and no tail to speak of. Unlike the average I was born of man. A mother fluttered in the offing but merely as a spectator. Father was the works. Sam Burns was to me what Whistler's mother was to him. He was tall and rawboned, had a Scotch burr, a red mustache and an awful gift for coining money. Awful because it made him conclude he knew everything else too. And he did almost. But not how to bring up a daughter.

Liz Burns was not brought up, she was made up, the ingredients being whatever Sam had yearned for and never got. Let it not be said however that he wasn't generous. He gave his daughter brains, and told her what to think; he gave her lungs and told her when to breathe; he gave her eyes and told her where to look.

A dummy, not a daughter. A gray-eyed, blond-haired dummy who was to go de luxe, prepaid. For Sam's kid, the sky was not the limit and the best was second rate.

"Knowledge, kid. College degrees, a doctor of philosophy. Travel, fame—find a cure for cancer, kid. For Christ's sake, use your *brain!*"

For Christ's sake indeed. For Sam's sake. For the sake of a Scotch farm boy who came over in the steerage and had to quit school at nine.

Never was there any time to waste on folderol like a home. Sam'l Burns, wife, child, and additional belongings, lived at the old Waldorf Astoria in New York City. A suite of high-ceilinged cells padded in mauve satin damask, every inch of wall space crammed with the tortured mahogany carvings of the era. Settees, tables, desks, whatnots. Homey like W. & J. Sloane Co.

In retrospect my childhood seems to have been spent perched on slippery brocade, fingers clutching, feet dangling. Eventually the brocade held tutors, every hour on the hour. The tutors came in assorted sexes, shapes and nationalities: "Nothing like speaking to a guy in his own lingo, kid."

Other children started school at six. Other children—

"Six? Goddam poppycock—you've no time to waste!"

There was to be no time for marriage either. Marriage was for fools, fools like Mother. Willowy sweet-smelling fools with enormous black eyes in creamy magnolia faces. Oil paintings would teeter and damask walls belch in and out from Sam's earth-shattering oaths against the holy state of matrimony; god-god-damning.

Brains were the ticket. Anybody could have a magnolia face, whereas *brains*—

I was not so sure. I used to look in the mirror and look at Mother and wonder. She was beautiful and aside from the quarrels I was beginning to overhear, she appeared to lead a lovely life. No being cornered, no questions, no proofs. Mother could say it was going to rain and nothing came of it but let me say it was going to rain and hell broke loose: "What makes you think so? Why? Can you prove it?"

Father was obsessed by logic. Many's the time I've fallen from chairs only to be lifted back, propped up, and cross-examined again because I had been unable to find an accurate reason for some unthinking comment. It sounds cruel, but then all obsessions can be. This was Sam's kid and not only was she his proxy, she was, from the beginning, a test case.

3

The day of my birth he did, for him, a Scotsman, a very odd thing. He had left the hospital and was passing St. Patrick's Cathedral when suddenly he whirled and went inside. It was dark and quiet there, in between services. He slipped into a back pew and sitting there, he started to think about women. He thought about Mother and about all the other illogical women; women whose response when cornered was: "Oh, you just *don't* under*stand.*" Then he thought about me, this brand-new four-hour-old woman. Without realizing what he was doing Sam slid partway to his knees. Hitting the pew in front of him with a clenched fist, he said out loud: "By God, *let's You and me bring up one woman who can reason!*"

It was a dedication.

Mother's luck was based on the fact that she was "hopeless." After you'd been thoroughly tested and found hopeless, you were let off the hook. You were free to read novels, to go to matinées and tea parties, to buy piles of rustly clothes. You had time to burn, time even to smuggle your child a kiss when Father's back was turned.

It is my ears and nose and eyes that remember Mother. I'd be in bed when all at once my ears would hear a *swoosh, swoosh.* Next my nose would pick up the scent of flowers, and in a moment there she was in the doorway, a finger on her lips. I could never understand why she was always saying: "Sh-h." Both of us knew this was a conspiracy; Sam was shaving but we both knew he shaved fast.

She would stand by my bed.

"Sh-h, sleep well, Elizabeth—" (She didn't call me Liz. Liz was vulgar.)

I'd fling my arms out. "Mama, you look so beautiful—is your dress *silver?* Where are you going—how *lovely* you smell! Oh, Mama—"

"Don't muss me, child. Hannah will be in soon. There. Lie back, sh-h. Sleep well."

4

The *swoosh, swoosh* would fade away till finally only the scent of flowers remained. My room would have turned into a garden and I'd lie there, sniffing deep, wondering what it would be like to be like Mama.

Hannah had come to us when I was seven. By then Sam was pretty rich and rich men's wives, especially handsome ones, require jewels and wardrobes and someone to look after them; Mother was "hopeless" but she had her uses to Sam. She and Hannah and the elegance belonged to a way of life and could be written off to advertising.

Hannah was far more than Mother's maid. She was my friend. She arrived right after I'd had a bout with typhoid fever, emerging from it with not a single hair above the eyebrows. I can see her exactly as I first saw her. Lank, sparse, ageless, with screwed-up hair and nose glasses. Father had introduced her as Miss Hannah Gundersen. She stood there in the brocade drawing room, a tidy island surrounded by carved claws and bowknots and cupids. She held out a hand.

"Good afternoon, Elizabeth," she said. "How are you?"

"I'm bald, thank you," I replied. "How are you?"

The answer pleased Father. He slapped a thigh and roared: "The kid's honest, by God! When something's wrong, she tells you."

The woman ignored him. She stooped down and spoke to me alone: "That must be very uncomfortable. But the new hair may be nicer—perhaps we could have a wig made. What color would you like?"

I appreciated that this was meant well, yet somehow I did not want a wig. The only hair I really liked was Mother's and it was white. Not old-white, a glistening silver-white that shimmered like the lovely ornaments on Christmas trees. I knew however that I was much too young for white so I said: "I guess I'll just have to wait and take my chances. Thank you very much though."

Sam roared again: "Don't talk rot. She's right—we'll get the best goddam wig in New York City!"

Hannah saw my face. What she saw made her speak to Sam as I had never heard anyone speak before.

"No, Mr. Burns," she said. "Elizabeth does not care for wigs. And I always say my friends have the right to look the way they want to look."

A friend? I'd never had a friend!

Well, I had one now. Hannah slept in the bed across from mine in my enormous bedroom. On one bureau was her hand-painted dresser set, her gray flannel pincushion, a group of small framed photographs of nieces and nephews in Norway whom I grew up to know intimately. And on her night stand was her Bible and a fresh-folded handkerchief. It was a great comfort.

Between our room and Father's and Mother's there was a tomblike bathroom. It was through here that I would overhear Father's voice and know my parents were quarreling again. The quarrels were coming closer all the time, so close that often they overlapped. In the middle of the night I'd wake up, raise myself on an elbow, trying to hear, trying not to hear.

I'd start shaking for if the mean talk lasted long enough, some strange unknown thing came creeping through the bathroom to wait outside our door. And it didn't always stay outside. Sometimes it crept in through the closed door and tried to grab me and when this happened I would scream and run to Hannah. Hannah always held me till I stopped shaking. She always said: "Now, now, say that prayer I taught you. Say 'Gentle Jesus,' and you'll go back to sleep."

In the three years ending in my parent's divorce Hannah Gundersen was the one completely sane being in that well-upholstered rat cage. Hannah and her Bible.

I never did hear the details of that divorce. Quarrel piled on quarrel; oaths, shouts, tears, moans, and then one day it was

6

quiet. Yesterday we were four people in a rat cage, and today Mother is being shipped somewhere and I somewhere else. It seems Mother is going to California and I to Switzerland, to a new cage, a series of them. I rarely saw my mother again.

And now if you'd care to drop a tear, this is the place for it. Recently I unearthed a cracked yellow photograph of Liz-on-board-ship, off to Europe alone. ("Make you independent, kid.") Independent—hah. That kid is scared silly. The eyes bulge, the lips are a rigid line, the jaw is locked, hoping to make like Mme. Curie. ("—a cure for cancer, kid.")

Europe lasted for eight years. Eight strait-jacket years of brain-pummeling, of weary mile on mile of churches, of art galleries, of scenery, in French, in German, in Italian. Of regimentation, especially at vacation time when Sam was on hand to be certain not one hour was wasted. Eight years of heart-stifling, of changing from a child to a woman in a foreign language under some prissy schoolmarm. Care without love. Growth without roots.

Maybe you fancy stuff like this. Maybe you think it's culture on a silver platter. Maybe you consider it too too cosmopolitan. Well, it wasn't. It was about as cosmopolitan as Alcatraz. By the time the first world war blasted me back home to college I was no more than a rubber stamp in English tweeds.

So don't think Smith College wasn't heady business. Here were girls who actually dared to say no, when they felt no. Who dared to dress as they liked, fix their hair as they liked, who even knew a boy or two. Liberation all over the place—have some, Liz?

Have some? The first two years I dipped with an increasingly larger spoon and the third year I dove in, head first. On one crunchy winter day Liz The Brain heard a call from across the street, gave a startled look, took a deep gulp, and commenced the very career Sam hated most. Liz walked out and began marrying. And it was not guts nor anything similar. It

7

was reflex, pure reflex, warning that wherever I landed, it must not be where Sam wanted or I would land alone in a padded cell.

That first marriage I took what turned up and the wonder is it wasn't worse. It hove from the right side of the Hartford, Connecticut, tracks; it had gold curls and a raccoon coat and a red Stutz to go with it. Strictly F. Scott Fitzgerald. Too strictly but who was I to guess that? Randall Trowbridge was precisely what he sounds, the prize of 1917, and nary a girl at Smith who wouldn't have swooned at him. The truth, so help me.

As I recall the 1917 model of myself, as appetizing as long winter underwear, I think I should revise Randy. Surely he must have been dumber than he was. Here was I, the girl who'd never heard she had a body, and certainly no tricks at all, not one measly trick. The wallflower never seriously sniffed at, the virgin to end virgins, each button buttoned. And up rolls golden Galahad to jam on the brakes and cry: "Who's that? No—*that* one. The one with the funny black eyebrows—"

Me? My God!

How do you figure it? Was it chemistry? But can chemistry cross a street? Can it drag a spoiled worldly youth out of a car and into a house to corner a tongue-tied girl who'd never inspired a wolf call and never hoped to? It did though. It did just that; lightning striking the most secluded, most sheltered, most unlikely spot.

Randall was incredibly handsome. He followed me into the hall of the house where I was living, while I cowered in the dark library and stared out at him, recognizing that never before had I seen complete beauty. He stood under a hall light which shone down on the bronze curls. The hair was cut close, probably in a useless effort to disguise the curls. It was his profile, however, which enthralled one, a profile as cleanly etched as those found on old Greek coins.

Two girls were with him, friends of mine. They were twittering. "She's got to be here somewhere—Liz," they twittered.

He had not spoken. Now he said: "Don't tell me her name —don't talk!"

I stood transfixed. And at that very moment he raised his head and looked straight at me. Before I could hope to pretend to collect myself, he had walked into the library, holding my eyes with eyes of the bluest blue you can imagine; the color of cornflowers except richer, deeper. When he came close I saw that the cheekbones were high, yet not too high. The nose was bold and below it the lips were full and curving and the jaw line was strong and perfect.

The two girls had remained in the hall. They'd stopped twittering and there wasn't a sound. Now he stood close to me, was looking down at me, saying: "I don't want this to worry you. Don't let it bother you or upset you in any way, but some day, I'm going to marry you."

Liz The Brain was a mouse and the mouse was bewitched and stayed bewitched. Sam Burns never had a chance. He was a pigmy, roaring on some far-off shore. Enraged, threatening, swallowing himself whole, except for his checkbook, Sam might have been six feet under, and knew it, knew it well. So, rather than forfeit the one thing he truly loved, Father paid and paid. And waited.

Had he been wise instead of shrewd, had he beckoned instead of shoved—but Sam is long dead now and presumably knows better than I.

Odd that of all the hundred violent storms, it should be the squalls that stand out clearest. Randy was forever sending orchids and I seem to remember that it was this that drove Sam craziest: "Kee-rist, more orchids—up to your neck now!"

By June the lovely fantasy was over. Come June, a crowded church, flower hung. ("If you've got to do it, do it right.") Ten chiffon bridesmaids, one chiffon maid of honor; ten ascoted

9

ushers, one ascoted best man. Come June, unlikely Liz quivered beside King Arthur's boy, vowing to forsake all others. (*What* others?)

At this point it would be delightful to pull the first blank. To pretend the next five years didn't exist, to call them a nightmare. Nightmares aren't expected to make sense—it was cucumbers, no doubt. You get caught up in a purple madhouse and you sweat your way out and it's over, thank God. Well, now maybe that's what this was—the description fits. We'll make it a nightmare. On me.

The switch from idyllic fantasy to realistic nightmare is split-second. The props have vanished as though they had not been. *Whisk* to the murmurs, music, moonlight; *whisk* to the man with the face of an angel; to the girl with stars for eyes. Gone. No premonition, no preamble. The nightmare has begun.

In this nightmare there are two central figures, heroic-sized, outlined against a lurid backdrop. A bull and a virgin, one advancing, one retreating. Present is a feeling that the bull has been alerted for a long time, has strained at some unseen, perhaps inherited stake which bound him. Now at last he is freed.

It is obvious that the virgin has not ever actually seen him. The virgin has been looking up and now she must look down and what she sees appears obscene, profoundly grotesque in its unfamiliarity. Body rigid, she shudders. Then violence is upon her. Violence with no hint of the tenderness King Arthur's knight had promised. Weighted down and down and down, the virgin's heart bursts, and from deep within there is a tearing, ripping sound as though a thing she did not know she had is being torn from her. A grabbing, thrusting, stomping at the very roots of a thing too fragile, too dormant, to guess its own existence.

The nightmare continues year on year, a contest macabre.

The one ever advancing, taking, doing what he has to do; the other, doing what she has to do, retreating, ever retreating. Underlying the early state of shock, and later a consummate distaste, there mounts a strange corroding shame. In the virgin's secret heart she has remained a virgin and yet she understands that in this act there is a part she is expected to fulfill. She cannot fulfill this part but notwithstanding this, the knowledge that she has failed is close to heartbreak. Failure is an old companion, better known to her than most.

There; that's done. Two paragraphs to mark five years. To tell it otherwise, this heartache for Randy, this for Liz; indignity, frustration, tears, suspicion, jealousy, accusations, a small blunt revolver, wild repentance, undying promises, fresh starts, quick failure, rivers of tears, more repentance, more promises, shame, guilt, lies, apathy, would drag this out and spew forth nothing new.

Curtain to curtain it is the same old story. The jaded pulp routine in which the gal runs from pa to wed the knight in shining armor and lo, when the knight takes off the armor, he ain't no knight.

It took much misery and many years for me to appreciate something of the frustration Randall Trowbridge must have endured. As I experienced other men and other husbands, occasionally I marveled that Randy had not killed me. As I chewed life into bits, I came to know too well that unrehearsed wedding nights are seldom perfect.

Sex is a duet, not to be picked up overnight. Divorce courts are way behind because a violet is a violet is a violet, rarely a Tiger Lily, and a bed-technician is a whore is a whore is a whore, rarely a buttoned-up virgin. A virgin can become a technician, sure, but this takes time. Time and training. Taking it for granted spells divorce. Books, ads, songs, plays to the nauseating contrary, the human race was intended to be perpendicular once in a while or it would not have feet.

11

Still even I, the double-breasted violet, might have acquired the knack of dividing myself into unrelated compartments, of being there without being there, as so many women do, had it not been for Sam. It was too badly botched for me to hope to enjoy sex with Randall, yet I might have come to terms with the night watch had Randy been merely a stud and not a fool. A stud I might have stood. And a thousand snide cruelties.

I could have stood, and did, his jealousy of an unborn child. Now that I've learned what glands can do, I understand both my inordinate love for the coming child and Randy's inordinate jealousy. Deep inside I must have understood then or I don't believe that even quavering I would have put up with what I did. But then Randy was such a fool as to ring in Sam; that did it.

Our son was four when his father did this stupid thing. He was named Alan, this sturdy little boy with smoke-gray eyes and crisp gold curls. Alan's one love was his mother. He liked his father and a nurse called Nora but his mother was his love and she loved him back enough to lose his love. There is such a thing as too much love, not necessarily the smother-mother brand either. Overconsideration will do it. Overgiving. Overgiving of crutches and bandages and ointment until the object, young or old, becomes overdependent and grows to hate his dependency and you.

In taking Alan as my heart's beloved, in cherishing him beyond myself, I was doing in a fashion what Sam had done, seeing that my child had what I had not had.

Like many cracked marriages, this one fell to pieces over nothing. We, Alan, Nora and I, had spent several weeks in New Hampshire. Our home was in Hartford and the day we returned there Randy was waiting for us. It was lunchtime. Nora had gone to the nursery and I was taking Alan to the kitchen to greet Posy, the cook.

Randy called from the living room. "Liz, you forgot to kiss me."

I let Alan go. Turning, I waited. Standing stock-still, I felt myself freeze in a horrible final way. Those weeks in New Hampshire had been a blessed respite and here it was beginning all over, before my hat was off. With some men a kiss means a kiss, with others it means bed.

He came to where I stood. At last, after my mouth was my own again, I pushed him away, crying: "No—no."

His eager smile died as swiftly as light extinguished behind an unshaded window. "What? What *is* it?" he asked.

I wiped my mouth frantically. "I don't know," I said. "Just don't *touch* me—*don't ever touch me!*"

He followed me from the room, his voice rising: "But *why? Why now?*"

Not stopping, I repeated: "I don't know. I told you, I *don't know.*"

It was the following afternoon that Sam appeared. Randy had phoned him, saying I'd had a breakdown, that I'd locked myself in the guest room and would he come and bring me to my senses? Perhaps today, thirty years later, we would still be together if Randy hadn't done this, but then, he could not have known how Sam despised marriage.

He'd met Sam at the station and was cut short.

"Women and children first," Sam told him. "I'll hash this out with Liz and see you afterwards."

But they never did see each other except with a battery of lawyers. Nor was Randall ever inside that house again, at least while we were man and wife. He may have gone there afterwards, when it was empty, when Alan and I and the furnishings had gone to New York.

The last thing in the wide world I wanted was divorce. I who own such an impressive collection of decrees, despise divorce as Sam despised marriage. Divorce is public admission of failure and I'd been taught that it was I and I alone who was to blame for failure.

Sam's tactics now were to trap me *between* failures. *Look* at me: *I'd failed my father by marrying and would fail my son by staying married.*

What was wrong with me? Was I yellow or something?

"No kid of mine should let God Almighty treat her like a bum. Where's your pride, Liz? Do you want Alan to grow up like *him*? You've got enough for *ten* divorces. We'll *crucify* Pretty Boy.

Over and over.

I'm not saying I was railroaded. I let myself be railroaded and not only by Sam. By a minister as well. The first minister I ever sought out.

Outside of social functions and college chapel, I'd never been to church, had never said a prayer beyond the one Hannah taught me, had never talked to a minister. But I did know of one and in desperation went to see him. I and the neighborhood knew beyond the shadow of a doubt what Sam was thinking, yet somewhere there was a God greater than Sam. Maybe a minister could tell me what *He* thought.

Lately I often wonder if the Rev. Edgar Carter is still alive. If he is, I wonder if he knows any better today what God thinks than he did then. If ever a minister muffed a chance, he did. Yet maybe it had to be this way; I never could learn easy.

The Rev. Carter's study was as cold as a Delivery Room. I sat in it, shaking to bits, hoping he wasn't cold. To untangle hearts you have to have one. What I was praying was that he would be against divorce—weren't ministers supposed to be? All he had to do was to show me how to live with Randy without hurting Alan, to show me how to find some way to be a decent mother and at the same time, a decent wife.

Ministers are not God however. God hasn't read theology. God hasn't heard how one rotten apple can spoil the rest in the basket; Christ either. Christ's rotten apple repented of his rottenness and came home to be welcomed with loving arms.

14

The Reverend Carter was a fat man who talked in quotes. His pink cheeks huffed and puffed a lot of junk. The eye-for-an-eye junk; Randy was not fit to be a father, and it was up to me to rescue my son. And don't delay too long; evil is catching.

The small mouth pursed. "Very young children can become blighted," it said, "like plants that never see the sun."

Finally, as I was leaving, he tried to drum up trade.

He said: "You must come to my church some Sunday."

His church!

If you're still around, I've got news for you, Mr. Carter. The Church is not yours, it's God's. And I've got more news for you. You're one of the guys who kept me out of church for thirty years.

CHAPTER TWO

From men did I learn about men and a part of what I learned
was that prematurity was largely responsible for botching up
Liz and Randall Trowbridge. How could it have been otherwise? The divorce decree says Incompatibility and how right.
Incompatibility at its sourest. One all timid pigeon, one all
ranting bull. On the other hand, pigeons do breed as well
as bulls—I know one pigeon who has enjoyed thirty years with
a ranting bull which just goes to show you.

Liz however was given neither time nor training so here
she is, her life in her lap. Released from nightmare, and therefore upright, she limps back to Sam, the decree in one hand,
a child in the other, an adoring, trusting, little son who lacks
nine months and ten minutes of being five years old.

The return to Sam and New York City could augur only
one thing: a diet of straight crow. Sam was jubilant: Now
was I licked? Now would I toe the mark? Now would I get
busy and finish college?

"Dammit to hell you're through with marriage *now*, aren't
you?"

Of course I was through, though not for any of Sam's reasons. Rather for the obvious reason that no man would ever

look at me. I'd hooked one lack-witted guy and fumbled it—how could I hope to hook another! At the tottering age of twenty-six I was scrapped, kaput, a Has-Been without ever being. To the end of time I would be Alan's mother and Sam's daughter, nothing more.

Liz, Liz—how bum a prophet can you be!

Should the coming account sound proud of myself, it is because I was proud of myself. In fact I grew crazy for me. A bemused, delirious Cinderella, counting her new-found scalps. It started with a natural hunger for approval, as innocent as a first cocktail, only to dead-end years later in moral drunkenness.

I fell flat on my face from love of men being in love with me. A disease which can land the patient behind bars because it so nearly resembles the real thing, and can last till she's ninety. Long before I was getting crocked on stuff in bottles I was punchy from an astounding and heretofore undiscovered ability to grab off men. What this knack was and whence it came is the mystery of mysteries, and still is. I can give some guesses but I can't be sure. All I can be sure of is that it *worked*. To a literal hell and back.

There are maladies, bad ones, which eventually wear themselves out but gluttony isn't one of them. Gluttony is like pregnancy; there's no such state as a little bit of it. Gluttony spreads and spreads and bloats and bloats whether the belly, the bladder or the ego. It mounts till insatiability sets in, and may God help you! You bust of it and finally die of the gimmes. The one cure is death, death of the outstretched hand. In 1924 however death was the least of my troubles—

The time is Prohibition, pre-market crash. Scrumptious days. The place is Manhattan. The heroine, a young divorcee with a budding taste for males but no taste at all for climbing into bed. The divorcee is tricked out in jewels and clothes that cost a million. Emeralds and smoky lace to match smoky eyes.

Giant topaz and satin the shade of honey to match hair of the same. The body is size twelve, a good healthy body which she is gradually learning to use. She is learning how it is supposed to act if not what it is supposed to feel.

There was a man who made some remarks about her which may be enlightening. He said she possessed every one but one of the qualities of a bang-up mistress and you were kept wondering as to whether she possessed this. He said she was alive but never bustling, responsive but never eager, intelligent but never brainy. He said she was full of surprises due to the fact that she had a man's mind in a woman's body. Moreover she honestly appreciated the attention you gave her and was happy to say so.

Madam, if the above does not read like a recipe for scalp-collecting, you don't know men. The not-crashing-through is the frosting, lady; the *sine qua non*. Gents prefer the chase to the kill, they really do. They choose to hope to conquer providing there's anything left to conquer. They'll ooze out of the wood to do it.

So far as I can make out, this is where they did come from. As little as I'd lived in New York my contacts were a few scattered females left over from college; no males whatsoever. Then all at once I was "it." Deluged.

From the dump heap to IT—try it some summer! I'll guarantee it will turn your head quicker than an acre of grapes. Indeed the day soon comes when you have need of the grape to endure the delirium of five different dates with five different men in five different places. Should you really desire to, you can't go to bed, yours or theirs. You haven't hours enough.

Nor did I. Close but no seduction. And it was this, I do believe, which accounted for half the men in town asking me to marry them. There is no other answer. They were so damn surprised the question was shocked out of them.

I will admit that the reign supreme of the pretty face was

18

over. Pretty Face continued to click the eye but the warm laugh, the quick response, the proper answer, properly timed, had nosed her out. Sam's kid had come in style. It was postwar. Men wanted a companion, not a doll, and when the companion only accompanied them so far, it was salt on the avocado; it brought out the flavor.

In those jazzy days, in the mad mad twenties—get a bottle, get a babe, go to it—the babe who wouldn't, whose eyes were understanding but whose gloves were on, simply mowed 'em down.

"Liz, I want you—"

"I know—I *know*. And it's so *sweet* of you. But, darling, I *can't*. If I could, it probably would be you—but, no, I just *can't*."

See the system? In the front door, out the back. Walk, don't run. The lady understands what this is all about and is deeply honored. (Sophisticated, see? And unspoiled. A terrific combination.) She understands and is honored and yet she just can't. One gets the notion that what the nice man wants must have rather extra ordinary value. The lady sees why the nice man desires such a pearl, and actually he may be worthy of it and yet—yet she must keep it for reasons too delicate to explain.

"But, Liz, you *love* me, don't you?"

(Love him! She loves men, *period*.)

"Of course—of *course*. But I—I had *such* a frightful experience. My husband—oh darling, *please* don't make me talk about it!"

See? The lady is not coy. She admits that the man has power over her but she is appealing to his higher self. His insistence has not offended her in the slightest. The contrary. In fact there is such a sense of obligation that she decides it is fairer to be frank.

The cause for her unwillingness to part with the pearl is that the only man who ever had it, mistreated it. Not that it is damaged, oh no! But mistreatment has frightened her—

Over a period of months, slowly, by trial and error, by cautious observation, I was mastering the come-on, the tricks, the patter. I was catching on fine. One never allowed the Mighty Question to be conclusively disposed of; it stayed on top of the stove to simmer.

The good God knows these men did not really want to marry me. Me or anyone.

I see a tall man striding beside me up and down a ramp at the Grand Central. A dark powerful man, very male, very buck-at-bay, and very angry. "All right—all right!" he explodes. "Then marry me—" A desperate alternate proposal. A last-minute substitution.

Delightful though. Delightfully delightful.

And every last smidge grounded on the most ancient of challenges; the goaded male snipping his single-blessedness to prove his prowess where another male has bungled. By comparison, to cut the nose to spite the face is infant's play.

Do I hear cries of, Teaser? Cheat? Understandable, but I was no teaser, no cheat. I had been lonely for a long time and starved. Now I was a parrot and a damn busy one. It was a question of memorizing the language of the time; the language of all time, I do believe, and if I got Honorable Mention, more power to me! Perhaps the "some day" angle was overplayed a trifle, and yet what is wrong with hope? You loved it, you know you did. You ate up the admiration and the thank-you-so-much, darling. You squared your shoulders at the great big wonderful men I insisted you were!

What I was was a diverter; I made trades. The precise method you use with children: "Baby, you can't have the pretty pink dish—another time maybe. Now, come—listen to the lovely bedtime story."

Oh, believe me, I paid through the nose for every single

front-row seat you ever sat in. Knocked myself out and glad to. I truly found it incredibly enchanting of you to desire me, the revamped wallflower. To permit me to repay you for supper clubs and drinks and love-making by telling you how marvelous you were—how there wasn't a thing on earth you couldn't do, except to me.

This was juggling at its maddest, don't think it wasn't. When occasionally one of you got dropped, it hurt me more than it did you, don't think it didn't. The juggler's shame was great. She was wholeheartedly distressed and said so and honest in it. Completely honest.

It's quite possible that it was the honesty, warped though it was, which accounts for most of the murder. There were lies, certainly. Fantastic ones, yet even the worst of these were a form of adulation, one more stroke to the glowing portrait of yourselves. If I lied and got caught, I didn't tell you to go jump as I would now. I rigged up some meticulously involved "out" that saved your face as well as mine.

Once upon a time a man suggested I get myself a job, do something really worth while. Well, this was Sam-talk, the talk I'd been rebelling against for years. Yet in place of saying so, I agreed it was a splendid idea, but splendid. I said I'd do just that, and then to please him, said I had and then got caught, and had to lie again. Pathetic, isn't it?

I'll more than admit that the lies were totally unnecessary. So was the whole shindig. Nevertheless and notwithstanding they did stem from a cockeyed gratitude. You were all so nice, so terribly, terribly nice that who was Liz to let you down: You were all so—oh, how funny and how sad that all of you should seem so important!

In looking back, the question isn't one of white lies or gray lies or black lies. The question is whether I remained celibate from decency or from fear of further failure. And might I have given in had I lost by not giving in? Who can tell? The system worked like magic so who can tell what I might have done if it had not worked!

Incidentally don't get the notion that I juggled every object in sight. Some got dropped and some never got into the act at all. Wolves, Casanovas—these were absent. These and the hearty ones, the Kiwanians out to paint the town. These are salesmen and know a salesman when they see her. Actually we were a lot alike. They dealing in gay times on the basis of rapid turnover, I dealing entirely in futures; "some day— maybe." Our goals did differ however. Theirs to get the goods; mine to keep the goods from being gotten.

Or was it? Was not my underlying goal to keep 'em coming? To hang onto the goods if possible but keep 'em coming? Only the Lord is in a position to answer this one. I do suspect that, intake and output, the entire performance was based on what everything is based on; *the thing you most want is the thing you work hardest at.*

Jesus once made a remark about people's hearts occupying the same boat as their treasures. My main treasure was pride-bolstering and I sailed with it. On the other hand, muddled and phony as it was, there was one thing to be said for me: I so terribly longed to give others pleasure.

However, as always, the hooker is this: *for my sake or theirs?*

Enough. This wasn't intended to be an itemized account of the irresistibility of one Liz Burns Trowbridge. The point in dragging it out has been to show that even though at long last she is making a success of something, she still cannot believe it. And when she comes to believe it, she still will not accept it. Her self-doubt goes deeper than the need to be needed and it is good it does because the need to be needed is the road marked Snake Pit.

The true thirst for approbation is Satan's bait. A nasty thing, clutching, fawning; no end to it outside of more and more of the same. And there comes the time when the supply runs out, for people do get weary, horribly, horribly weary of other people asking to be approved of. Of course self-doubt gets tiresome too, but in the end, if really faced, this can lead to glory. And then people are free of people.

Such a day was far off for Liz. Since Sam was a man and Randy was a man, and she had failed both, her starved self pointed to men and more men. And there was great personal joy in this. Giddy, triumphant joy, but it was not enough. It was glorious and at the same time, phony. The whirl is on and she, the central figure, yet the clock will strike and Cinderella will get hers.

Till then, make hay.

Sam did not put up the brawl I had taken for granted. Sam was giving up, exhausted from years of backing the same horse on the wrong track. Also he was ill though no one guessed it at the time. The arteries of his brain were hardening. Let this be a lesson to us all. The determination to force a round peg into a square hole chips the forcer as well as the peg. It was utterly inconceivable that Sam could ever be "poor" Sam but he was getting there.

It had never occurred to me that Alan and I would not be pinned to him, would not live under his hawk eye at the Waldorf, roared at, dictated to. Having leapt from fire to frying pan I so took for granted my return to fire that it amounted to a reprieve from the death cell to have him announce that he'd rented an apartment for us. The apartment was on Gramercy Park. The park was fenced in—good place for kids.

Good place? It was heaven! And in less than a week an angel showed up. One noon I was busily burning Alan's lunch when the doorbell rang.

"Come in," I yelled.

"Can't—it's locked," a voice answered.

Dumping the mess in the sink, I ran to the door and there

23

stood a wondrous sight. It was Hannah Gundersen. Hannah, my friend, whom I'd not seen since that awful day I sailed for Europe. I knew father had pensioned her, knew she'd been in Norway, but somehow I'd never expected to see her again.

Her sniffing nose cut short my tears of welcome. The greeting was so typically offhand that I laughed instead. Presenting me with a swift peck, she turned to Alan, her latest child.

Your lunch is burnt," she said. "Come help me fix a new one."

I closed the door and leaned against it, heaving a tremendous sigh. The nurse problem had been solved, the meal problem— all problems. How good of Sam.

I watched the incongruous pair march up the hall, hand in hand. The small boy in the blue and white striped playsuit and the sparse woman in gray serge who didn't appear to have changed a particle in fifteen years. They would be friends, these two. Alan Trowbridge was on the brink of a rare experience. He had just met a female he could trust.

Evaluating myself as a young mother, I wonder whether I might have done a better job had Sam stuck to the steerage. While I spent hours with Alan, hours on end, I never had to. Alan was mine to love but not mine to care for, the reverse of my own situation both at the Waldorf and abroad where I had too much looking after and no love. Suppose I'd had to wash, cook, scrub—would my love have been wiser? This could be. Love isn't so much a matter of words and caresses as it is deeds for the beloved.

How can I tell? Especially now when it has long been too late. The period shortly after Hannah came was the period when the whirl began, when even Alan was sandwiched in between a man here, a man there, then men—men! (Where did I meet them all?) Soon it was days with Alan and nights, night-clubbing, from Harlem to the Village. I said yes to every date, overlapping, undercutting, dividing myself like the loaves and fishes to be shared by 5,000.

24

For such were martinis invented. The small glass, the quick return; gulp one, gulp two—

"Darling, I'm so terribly sorry I'm late! Yes—I'd love one."

"Darling, I'm so terribly sorry but I have to run in just ten minutes! Yes, please—one for the road."

"Darling, I'm so terribly sorry but I can't *possibly* make it—oh, all right! Start mixing—yes, five to one."

Here is the perfect soil for the embryonic drunk to sprout full-fledged. Deep subsoil of hurt and fear and guilt, middle layer of self-pitying rebellion, top layer of frustration sprinkled with some new and unimagined and unbelievable elixir of power. The drunk *has* to doubt this power because he doubts himself. Over and over, despite proof, he doubts, and so sprouts immoderation. The need comes to reassure himself again and again, to bite into life in bigger chunks than can be chewed. More and more and more and more. The burning yen to do something—anything—oftener and better than it can be done. Just-as-good is not enough. The drunk is no halfway guy. He is the self-flagellating perfectionist, goaded by ideals he is unwilling to discipline himself to fulfill. Eventually this ceases to be choice, it is compulsion. Add gin and juniper to compulsion and the skids are right around the corner.

The nonalcoholic, stuck with an alcoholic, thinks *he* pays. No, brother, you pay in chicken feed; we pay in lacerated souls. *We hate ourselves far worse than you could ever hate us.*

Through the blur of thirty hung-over years I recall distinctly the first hangover. That first down payment of the soul. It was past midday; it had to be for my room was sunny. Horribly, horribly sunny. I could not bear to open my eyes because when I opened them the sockets were lined in pain. Whether the eyes were open or shut, the top of my head and the base of the so-called brain pulsated from blows of tiny angry hammers, striking offbeat. My lips were made of sandpaper and my mouth tasted—well, you know or you can't ever know!

The glare was unendurable—*I must* get dark shades. See,

this is interesting, isn't it? Not, the glare is unendurable, *I must never drink another drop.* But, the glare is unendurable, *I must get dark shades.* The sprouting alcoholic, adjusting, compensating, passing the buck.

Outside was a motor horn, the type laughingly dubbed "musical." Inside burred a vacuum cleaner. The glare combined with the assault of these two forced me out of bed. Moving cautiously like a commando in an enemy forest, I could feel my insides answering roll call; here, one hammering heart; here, two part-time lungs; here—coming right up!—one stomach.

A long mirror across the room showed me that a yellow chiffon nightgown, worn backwards, might not have been the happiest of choices. The face above it was a dim green and had a choked look, but what are looks when you are dying!

Groaning, I teetered to the door. I discovered in transit that my stomach was not coming up, it was falling out. I wished it would, and fast, because at each step, it slipped a notch, vibrating delicately from left to right.

The vacuum cleaner had stopped but stretched from wall to wall outside my room was the electric cord. I stumbled over it and died a little.

"*Damn* people," I gritted.

In the kitchen doorway stood Hannah. As ever her finger marked the place in a closed Bible. She was looking me over.

"Did you say something?" she asked crisply. She was so horribly intact. So neat. So in her right mind. "Did you say something, Liz? Are you ready for your orange juice? How was the party? Say—what's wrong with you?"

I whipped myself into a lather.

"For the love of Pete, *stop asking questions.* Outside of the small item that I happen to be dying," I replied icily, "there's not one thing wrong with me and the party stank, thank you— my God!"

Hannah's nostrils quivered. "Now don't you start swearing. Well, I guess nobody made you stay till all hours. I bet Mr. Silas was ready way before you were."

Mr. Silas was Silas Addams, a recent appendage. Hannah liked him. He was "nice," she said. "Nice" included everything from kind hearts to polished shoes.

"Oh, you do, do you?" I replied nastily. "Well, it's a pity to disabuse you but Mr. Silas adored every second of it—talked stocks right to the elevator! Why am I always the one to get the blame?"

Exchanging the orange juice which I had not touched for a cup of black coffee which I needed to live, Hannah said: "Who's blaming? Get your shower. Sausage and eggs are about ready."

Sausage and eggs—my God.

I had another new appendage. At least I thought he was one. He wore pants and was around. He was an actor and his name was Gregory—why is it that children named Gregory always grow up to be actors? In a Byron way, he was good to look at, lean and dark and very sensitive. Too sensitive to abide common people and common talk. He loved money though, emeralds and topaz and mink. I thought it was me he loved until Sam got in the picture.

Now that Hannah was there, Sam was away a lot. Off at some sanitarium or other. During one of these periods I met Gregory at a cocktail party and we had started going everywhere together. We even rated the Smut Sheets; "a News-some Two-some." To me, this seemed divine, an actor and all, but it was scarcely divine to Sam.

Sam returned and it was several days before he was able to get hold of me. When he did he nearly tore my ear off.

"Where in hell have you been?" he shouted. "Get the devil up here, young woman—I want to talk to you!"

I turned from the phone to Hannah. I remember her sitting

27

by a window with Alan on her lap. They were reading *Little Sambo.*

"What have you been telling Father?" I asked her.

Sliding Alan off her lap, she closed the book and got up.

"Come, boy," she said quietly, "you never finished that drawing. Go do it and then show Mommy."

She closed his bedroom door behind him. Not till then did she answer me.

"I only told your father what I know, which isn't much," she said. "I've not told anyone what I think. Maybe I should, Liz. I guess it's my duty to Alan as well as you—"

"Leave Alan out of this," I broke in.

"How can you leave him out?" she asked. "Alan is—"

"Oh, *please,*" I broke in again. "God, will I *ever* get the chance to lead my own life! You all treat me like a child—I'm *not* a child."

"No," she agreed, "you just act like one—that *nice* Mr. Silas."

It sounded like a *non sequitur* but it wasn't.

"Okay, so he's *nice!*" I yelled. "I *hate* nice people—anyhow what's childish about preferring one man to another? Suppose you do what you're paid to do and let me attend to *my* affairs?" (Hannah, forgive me. But of course you did, before the horrid words were out!)

Already she had crossed the room. Taking my hand, she said softly: "Nobody can be paid to love you the way I do. But you're sorry you said that, Liz—I know what's inside you. That's why it hurts to see you all worn out, drinking that awful stuff, spending your nights with the wrong man—"

"Spending my *nights*—!" I howled. "What *do* you mean?"

She put her arms around me. "Now, now, not what you mean and you know it. But what about Mr. Silas? I like him and Alan likes him—he keeps asking where he is. Liz, where *is* Mr. Silas?"

I burst into tears. "I don't know," I cried, " I *don't know*—"

But I did know. And I knew why he'd stopped calling.

In his apartment in the Waldorf, high above Fifth Avenue, Sam was pacing back and forth. He began the attack before I took off my gloves.

"Sit down and keep your mouth shut," he commanded. "I've told you that before you were ever conceived, I made up my mind I wanted a daughter. Most men want sons but I wanted a *girl*—"

This touched me greatly.

"I know," I said, "and it's nice, terribly ni—"

"Don't interrupt," he commanded. "Are you going to listen?"

"I am listening. I'm pleased," I told him.

"You won't be so pleased when I get through with you," he told me. "The reason I wanted a girl was to prove they could use their heads if they had a mind to—I was so goddam sick of your mother! *But now I'm goddam sick of you*, see? Before you even finished college, you married a poop—you got yourself in one hell of a stink. All right, I got you out. I got you an apartment and let you live the way you wanted to. I gave you Hannah and more money than you could spend. *But I did not* do this with my eyes shut. It was a test. If you passed, good. But, by Christ, you haven't passed! You've flunked flat on your face—*don't say a word.*"

In total silence I waited while he blew his nose, while he started in again.

"What do I find when I get back? I find you've gone haywire again—in every gossip column in town, linked with some cheap Broadway gigolo. I'm just the guy who knows—I make it my business to know! So, sister, as much as I hate threats, here's what's going to happen; you give this bum the rush and straighten yourself out—and fast!—or I'll cut off the gravy-train. Like *that.*"

I was at last permitted to speak. I said: "Gravy-train? What's that?"

He snorted. "That, sister, is the do-re-mi—what buys emeralds. What'ya think the pansy's after, your gray eyes? Not by a damnsight! Well, no pansy's gonna bloom on my dough—this is the word with the bark on it."

I sat perfectly still for a moment. I knew very little about the homosexual but as I thought of Gregory, I knew father was right. Some of the very qualities I had liked, his indifference toward me as a woman, the making love with words instead of action, the scorn of marriage, were so unlike other men, that while they'd been a relief, they seemed queer, too. All right—so they were queer.

I was sorry for Greg but as there was nothing I knew to do for him, I was quite willing to let him go. There was however something I was not willing to let go!

Suddenly I stood up. Suddenly, for the first time in my life I was free of fear of Sam. It could have been his use of the word, "sister." I detest people calling people sister when they aren't sister. At any rate I suddenly heard my voice say: "You will never speak to me this way again."

I saw Sam's eyes pop out on his cheeks. There was a strangling noise but no words.

I picked up my bag and gloves and walked past him to the door. There I turned and said: "You have just lost yourself a whipping-girl. Alan and I'll make out without you and without your gravy-train. I can learn to scrub floors—in the meantime we'll eat emeralds. Take your goddam dough and—"

Behind the closing door there wasn't a sound beyond the sound a pair of eyes might make if they should bounce to the floor.

I escaped barely in time to vomit in the nearest toilet. The Waldorf plumbing got everything I had except my determination to stick by what I'd said.

And actually the truth is, from then on, I was more nearly Sam's kid than I ever was. Once he'd picked up the eyes and popped them in place, once he recovered from shock, he was tickled stiff. This was his kind of talk. Sam's chickens had flocked home.

The pity is I didn't do it before.

Before the merry-go-round got going.

CHAPTER THREE

Alan was the one who started me thinking in terms of a second marriage. Alan was going on six and six meant time for school. I was determined that he try public school which meant moving to the country. Moving to the country meant a house, a house meant a home, a home meant a father and a father is a man, not men. Though it still seemed hard to believe, the past year had shown that if I truly needed a husband, the chances were I could snag one.

The main requirement in husband No. 2 was that he be as dissimilar to husband No. 1 as could be found. Not only could husband No. 2 not be beautiful, he must not be God's gift to the ladies and above all he must not be studdish.

Hannah's "Mr. Silas" was my boy. Waiting faithfully, aloofly Yankee, on the fringe of the mob. This was the precise man to be safe with, this Silas. The pleasure craft would make for harbor. Silas was monosyllabic, contained, trustworthy, and he damn near fell dead when I took him up on what was never actually a proposal of marriage or anything else. It took a bit of doing but after I pointed out to him how fine he was and how deeply he loved me, you couldn't conceive of anyone more surprised and pleased.

Everybody was pleased. Everybody except the mob and even it was relieved in a groaning sort of way. Alan was delighted, Sam was as near delighted as he ever got—"a guy with sense, for a change"—and tired old Hannah was so delighted that I lost her. Now I would be all right, she said. She could retire now; Alan and I would be safe with Mr. Silas.

And I? I was in harbor. A house of our own in a small Jersey town with lawns and birds and playmates for Alan; as the soap-opera slop says, "Life Can Be Beautiful." I alone made the choice and it was a good one. The fact that it did not turn out to be in no way disproves this.

Silas Addams was good and is good. All wool and a yard wide, whatever that may mean. Born of a long line of Ver-monters, he might have been named Prudence, had he been a girl. Medium is the word for Silas, medium height, medium coloring, medium tastes, viewpoint, husband, father, citizen. Prior to being lassoed by one Liz Trowbridge, his history had been straight down the line; school, college, first world war, brokerage business. It was an inexplicable deviation for him to let Liz marry him; however, this lapse did not disturb the pat-tern. Remaining essentially as before, Si was as dependable as a padlock, sweet, even-tempered, undemanding and infuriating to live with because he was never there. A fog of a man.

To describe this second marriage is to describe a relay race with yourself the only entry; a runner in search of someone to accept the blazing torch. It's difficult to place Silas, to remember much about him. I remember each room in every house we lived in, and the servants and our friends, I remem-ber too much of what I did and too much of what I said, but what did he say? And, outside of stocks and bonds, what did he do? He worked his head off, I certainly know that. He made money and became a partner in the brokerage house and when this occurred I remember the exact words his senior partner used. "Well, Liz, you finally did it," he said. "When you married Si, if you'd told me he was partner material I'd have laughed in your face. Three years—it's astounding!"

Nothing so astounding about it; I was like Sam, only better. I kept drilling into the guy how fine he was, how this, how that, kept urging him to believe in himself and his ideas until at last he did believe. As simple as that. Sam and I were both tooters but he tooted his horn and I tooted Si's; there's quite a difference.

The trouble with this is, it gets away from you. You convince a person of what he can be and before long he's devoting his time to being it and where are you? You're high in drydock. You sit there, peering down at your barnacles commencing to see how really still still harbors can be.

From here in, the marital and moral acrobats of Liz, born Burns, cannot be squeezed into either fantasy or nightmare. The years with Randall Trowbridge might be ducked but the Addams' household is too clear for comfort. What with hindsight and rehash and self-castigation I see Liz-on-the-skids yet I can see Silas too and it's about fifty-fifty. I didn't used to think so. Si's intrinsic goodness used to befuddle the issues, jockeying me into position of prime goat with the haircloth hide, but not now. I know better now. Nobody is all good and nobody is all bad, even Liz.

Put it like this; say a woman seeks love, being formed for it in the nicest way; say she is pushed around in childhood, and abused—or so she thought—in a first marriage and is deeply marked but keeps on searching. Does she stop to say, could anything be wrong with my ideal? Not once. Clinging like a cactus to House and Garden ideals of marriage she deliberately picks on some poor bloke who never reads House and Garden. His dish is the Wall Street Journal. The man is a Business Machine registering all emotion, all pleasure, distress, interest, disapproval, by a single method, the protrusion of his lower lip. So what happens? You bet it does!

It starts off great. The man works and the woman rehearses

the role of perfect wife. The house in Jersey is to be the home of homes; she thinks of it as a haven and there will be bigger and better havens as the man gets a leg up. Business problems are trundled home for her to listen to and this she adores. For instance she is very glad to help in the small matter of how to get rid of gabby customers who waste time.

"Liz, I don't know what to do about them. When people finish their business, why do they sit there? Why don't they get up and go—drives you nuts."

Liz nods. "I know, darling—but why don't you get up? Get up. Courteously, of course. Stand at your desk and give them the pleasant Good Afternoon look. It's been done to me and it works."

It worked. Before the month is out, she is overhearing: "Sure, I know. But if you'll stand up yourself you'll get rid of them all right. They get the hint. That's my system, isn't it Liz?"

"It is, darling."

And the not so small matter concerning a salesman whose hand is in the till. Silas is branch manager now and is expected to make recommendations but here is a touchy situation.

"Liz, the man's got to be kicked off the Street. If it goes to court, though, it won't help the firm any. I don't know— maybe I should turn it over to the partners, they'll decide anyway."

Liz shakes her head. "Could you get the money back, Si? Is any of it left?"

"Not a dime. Wasn't much, only a couple of thousand."

Liz, chewing a pencil: "Darling, doesn't the Stock Exchange have a way of handling such problems? I'd think the directors, or what-have-you, would hear the case and take the necessary steps—why not ask around? All you want is no more of the man with the leaky fingers and no publicity—don't make your report yet. Inquire around."

Before six months are out, she overhears a partner: "That

Exchange groundwork showed initiative, Silas. We need men like you."

Silas works harder as Liz grows letter-perfect. To further her role, she prepares to contribute a child; it necessitates a second Caesarian but what of this? She bore the bull a son so the Business Machine rates one too. And Alan, Alan the beloved, ought to have a brother.

Naturally she will love the new baby but—but Alan is her beloved. At his slightest frown, off come the party clothes, forgotten is the gayest party at the country club. She does not guess what the world can do to someone who has been over-nurtured: "Sorry, chum," the world says, "sorry you feel bad—see you a year from Sunday." The woman is concocting bliss and all will continue to be blissful for the reason that she wishes it to be.

It is summer, the season for bliss. The moon streams across a screened-in porch. Tree trunks, whole branches, the leaves themselves are outlined in minute delicacy and now and then a breeze stirs and the leaves ruffle gently. The man and woman are sitting close on a wide cushioned chaise. Immense with child, the woman smiles tenderly and the man looks up and says: "A penny for your thoughts."

Her smile deepens; how like him. Not: "What gives, toots?" but, a penny for your thoughts. She takes his hand. "*Feel.* Feel how he pushes—darling, if it is a he, what about the name—Peter? Peter Addams. It sounds like you, sweet. Early American."

The man removes his hand. He yawns. "Sure, why not? Say, suppose we threw a dinner at the club—would we dare ask a couple of the partners and their wives? You know—shoot at the moon?" His expression is naïvely eager and his lower lip protrudes.

She laughs. "As Father would say, 'Shoot at the moon, you may hit the top of a bank.' Of course, darling, ask anyone. With your head and my gall, we'll get places."

The man grins, yawns and goes to bed. She stays to watch the shadows.

Would the lady like a little drink?

A *drink?* Oh, no, no thank you. There is nothing to run from any more.

It is late fall, three to four years later. The house is a larger one, twice the room, twice the servants, twice the entertaining. This is 1928. Silas is a partner and in '28 no partner in a good brokerage house can miss. The guests who are being entertained however appear fairly reminiscent of former guests; this fall's crop of those to whom Si is selling stocks or preparing to sell stocks. Actually the stocks sell themselves but the personal touch is a must.

Month after month black-tied males talk business and low-necked females rotate from offspring to clothes to servants. Certainly there's no harm in talking offspring except that you now see your own so seldom. You really should say, I'll ask Edith. Or Maggie. Or Gracie. This is what you should say but you don't, you say: "The boys are wonderful, thanks."

There's no harm in talking clothes: "What a divine dress—where did you find it?" But you know where they find them, Bergdorf or Carnegie. And no harm in talking servants: "What a lousy life—how do they stick it!" This is about all you are able to wring out of any of these topics, whereas these other women—! Nice women, really. Pleasant, friendly, stable. Too goddam stable.

Life is a stepladder resting against the New York Stock Exchange. Each year is a rung up until eventually you get to where you yourself started from, the top. This dinner and the memory of like dinners are so deadly, so politely, insistently deadly that on occasions the woman feels her throat close. Last year was filet *mignon* with watercress and vice-presidents. This year is terrapin with artichoke hearts and presidents. The year after will be pressed duck with iced persimmons and chairmen of the board. Sometime it is to be hoped they

37

would all be too rich, too attenuated, too pooped from clipping coupons to be able to eat at all.

Now, *would the lady like one more glass of wine?* Shouldn't it be passed again?

Yes, you bet your bottom buck it should. The lady is growing desperate. Desperate from the monotony of clichés plus lower lips which stick out. It isn't the Four Horsemen that drive people nuts; it's the whine of mosquitoes. The knowing, hour in, hour out, what someone is sure to say, sure to do. Elizabeth Addams tries desperately not to listen, not to watch, yet she does listen and does watch and despises herself.

Hear now:

"It's difficult to get steady salesmen," Silas is saying. "I always have to remind them that rolling stones do *not* gather moss."

A female sparrow in medium-sized rubies contributes a scintillating aside: "My dear, I simply told my waitress to take it or leave it—half loaves are better than *none*."

Rolling stones. Half loaves. God. Her nerves tightly clenched, Liz thinks, I'll play too. I'll say, any of you savants ever hear the one about all is not gold that glitters? And about wise men knowing their own weakness? And—and—about hope deferred making the heart sick? Never did? Well, look around, you wordy bastards!

Imagine if just once a person next to you would turn and make a thought-provoking statement. Suppose he should say, "You know, I often wonder if part of the trouble between men and women comes from man's envy of woman."

"Envy?" she would say. "Why would men envy women?"

"Oh, easy," he would reply. "The purpose of life is procreation, right? And women, well, women are equipped to do their job, desire or no desire—hating it, even. But men, poor jerks, aren't equipped for first things first, they've got to get steamed up. The female can conceive without passion but the male—no likee, no soap. In his soul this must gall the male. Must make him want to get even."

A thought worth considering. Her mind would immediately go back to Randall and from him to a world of males urging females into bed when, often, very often, the males themselves didn't actually want it. An idea with possibilities. And what could be more interesting than the secret underlying the mess between the sexes? There had to be an answer somewhere.

In some wide-open room in some far distant place there must be men and women who could talk to each other, who had ideas worth exchanging. Not necessarily brilliant nor profound. Merely provocative. There had to be people somewhere who played with thoughts, running them back and forth on colored strings, experimenting, interchanging, sharing. Conversation in place of monologues—surely this was so. Surely there were those whose speech was the result of thinking, who laughed from humor, who made you come to life because they themselves were alive. What must this be like? What would it be to be with those who were bullish on perception and bearish on quotations rather than on stocks and bonds!

"A penny for your thoughts, Liz—"

"You'd be gypped, baby. How about a round of wine?"

Soon the women would leave the dinner table. Soon she would say cutely: "Any of you gals like to powder the nose?" Some night she'd be looped enough to tell them all off, for no other reason than to watch the stunned reactions. After all a spade *is* a spade, as Si would say. And more and more frequently she found herself wanting to say so, wanting to call a smell, a stink, even when it wasn't. You could put it down to Sam's peasant blood or it could be just plain nausea from a topheavy pinnacle of boredom.

Boredom could build up only so far and then it crumbled. Then it wouldn't matter how good someone was, how kind and trustworthy. Sam's values, his extreme standards, must have bitten deeper than she'd realized. This rambler-rose-green-shutter existence was a haven all right, a haven like the grave. Being loved was evidently not sufficient. The love of a good man, and the patter of tiny feet did not of themselves bring fulfillment. If there was such a state—

No one could say you didn't love Si—what was there *not* to love? And you loved your sons. You loved Alan and Peter to the walls of your heart yet somehow you had become an Emergency Mother. In case of emergency you were called in—nobody like a mother in emergencies. In between however servants did a better job than you because, face it, you loved your kids to death but this didn't mean you could be with them overmuch. Not any longer. You'd die for them and still not be able to live with them—not for long. Was this monstrous? Yes, it was monstrous. Just the same, it did take a special kind of mind. Not a mind necessarily inferior, merely capable of suspending itself, of adapting and yet not losing its flavor.

To rise to kid-crises was a cinch. Kiss the knuckle, mop the blood, praise the triumph, referee the battle; these and read a book, toss a ball, make a screwy face—yes, yes! But: "Mommy, watch; mommy, why; mommy, what?" No, not any longer. Not even for Alan. And as for Peter, well, while you'd probably spawned yet one more customer's man, it was a sure bet that, forever and forever, with or without you, Pete Addams would be staunchy and exactly what he was; *himself*, hell or high heaven.

"Liz!"

Slowly the woman drags her thoughts back to the circle of faces. "Forgive me," she smiles, "I was off on cloud fifteen. Any of you gals like to powder the nose?"

"Liz, you *missed* it. We're talking servants, and what we want to know is, did you really mean you're sorry for them? Nowadays? When they have everything but your mink coat?"

"Toss in the mink coat. It won't help matters a particle," Liz says. "Till they're allowed a little privacy and dignity and a last name and hours not invaded by a million petty whims—"

"But that's—"

"Sure, that's mutiny. I'm the traitor to my class—class, my foot. My father, Sam Burns, arrived by steerage. If giving every human being space for his soul to breathe in makes me a traitor, I'm a traitor and proud of it. If giving every last human being the privilege of being as good as I am—"

"Wait a minute—what about *niggers? You can't think niggers* are as good as you are?"

Oh God!

"Not only are they as good—but the word *nigger* is not used in this house. They are Negroes, colored people. People whose skin is dark instead of light. It's a pity God didn't see fit to endow humans as He did chickens; light *and* dark in the same setup. In that case the problem would never have arisen. But I guess He didn't imagine we were going to turn out dumber than the chicken!"

The gray eyes smolder but the wide mouth has maintained its grin. It has been said of the woman that she slaps you with the right hand and keeps you from toppling with the left. Here is one subject however which makes her want to topple right and left.

Before her ever-present is the picture of a blond-braided little girl, elbows on table, sitting in a dining car listening to her father. Sam is explaining where they're bound for; they've been invited to the home of one of the few truly great men in the world. He considers it a tremendous honor, one which she must always remember. "His name is Booker T. Washington, Liz. Be sure you're damn good and quiet and hear every word he says." As they'd left the train she'd been surprised to find that Mr. Washington was colored, yet not too surprised. Sam collected a great variety of friends. She had

41

liked Mr. Washington, liked him fine. And she had never forgotten him.

The memory fades. The chatter around her causes the woman to shake her head, a little dazed. She pushes back her chair. "Come, we'll tear ourselves away. That is," she smiles, "if the gentlemen can manage to exist without us. Try talking business, why don't you?"

The years pass. The Stock Market crashes. Men leap from windows and other men stand on street corners, selling apples. And Sam has died. In a Boston sanitarium Sam Burns died asking for Liz but Liz was great with hangover and the maids could not disturb her. They'd had strict orders but they positively would see that she got the message that Boston was calling. So by the time she reached the sanitarium, Sam had been dead the better part of a day.

From what the doctors told her, he died as he had lived. Barging roughshod into the Hereafter as though it were a new real estate deal to be cut up and sold for lots. Due to Sam's vitality, the end was not foreseen. He'd shouted orders with his last breath: do this, do that, get this, get that. Get his daughter—*where in hell was Liz?*

Sam and his daughter had not seen each other in months nor could his daughter see him now. Sam's body was at an undertaker's. Had the sanitarium heard from her, had they been certain she was coming today—here was the address. Did Mrs. Addams have someone with her?

Yes, Mrs. Addams had a taxi driver. She would make it, thanks.

The undertaker was relieved. It seemed this dumping of bodies without authority, with nobody responsible, was highly irregular. Undertakers took awful chances. She stood gazing down at the wasted form of what had been Sam Burns while the man went on and on, enumerating what awful chances undertakers took. "Look, lady," he whined, "we have to eat too."

The lady looked up at the whining empty face. It was a putty face, as featureless as a peeled onion. It was this man who was dead. *He* should be lying there in place of Sam.

In sudden fury, Liz struck out at the face. "Shut up—that's my father!" she screamed. "*You damn ghoul—that's the greatest man who ever lived!*"

Silas flew home at once. This was good of him because it was not his weekend to be home. Since the Market crash, four years ago—or was it three?—Si had been in the Middle West, something about branch offices, about reorganization, about merging. The crash had not affected their lives except for this separation but it was a curious way to live. Curious indeed. Even Alan had wondered at it. He'd asked, sometime back that was, before he went away to school.

"Mom, seems like you're tired all the time," he began. And then he asked: "Mom, Si's our father, isn't he? Well, why doesn't he *live* here? He used to—who're all these other men? Why isn't Si home?"

It wasn't easy to satisfy him. She didn't suppose she had— what was it she'd said? There wasn't any answer which could honestly satisfy anyone. It had started out as a mere matter of months and had continued on and on.

The seasons come and go. It is winter. The ground outside is heaped in snow. Behind the drawn draperies the sleet snaps at the windows with the sound of a million mice cracking grain. In the large and gracious living room, varying little from other large and gracious living rooms, sit the man and the woman, their low cushioned chairs on opposite sides of the fireplace. It is a stage set. A play seemingly for the deaf and dumb.

The woman drops her book to stare at the figure whose head is hidden behind the folds of the *Wall Street Journal*. Lighting

43

a cigarette, she inhales deeply and leans forward, her features strained yet bright with animation.

"Si—Si darling, couldn't we go away, the two of us? To—oh, to Pago Pago or Buenos Aires or Guadalajara, such lovely names! Think of it—you're listening, aren't you?—think of no telephones, no parties, no ticker tape, no—"

From the sagging folds of the *Wall Street Journal* comes a snore, and another and another, as rhythmical as a metronome. Liz starts to speak again only to give up and go to stand beside the sleeping figure. The body is crumpled and the face lax and drained. She knows he is exhausted, but, God, so is she! This monthly visitor is now an interruption who pays the bills and damn little else. Looking down, she protrudes a lip in bored imitation and begins to tiptoe backwards from the room. In the hall she halts a moment and then knowing she is safe, hurries to an opening in the paneled wall. From the small compact bar with rows of shining glasses and rows of shining bottles, she picks a bottle at random. She pours a stiff drink and gulps it.

One more quick drink for the lady?

You're goddam right—the lady would be able to forgive adultery, murder, mayhem, but *fog!* Fog is the three monkeys, seeing, hearing, saying *nothing.*

Weak from self-pity she leans against the bar. She has tried, torn herself to shreds trying. If only they could get away, take a year off—but no, of course not. Next year, perhaps, or the year after they'd take a month, some stinking tour somewhere, and in the meantime charm yourself with the thought of two dazzling weeks at Palm Beach.

"Mr. and Mrs. Silas Addams in the giddy whirl at Palm Beach."

Giddy was the word. Giddy as all get out; two strangers of the same name in the same room.

As Si was always saying, always, always, *always* saying: "No-

body but a fool keeps on running after he's caught the train."
It was a pet phrase of his. Yet—yet might not the train lurch
unexpectedly? It might. It might lurch very hard and then
couldn't the somebody who wasn't a fool just happen to
get dropped off?

CHAPTER FOUR

A year and more have passed. It is early spring. A ship glides through a night radiant in full moon, its stars glinting like diamonds against a dark blue ball gown. On board there is dancing, music, voices, laughter intermingling in the moonlight. Far in the stern stands a solitary couple. A distant plane blinks red and green and the man watches this, his arms resting on the rail. Down, down, the ship's wake tears at the velvet sea and the woman watches this, her breasts rising and falling in dry sobs that rack the slender body. Her husband reaches to pat her hand.

"Hadn't you better tell me?" he asks. "It might relieve you, Liz. Nothing ventured, nothing—"

The woman moans. Then suddenly, for the first time in many weeks, the tears pour down her face. Her head drops to the rail and she cannot tell whether the taste of salt is from the sea or from her tears.

Breaking the sobs, she jerks upright. With a vehemence out of all proportion to her request, she cries: "All right—only for *pity's* sake, find *chairs! I cannot stand another instant.*" While she waits, although the night is mild, she pulls her furs close about her, shivering from the uselessness of what she is about to do.

He returns and after they are seated, she begins haltingly: "Si, I'll try—I'll—*oh, Silas, I killed him! killed* him just as surely as though I'd turned on the gas—first my father and now this!"

Silas clears his throat. "No, Liz, that's morbid, melodramatic. You had nothing to do with your father's death."

"Oh, yes—yes, I did! If I'd been there, if I'd been sober—Oh, Si, Si, imagine Sam wanting me and my not being there!"

"Steady, Liz. Sam hadn't recognized you in well over a year. Steady now. What was this man's name?"

"His name was—oh, David, *David!*" Biting her lips, biting down hard, she catches herself. "David Boothe was his name—clever of his parents not to call him Edwin, wasn't it?" The bravado crumbles as fast as it had come. "Si, I can't do this, not without a drink anyway—get Scotch, anything. I mean it—I can't go through this on my own."

He gets up slowly. "Will you want a chaser?"

"You ought to know better—but bring a glass. Hurry."

By the time he returns the thought of the bottle in his hand has already quieted her. The glass is a water glass. Filling it three-fourths full, she drinks the contents.

"All right," she begins again, "I'll have to try to tell this as though I'd read it in the papers—it *was* in the papers, Si. Headlines. Oh, it was perfectly horrib—"

"Start over," he tells her.

"Yes, all right—only don't interrupt. Just sit there as though you were asleep. Can you please do that?"

"Certainly."

Her wide mouth breaks into a grimace, edged in bitterness.

"Why, certainly you can—how silly of me. Well, we met, David and I, at the Parkers' whingding New Year's eve. Three months, seventeen days ago. I'd think the Parkers'd get damn sick of that yearly bout—you'd promised to fly back, remember? When you didn't I was stuck with the Jersey locals

47

and pretty annoyed. But then, when we reached town, there was David.

"He was attractive, Si. Good-looking in an Abraham Lincoln way. He was all by himself too and you know how that is; we got to talking in snatches, about this and that, mostly about people. About how awful they are and where did they all come from? The apartment was mobbed. Everybody wedged in like cows on a freight train. No hope of our ever reaching the bar, no hope, period. This David was very tall, able to see over others and pretty soon I saw him grinning at something and when I asked, what, he lifted me up. Some fat dame in sequins was taking a sock at her husband. I suppose it was her husband—God, I hate sequins!"

Then later when he'd tried to put her down, every smidge of space was filled in so there she was, all dressed up and no place to stand. It was fantastic; millions of strange faces staring up. It was so embarrassing she'd begun to clown, to mimic an opera star in a horrible falsetto, trills—the business—then throwing kisses and grinning like a fool. Soon she'd realized they were moving a little, that David was pushing toward the hall door, with her still up there. It was fun, kind of. She'd pulled his ear. "Where are we going, sir?" she said.

"Miss, you and I are on the lam," he'd called back.

It turned into the nicest New Year's eve, the two of them before a roaring fireplace in his apartment. Not one bit like an apartment, really; half of a ground floor in an old brownstone on the Square. Bath and kitchen and a big double-sized room with long windows on three sides. It was perfectly kept, a Filipino came in daytimes. There were charming things about: old glass and lustre and pewter. Not junked up—extra-special pieces, collector's stuff. The evening was painfully circumspect, no passes, no you-and-me talk, not even too much drinking. Si knew how often she got to know people right bang off? Well, that was all this was. Until the next day.

48

"But that next day, Si—well, David had fallen in love. He was younger than I, a few years, and never had married and never truly been in love. Because of this, I guess, and because of the kind of person he was, it hit him hard. He was especially sensitive, not easily hurt sensitive, aware. Open to nuances and undercurrents, introspective, apt to throw over the concrete in favor of the abstract and always either way up or very down. Somewhat like me, in fact. The more we saw each other, and we did almost every day, the more we clicked —you know that guck about opposites attracting? May be, may be, but they don't stick because what on earth do they have to talk about? David and I were quite alike and up to a point this was simply wonderful.

"But he—pretty soon he wanted me to leave you, Si. Wanted us to go off somewhere, anywhere. It got to be frightening, the intensity, the sort of brooding, smoldering thing which can't be laughed off once it starts. I tried not seeing him and this was worse. The phone rang day and night, and I couldn't always be out, so finally I—I have to tell you this— I offered to have an affair with him. You know I've never done that. At least I hope you know it—but this didn't work either. David didn't want an affair. He wanted me, he said. For keeps."

The whole performance, start to finish, lasted less than two weeks—God, was this possible! She'd gotten that strep throat —or hadn't Si heard about that? Seeing so little of him she never knew what he knew and what he didn't know. Anyway she'd been laid low with strep but after a day or so, because David kept calling and calling, she'd gotten out of bed and driven into town. There was a full moon that night too, except cold of course, cold and crackly. The night air made her throat pulse and she'd known her temperature had sky-rocketed; she could remember turning the heater off and on, off and on.

49

She was meeting David at a party, friends of his across the Square, and when she got there dear David was tight. Not drunk, just a handsome start and there she was, sick to death and cold sober. Something snapped. Suddenly she was simply livid and said so. She told him that the whole damn act was completely ludicrous. What with Alan and Peter, by God, this could not go on!

"I told him I was never going to see him again, kept telling it, kept telling it over and over, but, Si, he just wouldn't understand. At least I thought he didn't and this made me madder. I said he was an attractive, self-centered pig, that I could not face another divorce, so to hell with it, and with him too. And all he did was laugh. He looked at me and laughed and laughed, with his mouth, not his eyes. His eyes were a coal black and they were burning into me, eating me. It was terrible, and you couldn't decide exactly why. This went on and on. We were sitting away from the others. The radio was turned up too high and everybody yacking, everybody but me drunk, for once, and my head splitting and David laughing and acting like a maniac. At last I couldn't bear it another minute. I stood up.

" 'Goodnight, Junior,' I said. 'Give me a buzz sometime. Sometime when life is half as funny as you seem to find it.'

"Out in the street he stood staring in the car window. I already had the motor going when he motioned me to wait. There was a tiny yellow rosebud in his buttonhole and he took it out, very carefully, and handed it to me. 'Here,' he said, "here's something to remember me by'—you know that song, Si. I took the thing and banged the gears and drove off like crazy. I think I was crazy. Am crazy," she corrects herself.

The ship throbs on through the Caribbean. The music stops and there are goodnight calls and then silence. Moonlight floods the deck and the stars are as bright as before. The silence is vast, as vast as only a sea or a desert can make it. The man sits very still, head lowered. The woman, in light-

50

ing a cigarette, drops it and, fumbling for it, her hand touches the bottle. This time she does not bother to use the glass but lifts the bottle and tilts it to her lips. As she leans back she sees that her hands are shaking and that when she clasps them the fingers bend rigidly to pluck at the knuckles. Watching them, they do not seem to belong to her.

As she speaks again her voice is even huskier than before. "Si, when I got home I was completely bushed, drained. Dragging myself upstairs, I remember seeing Alan's open door and thinking how lucky that he wasn't there, that he liked prep school so much. You know, Si, Alan loves you—loves you dearly, did you know that? Well, anyway, Pete didn't move as I put an extra blanket on him and there wasn't a peep from the servants' rooms. I felt peculiarly alone—of course it was late. Close to two, I think."

As Si knew, her very last act every night of her life was to click the off-button on the telephone and yet, incomprehensibly she forgot it that night. Weird. She'd taken three pills instead of two— Sleeping pills, God, they were worse than liquor! Well, not worse maybe but once you drifted into the routine the damn things *owned* you! You could live without air, arms, legs, but not without the nasty little pink jobs. So she'd taken three of them and was stunned into sleep, not remembering David or anyone. No one would ever know how long the phone had been ringing before it got through to her. She supposed she must have been in some deep dream because trying to awake was like trying not to die.

"My hands were stumps, Si. My throat hurt and my ears hurt—I couldn't seem to make sense out of what I was hearing; there were a number of voices, cross currents. Then I heard David. It wasn't so but at the time I took it for granted that the party was still going strong and it made me absolutely *wild*. 'What in the *hell* do you want?' I screamed. Oh *think* of it, Si—*think of it!*"

Silas coughs discreetly. "Yes, Liz. And what did he want?"

"I can't—I—" Liz stumbles, waits, starts over. "He—he said, David said: 'Sorry to disturb you but I did want you to be the first to know I've just turned on the gas.' But, Silas Addams, do you think for one moment I believed him? Oh, can't you see how *horrible* this is? I thought he was drunk. I screamed: 'Stop it. Stop being so goddam dramatic!' and slammed back the receiver. The clock said twenty-five minutes to four, and I flopped down and went to sleep, loathing David, loathing everything.

"Four hours later, about eight o'clock, I found myself standing in the middle of the floor falling apart, hanging on to a bedpost, teeth chattering so that I could hear them. Something was compelling me, something I had to take care of. And whatever it was it was more vital than Judgment Day. And then it came—*David.* David had said he was going to kill himself and if it was really true, it was I who'd killed him! I grabbed the suit I'd worn the night before and you can imagine the maids when I tore through the kitchen; *Mrs. Addams up at eight*—well, you know. As I backed the car out I hit the stone wall and rammed the gas tank and the stink of gas went with me all the way to David's. Traffic was ghastly—Si, how did you *stand* commuting?"

There'd been space to park almost directly opposite the red brick house. It was a gleaming morning. The kind of winter morning that points out things, that makes windows look especially dirty or especially clean. She'd thought at the time how much drunks miss, why, they—she—*miss* mornings!

As she went up the steps she'd noticed how that long front window sparkled and then she thought of Pedro, the Filipino, and right away her mind froze because the door was locked and no one was answering the bell. She pressed and pressed. Occasionally somebody would come down the hall stairs and she'd felt a fool, like a door-to-door salesman. And anyway she was being hysterical; David would be at his office—of course he was at his office! But where—*where was the Fili-pino?*

The house was on a corner, one of those old Washington Square houses which still have small lawns. In front the lawn sloped sharply but at the side it was comparatively wide so she'd gone there and stood close to a window, expecting—well, she didn't know what she was expecting. She did see however, at first glance, that Pedro had not been there. A coat of David's, a brown polo—she never liked it much—was dumped on the floor and there were liquor glasses and filled ash trays. Panic sucked at her, a creeping kind of thing—

"There were two side windows, Si. Both locked. I couldn't just stand there, I had to do something, and right at my foot was a small rock. I took the rock and smashed a window and the gas poured out and smacked me in the face. Then—then I reached in and unlocked the window. I raised it, stepped into the room, and nearly tripped on a low narrow radiator directly below the window. I hadn't ever noticed the radiator before, and I—I do thank God I hadn't.

"After I'd closed the window, I stood there. Simply stood there, nailed down. I couldn't bear to look around and for a while I didn't. Then I moved my head and over in the corner was the day bed and David was on it and he was dead. This I knew absolutely. David was very, very dead and parts of me were dying too. The kitchen door was open, so was the stove oven, wide open, and all the little white knobs turned out toward me. Five of them, all on, all going full blast. The smell was sweet, vomitous sweet, and my head was pounding and my eyes and nose ran. Si, I think I know what it means to go berserk because I did the strangest thing. After I'd turned off the stove, I thought of David's last phone call and knew it would show up on the toll bill and nobody could stop it, but I got smart—crafty. The idea came to tear up the A's for Addams on his private pad, as though *that* would help! As

53

though the toll operator couldn't link up the number in two seconds—crazy."

The phone was close to the day bed. Maybe—maybe David was already groggy when he made the call as the phone was lying on the floor with the receiver off. As she'd reached for the number pad, holding her eyes carefully from David, there was a movement beyond the front window. It couldn't be called a movement exactly; a change of light, a thing that was there, then not there. She'd taken the A's and crushed the heavy paper and put the pieces in her bag. Then finally she looked at David.

"He was fastidious, Si, and—and he was then. Aside from a jacket, he was completely dressed and not even wrinkled—lying on his side, face out, an arm dangling. The top button of his shirt was undone and the tie loosened—brown foulard tie with yellow dots. He seemed quite natural until I made myself touch his forehead and it wasn't natural, it was ice and I felt my legs turn to ice. Right away I was aware of one perfectly definite fact: I was going to have to carry David Boothe around with me the rest of my life, so—so how much better it would have been if I'd left you and married him! It was at this moment that I heard the noise, not hearing it, registering it. The noise didn't alarm me, still it did make me realize that I should get out of there. I turned, took a step or two and then turned back to ask David if he could ever forgive me. After that I went to the hall door and unbolted it.

"The hall was empty. I closed the hall door and opened the one to the street and walked out and down the steps. As I did this, two men in uniform came running at me, a cop and a messenger. They didn't stop though, they brushed past, and I knew exactly what I'd seen from inside that room. It was the color that registered, the color of the messenger's uniform. And I knew what had happened; the messenger had gone into the hall, smelled the gas and run for the police. I was positive this was the truth. And it was.

"I must have flooded the motor, Si. Even with the leak in the tank, the gauge said half full but it wouldn't catch so in desperation I chugged around the corner on magneto. I had to get away. You see, I was so sure some smart cookie would spot the license and remember how often that black Packard had stood in front of that house. I wouldn't have been able to drive, though, flooded or not. I was shaking like an aspen —Si, what is an aspen? Never mind, I'll get on—I was shaking and so terribly sick I was afraid I'd urp all over everything so, because I couldn't get away, I started to wishful-think. You know how terrific I am at that. I started to kid myself that David wasn't dead after all. Everything was going to be all right, the police were there, weren't they? And a pulmotor would come and sure enough it did and the chief's car and a crowd gathered and men dashed in and out.

"Never have I needed a drink as I did then. I kept expecting somebody to come up and ask who I was—you know, the way they do in books—but nobody did. I waited and watched and hoped, certain in my heart that David was gone but if he wasn't—oh, Si, think of all the time I'd wasted! Maybe if I hadn't torn around, tearing out telephone numbers, behaving like some dumb cluck-head in the mysteries. Priceless minutes wasted on antics like that—well, anyway, he was dead all right."

It was singular how this had become evident. She'd been watching with her whole body, still hoping against hope, when all at once she saw a priest trying to get through the crowd. He'd gone past the house when a cop spied him and ran out and spoke to him and a minute later the priest turned back and went up the steps. A priest, for God's sake! She could have told them David was no Catholic—but then, Si knew cops. The shaking got worse and worse—this was curtains! The cops were shooing the crowd and the cars would be next. She might as well go home. Where else was there to go? So she'd driven home and there on the garage floor, crushed, stepped on, was the yellow rosebud David had handed her. It looked up at her like some goddam symbol.

"And that's about all, Si. Except for the shouting. I didn't see the papers that night, I was blind drunk and couldn't have read them if I had, but the morning papers! David's uncle was a bigshot politico and they gave it the business, headlines. And do you know what? Not a paper, not a single paper, said one word about suicide! They hinted around it; one headline said: IN SPITE OF BROKEN WINDOW POLICE STILL INSIST DEATH OF DAVID BOOTHE ACCIDENTAL. They couldn't have wanted to know, they just *couldn't*, because Pedro, the houseman, showed up with a note which had been thumb-tacked to the door. The note said not to come that day—now how *could* they get around that? They did though, they said David hadn't been feeling well and didn't wish to be disturbed. He won't be, *that's* for sure."

The low voice drifts off. There is no sound at all until at last the man stirs, moving his body sideways to look at her. He says: "And how did they account for the gas? You'd turned off the stove."

She laughs harshly. "You bet, I'd turned off the stove but the radiator, the one I almost tripped on, was a gas radiator. Naturally if I'd known it, I'd have turned it off too. The papers said the radiator had a leak in it—but what's the difference? Leak or no leak, David Boothe is dead and I murdered—"

The husband reaches over to touch the knotting fingers. "No. No, Liz. If you don't mind, I think you've overdramatized this too. A man falls in love with you—and that's nothing new—and when you refuse to do what he asks, he takes his life. In all probability he'd have done it later, over something else; you're the suicide type or you aren't. I'm glad though that you told me. Perhaps now you'll be able to forget the whole incident."

56

The wife stares at him, her features twisting in anguish. Interpreting his words in her own fashion, she says: "I see. It was simply an incident, was it? And I'm to forget it because two wrongs don't make a right—*Christ*. I should have done what David asked, *leave* you!" '

Jerkily she gets up and walks to the ship's stern. She stands there, staring down, then swiftly, urgently, she grips the rail in both hands like someone about to vault a fence. But the man moves faster than she. He runs and clutches the body, forcing it back, forcing the hands loose.

"Liz—Liz *dearest*," he cries.

The body shudders and at last the arms go limp. Tears come. Weeping convulsively, she says: "Si—Si, *forgive* me. You've been sweet—perhaps it *will* help. I—I hope so."

As he leads her past the deck chairs, the man's face sags piteously, the lower lip protruding like a weary child's.

CHAPTER FIVE

In standing aside and looking back at this woman I used to be, it is more and more possible to detach myself, to view her in third person. She was she and I am I; Siamese twins perhaps, one of whom must die that one may live. However some of her blood is in me, particles of the gene of her. I do not think as she thought, feel as she felt, do as she did, and yet there do remain leftovers, tag ends, at least the memory of urges. One of these urges, more clamorous even than that of telescoping the nightlife of bull and virgin, is to brush off the Liz I must now deal with. To burlesque the act by simpering: "My, my, will the woman never light!"

It is not that simple. From my present seat, sin is not a joke. The Devil, wily fellow, begs us to think it is. With crafty gaiety he shifts to meet our humor, our minds, on their own level; a wisecrack here, a psychiatric term there, and shame dissolves. Shame is a bore, not chic. The autobiographies of other pagans find me unprepared for the gusty lip-smacking their sinning seems to bring them. In a way they are fortunate since if one is bent on playing pig it must be nicer to enjoy it.

I did not. That life was work, extremely complicated, always just about to be worth it. There was fun of course, case upon case of 98 proof fun, but fun of whatever proof is not joy, is not contentment, is not happiness. Fun is excitement-eating, a dietary substitute for growing up. There comes the day—you'd better *hope* there comes a day—when the merry-go-round stops twirling.

Therefore, as cheery as it would be to dish out tales of joyous amblings on the downward path, the scent of primrose in the air, the sound of naughty kisses, that's not the way it was. Not for Liz. Liz sloughed down the path, paying her toll in hard-earned charm. Don't think there isn't toll. And don't think charm is not earned.

You are thinking I think I was a congenital killer-diller, history's *femmes fatales* wrapped up in one. Well, you couldn't be further off; I was a congenital *wallflower*. What I acquired, I dug for; slaved for; observed, compared, maneuvered, backtracked, foresaw. Success is ever thus. From Eve on down, no all-things-to-all-men dame has got that way without thought and effort *in excelsis*.

If you're a gilt-chair-sitter, one of the army that parks its rear and whispers: "What *do* they see in her?", stop wondering—I'll be glad to tell you. To begin with, what "they" see is a woman who's kept her own rear down to size 14, and you know what a job *that* is! They see a woman able to criticize herself, who therefore does not wear plaids if short or stripes if tall. They see a woman conscious of self and not self-conscious. Who has daring, not gall. Who adores the limelight, and is careful never to hog it. Who knows an answer or two and doesn't have to interrupt to tell it. Whose discretion can be trusted, whose anecdotes do not go on and on and on if the Big Freeze is on—you see, she *feels* the Freeze! Who has not the arrogance to slide into deadpanism, who—and *this is it*—is more concerned with how you are than how she is.

This all-things gal is a Feeder in place of a Monopolizer. Above and beyond all, she is a *listener*. The gal *actually listens*. This she proves. She proves it even to other women by laughing at the right time, weeping at the right time, asking the right question at the right time.

See, this is what "they" see in "her."

The point with Liz is that she has been a wallflower and has not forgotten it. Still unable to believe her senses, she is grateful and has acquired the habit of appreciation.

Like the word glamour, the word charm has been worn to a nubbin, to an extent where it's almost negative. If someone isn't a dope, a frump, a shrew, she's charming. The heck she is! While we're at it, take the word attractive; the word lady. Attractive is what a baby is if it doesn't bite you and a lady is a female who will never pick her nose in a glass house. Fuzz.

These words are words intended to denote an *inner* state. To call a female charming, attractive, a lady, ought to indicate a quality extremely special, an inner glow so outreaching as to include all around her. A something which is the result of other somethings and so how could it be easy? It could not and is not. It is not caught like measles, is not picked up from how-to books. You cannot buy it, you can only sell it. You cannot eat it yet when you possess it, you can be sure you'll always eat.

In fact it is an art. An art akin to selflessness. And it is the use, and the motive behind the use, which together determine whether the kinship be bastard or legitimate. And here was where I failed. I was now charming others to charm myself and this is bastard.

A new game was in process; the game of soul-collecting rather than mere scalp-collecting; cyanide to buttermilk. A quicksand diversion. Warped. Evil.

I believe I knew that it was evil. Often I am told I'm far

60

too tough on the self I was and here *is* a joke for only I can know the thoughts I had, the compulsive will to power, the conscience-muzzling. The darkest sins in 2,000 years have been psychological sins; stealing someone's rights is worse than stealing someone's right of way. Far, far worse, since this demands a smarter thief. The Ten Commandments may have covered Moses but they don't cover Liz.

Because Liz knew what she was doing. Knew and hated herself and thus the circle became a vicious circle. The less she could abide her actions the greater the need for someone who could be counted on to whitewash them. The viciousness lies in the fact that a time comes when one goes further and further, solely to test whether this too will be condoned. ("You think you can't take *more*? Just wait; just wait.")

Power and cruelty are recognized as brothers. Power comes through making yourself indispensable and cruelty follows from the need to prove your indispensability. However it is proved, by guns or wit, you rob the victim of all critical sense, all discrimination, and lastly of will itself. The human version of cat and mouse. The adult version of de-winging flies.

Obviously my men who let their wings be pulled were not strong men. The greater number were young and dazzled, or maladjusted, but of one thing I am certain; *every single one was a human being.* And no human being was put here to play spare tank to augment another's pride. Such a game is not allowed to last and oddly it is the starter who stops it for sycophancy is an echo and echoes hold little lasting interest.

Aware that what I was doing was beyond decency, it seems I had to do it, *had* to, just as I had to guzzle, hating both, hating me, yet having to. A strange strange war between two selves, the one self running headlong, faster, ever faster; the other alongside, crying out, abusing, warning, pointing to the finish. There are numerous levels of escape. Some crude, some insidiously refined, and their consequences match them.

61

Snitching a person's purse can be repaid but nothing can repay the snitching of a person's soul. If Heaven chooses to forgive this, I shall be surprised and will put it down to just so much celestial gravy.

It appears so odd that Liz could not foresee the finish. She had a brain, imagination, a twisted yet terrible sense of honesty; the gods had emptied goodies in her lap. She was given all except a face to launch a thousand ships and what woman gives a hoot for one ship, let alone a thousand? Sam, with great love, had handed her the moon framed in platinum; health, opportunities, position, money.

And Randall Trowbridge; why had not the triumph of snaring the fair-haired prize counterbalanced the bullishness? There be those who dote on bulls, in truth, *insist* upon them, and here was such a *pretty* bull! But, that is past—she didn't *wish* the bull. Peace of mind was what she wished. With Silas however she has found that there are different kinds of peace, each demanding a certain compromise. But compromise she will not, any more than she will call amusement, happiness. For a period, yes, and then some goad pushes her, hurries her on, *on*, and always in the wrong direction. This was Liz Addams the year of David's suicide.

I see this Liz. I feel her insides knot. I hear her silent cry and also I understand why no one dreams of listening. Who, who could pity Liz? Why *look* at all she has. See—see *this* and *that*, five of these and four of those—good God, Liz is to be envied.

Lost, ashamed, confused. As lonely as the call of mourning doves—*and to be envied?*

This is a woman whose need is great, is ripening, is coming to a head. Good, fine—go buy a diamond bracelet!

Mankind has stock comments for the misery of the well-upholstered: "Jesus, if I had all *their* dough—!"

And: "With a million bucks, what's *his* excuse for suicide?"

And: "Nothing wrong with me a lotta jack wouldn't fix."
Is that so?

Well, I wish you'd try it! I wish you'd try a bed of roses
—sit on roses, sleep on roses, eat roses, breakfast, lunch,
dinner. Until you have tried it, day in, day out, for forty years
and over, your opinion isn't worth one damn. Comforts, yes
indeed! The right amount to lead a healthy, free from worry
life, but duplicates, and triplicates—! And nothing from
dawn to dark, nothing at all that *needs* doing, that is *death*.
And not the cozy death you might imagine either. A satin
pillow will smother you as fast as a burlap bag; a rope of
diamonds for which a man has hocked his heart will gag you
as surely as a dirty rag. Then, in addition, the frosting on
this towering layer cake is *guilt*. Always and always there is
guilt because you are so terribly aware of how much you have
which others lack.

Surfeit and guilt. A combination that is preposterous and
yet one which tortures every sensitive person. But the hooker
is, while you know that others lack, you do not *know* these
others. You don't even know *about* them! They live in tenements and you don't go to tenements. And what you haven't
seen is pretty hard to picture and what you cannot picture is
pretty hard to feel responsible for. You look at photographs in
magazines and papers, and think, Suffering Lord, isn't it
simply *awful*, but pictures are not people. Now maybe it's
your bounden duty to barge into tenements, to wring gloved
hands and cry: "Oh, missus, what—what can I do?" Maybe
on the other hand you happen to be the kind who has the
sense to feel that Lady Bountiful is a Grade A pedigreed ass.

Give, of course, and you do give and give. Not till it hurts
perhaps, yet a great deal and consistently; in quotas, donations, taxes. In addition you're the town's pushover for every
Mac who rings the doorbell. You buy a dozen yellow pencils
when you've got a gross of yellow pencils; you buy boxes of

red apples when you've got an orchard of red apples. And none of it is worth a hill of beans because it is utterly impossible to *feel* a need you haven't had.

Charity is love and love is understanding. To give to others without understanding is the boy with his hand in the dyke. A stopgap, little else. Not for a single moment do I mean that we should stop giving; what I mean is that to give money with no understanding cannot be true charity.

Nor is this in any sense a plea for a poor little, lucky little rich girl. This is the other side, a side which maybe you don't know. And there are two sides to the money angle as well as everything else—for crying out loud, there has to be! The rich bastard with an aching heart hears plenty about the poor bastard with the aching back but how about the other way round? Try the other team for a change.

Try the team that's up to here in material junk it never asked for, doesn't want, doesn't need, doesn't value and so doesn't use properly. Liz had desired none of it; every bit of it was a redheaded farm boy's idea of what *should* be desired. The Scotch kid climbs out of the steerage, peeks into showcases, spies the fancy junk and decides this must be essential to achievement. Though it'll have to be said for Sam that he never *settled* for Things, not once, nor valued them *per se*. Money had a purpose. Money was the stuff that made the mare go, but it wasn't the mare.

In retrospect, this particular Liz is a Liz-without-Sam. She spends a lifetime running from Sam, in rebellion to him, and yet the same lifetime is spent comparing every man she meets to him. Material possessions in the light of Sam's use of them had not appeared so senseless. They were merely part and parcel. Sam's vitality had changed all possessions, all acts, all people. In the light of him, other men were shoes without laces, potatoes without salt, motors without batteries. Self-made, impossibly tough, but, by the Lord God Almighty, a

64

man! A man who had made the bull naught but a bull, and the fog naught but a fog.

Now that the blinding glare of Sam's tremendous maleness has gone out, life is quiet and it is stale. Liz is Liz-without-Sam and must take it from there. Take what? And where? What *is* it that Liz Addams wants?

Well, I will tell you what she wants! She wants to point to one thing, almost any thing, and say: "This I *earned!*"

With this in mind, we will return to Si and the Jersey household. As you may have noticed, the yard-wide wool has raveled and is greatly patched. A temperament such as mine used to be does not think however of making over; it has never thought of revamping a worn coat into a good short one. It yells: "*That* old thing!" It throws it in a corner and some day soon it shops around for something new. Perhaps something the very opposite.

There were several other things I could have done. In spite of Si's saying he was coming home next month, next month, *next* month, I could have insisted upon moving to the Middle West with him. By now Alan was away at college and Pete, six years younger, would be ready for prep school any day. These two had been born as I was born to a group which palms off offspring early. Children come and that is good. Nurses are hired and that is better. Children outgrow nurses and go off to school and this is best. Good, better, best: the philosophy that children are delightful if somebody else brings them up!

Or I could have sat by the fire and sucked my thumb. Or I could have done what I did do: raise hell.

Now swoop the if's. If Silas had stayed at home, if the all-wool boy had seemed to place his wife and son ahead of business. If I had ceased to be Sam's daughter and dared to become myself. If along the corridor there'd been a door marked A.A. and I'd stopped to open it—

65

Before dawn is the darkest and while the darkest was still ahead, this period was very dark. So dark that it is with wonder that I recall a statement made by a friend named Debbie. A chipper, rounded, little thing, Debbie, who lived across the road, would drop in as though by chance all through the aftermath of David's suicide. Days and nights of morbid hysteria, of incoherent black, black guilt, of drowning guilt in liquor and never drowning it. Debbie would sit quietly, ignoring the clenched hands, the bloodshot eyes, the mad scrambled talk.

Once the mist surrounding me must have lifted for I remember her saying rather sternly: "Liz, yours is a strange, strange pilgrimage. It leads you into very very odd places where you pick up and discard, pick up and discard, but all the same it is a pilgrimage. For truth, the Truth. And they who search, find, and some day, you will too—you'll find the Truth." I felt she too was mad but now I know that she was not.

The Caribbean cruise over, Si went back west and I, Liz, scrutinized the raveled marriage and began to shop around. The shopping wasn't deliberate; none of what Liz did was done deliberately. Bad, bad but not deliberate and probably this too is typical; the total lack of deliberation. Here once again she stands knee-deep in men yet still no actual realization that one and one and one eventually makes three; three *husbands*. God knows she wasn't doing this with open eyes and God also knows, and hasn't hesitated to point out, that she had two eyes to open, both twenty-twenty.

Her state of "extra" woman-though-married continued one whole year more, and as war wives have discovered, it's a state similar to a meal consisting entirely of desserts. No soup, no entree, no salad. Bloat without nourishment. In reappraising it appears quite remarkable how comparatively easily Liz was able to digest her males. If there was scandal either

66

she was too swacked to notice or no one had the nerve to tell her. I wouldn't have had the nerve myself; the Liz I used to be wasn't exactly a dame to tangle with.

The one Force which could have tangled with her was her Creator but she considered Sam her Creator and had put no other God before him. No one she knew knew God. For some He was a rabbit's foot, for some, the Bogeyman, for some, St. Nicholas, for Si and his Vermonters, He was a giant in whiskers and a Prince Albert coat whom she never ran into unless she went to visit in Vermont.

This woman seeks the Truth, yes, but the only level upon which one can seek Truth is the level one is on at the time of search. The wisdom of Plato is not dreamed of in kindergarten; Bach is not played in honky-tonks. Liz Addams' search was on the level of a pasture overseen by some man as vital as Sam without Sam's demands. Armed with the sure appeal of the sex-unconquered she shopped for greener fields, forgetting Randy's once-lush greenness, forgetting Si's once-safe, gentle green. This was to be permanent. This would have everything.

As in all quests Liz found precisely what she deserved. They both did. His name was Jim Hatch and they deserved each other.

The year of shopping was over. By now Pete was twelve and set for boarding school. And at long last Si, after four years, was coming home to stay. It was this more than anything that accelerated the trip to Reno. Liz could not live with the little man who wasn't there and now that he was there she could not live with him.

It was too late. These two were strangers. Strangers who knew each other's most intimate habits and this is disconcerting in the extreme. They now had separate rooms. Between the rooms however there was a door and occasionally when the door stood open, they would make like lovers. It was one such night that the new love, the man called Jim, seemed to come and stand in the doorway, stand there waiting. Then Si's arms were no longer tolerable and she had to break away. She had to tell him.

The memory of this woman and her words are quite distinct. I remember leaving Si and getting up. I remember the color of the robe I pulled around me. It was a sharp awkward green, a kind of peacock, a robe Si had bought me. I remember thinking: at least he'll notice I've kept his gift. (As though a gift not discarded could soften what I was about to say!)

"Si, Si dear," I began, fighting for calmness, trying to give notice quietly that he was about to lose his wife, that I'd found someone better suited, someone named Jim Hatch.

But I could not contain myself. It was as if inside me a wood fire had smoldered in secret until now the very breath it took to tell about it was causing it to burst into flame.

"Silas," I cried, "I have found a man—"

"A man?" he repeated as though the idea of another man were wholly new, as though there'd never been a David or any scalp collection.

Such artlessness appeared cynical. It made me want to hurt him, made me cry: "A man, yes, fancy that—a man, do you understand? An honest-to-God man—we are so right for each other that even you must see it, Si. I love, no maybe it isn't love, maybe it's a kind of madness, but you, nobody can stop it! You could no more stop it than you could stop a hurricane."

Silas was not one to change moods easily. His expression had been sweet and drowsy and only a little questioning but now pain began to come, the old inner pain. The eyes looking at me grew raw with hurt, a hurt exposed and quickening. Once or twice his head turned on the pillow and then slowly he pulled himself up.

68

"Stop what?" he asked.

In spite of the myriad causes for pain I had already given him, his face was so guileless, so unprepared, that my cruelty was at once monstrous. I began to weep in a lost, weary fashion, almost without changing expression. I recall wandering around the room, straightening objects that were already straightened, moving a chair an inch or two only to replace it. Finally I reached the bed where Silas sat, not going there deliberately but because he happened to be in the path of my aimlessness.

The futility of reaching him, of finding words ruthless enough to convince myself as well as him, filled me with despair. For the moment I was quite positive that nothing was worth this, nothing in heaven or earth. I would never leave Silas. Never leave that round face, this house, this room, this very furniture. Suddenly my hopelessness fastened itself on the things around us, the inevitability of inanimate objects.

"Look at all this junk." I pointed. "Look at it! Then think of all the millions and millions of other crackerbox-houses filled with more and more junk. Beds, tables, chairs; big chairs, middle-sized chairs, little chairs, like the three bears. Chairs to fit the behinds of millions and millions of people—what waste! What damn idiocy when all anyone ever needs is a pine box—no, Si, don't touch me. *Don't.*"

He had gotten up and was about to put his arms around me. Letting his arms fall, he said: "Never mind the furniture. What was it you were trying to tell me? What is it no one can stop? Whatever it is, Liz, I'd like to help if I can."

Here was the spur I had needed; this terrible unfailing kindness, this undemanding blind acceptance that what was could be made to go on forever. With the type of honesty that shifts its guilt by confessing it, I burst out: "Oh, Silas, don't you see how I detest what I am doing to you? Oh, you're good, you're everything people ought to be, everything,

69

and that's the trouble, that's exactly what's wrong! I can't stand it any longer. That's what I meant—when I said I'd found a man—a *man*, not a saint! Somebody who won't *let* me win. Never, never, never, if he has to kill me."

"You had that in Randall," Si said. "You used to tell me—"

"*Randall*," I jeered. "How very plainly that shows your lack of understanding. Randy was a child. Jim Hatch is a man. He's what I've always needed—oh, can't you see I'm sick to death of gentleness? I have to go, Si—please let me go!"

He stood there, staring, and tears came and ran down his face.

"What will I ever do without you?" he said.

Grief could not alter the shape of his face; it was just as round, just as childlike, but before my eyes the features changed. It was like some child at Halloween taking a pumpkin and cutting a happy face, mouth tilted upwards pleasantly, but all at once the knife slipped; the mouth was gashed, stretched painfully beyond repair. Si's eyes, usually bland, not overly aware, were now defenseless, not yet able to conceal their grief.

We stared at one another.

He said: "I love you, Liz. I've always loved you. But—but somehow I never seem to find the words to say it."

(*Father God, is there some very special hell for the Puritan Founders? A very prissy, self-contained hell where Ramrods stand and meditate upon the curbs they handed down to inhibit their poor progeny forever?*)

And I, the noble martyr, what did I reply?

"And now it is too late," I moaned. Then, like explaining to a child why you had to punish him, I said reasonably: "You see, Si, it's that this feeling, Jim's and mine, is greater, greater than you and I, greater even than Jim and I. It's—"

"Greater than Peter?" Si asked.

That frightened me. I remember my hands flying to my

face, remember crying: "Si, you wouldn't! That isn't like you—you're too kind to make me make that choice." Then, watching him, seeing that I was safe, I dared to say: "Silas, you keep Peter. You get the divorce. On any grounds. On drunkenness."

His answer stunned me. "I think I almost could," he said.

Faced with the stark truth, my bravado crumbled. "No, Si. No, you won't do that. And you won't take Pete—oh, if only there was the slightest chance of justifying what I'm doing, doing to Alan as well as you and Pete! It's all so frightfully mixed up because I do love you, love the part of you that is what I used to be, or longed to be. How can ideals curdle so? I had them once—where are they? Have I traded them all in for lousy *charm*? I don't know, Si, I don't honestly know. But just the same I have to leave you—*have* to, Si. For God's sake, let me go!"

Yes, he would let me go, he told me quietly. Unless—?

I shook my head. "No, don't hope. There isn't any—and don't look that way. Oh, darling, darling, you'll be better off. I don't imagine you ever really loved me anyway; it was just that you had no basis for comparison."

At this he smiled faintly.

"Liz, don't work so hard," he said. "You can go. All my life I've believed that people have to do what they have to do; it's some kind of pattern. The one thing is that you—you'll have to be the one to tell Pete. And Alan. That I can't do."

After he'd closed the door I sat and wept my heart out. I sobbed and sobbed and got the sherry bottle and slugged myself and called James C. Hatch and gave him holy hell and got hell back.

(Oh, Si, that's what you should have done. Given me blow for blow. But no, no, I guess not.)

(Oh, Si—what were your thoughts? When I told you of Jim, what did you think? Did you think I was living with *both* of you? Or did you trust me? Or didn't you dare to think of it

71

at all? But then, I never did know what you thought, I only knew what you said, and that so little. But you did say that people have to do what they have to do and I guess that's right. What I believed I desired doesn't exist at all, but I had to find it out myself. Had to find that what I was asking for was a grab bag marriage full of fancy prizes just as later I was to try for a grab bag God full of fancy miracles.)

It was September before I got around to telling Pete that he'd lost his home. He and Alan were back from summer camp and Pete was packing, sorting his belongings for his first year at prep school. Excited and happy, he came to my dressing room, a rain hat in one hand, a ski boot in the other.

"Hi, want me, Mom?" he asked.

To tell Alan would be a simple matter. After all, Si wasn't his father—but Pete. I looked at this young son of mine. His hair was blond like mine but the eyes were my mother's eyes, exceptionally dark and full of sweetness. Pete had my hair and Mother's eyes and Si's simple goodness and there was something else, some quality that was Sam. Integrity perhaps.

He was smiling up at me. "Gee, Mom, you're interrupting an awful busy guy. What was it you wanted?"

Glib approaches left me. I swallowed hard. "Pete, listen— I, well, Daddy and I—well, from now on we're going to live in different places."

His grin widened. "You mean cause Daddy snores so awful?"

"Well, y—es. I, we—we both think we'll be happier apart."

The brown eyes smiled confidently. "Yeah, Mom. And where'll I be happy?" This did not mean that Peter was troubled, merely that he was asking for information.

It made me sick. Soul-sick. It made me cry out: "Oh, Pete, precious *precious* Pete, you're the kind who'll be happy always!"

"Sure, Mom," he agreed, "but where'll I *be*?"

"Oh, that—?"

I went and put my arms around the sturdy body, smelling the familiar smells; soap, dirt, corduroy.

"Oh—that'll be all right, Pete. Why, you'll have two homes. Two, instead of one."

"Alan'll have three," he said. "Cause even if he doesn't see his dad, he could always go there if he had to."

The eyes were no longer smiling. They were gravely searching mine. When he spoke again the words were slow and stressed.

"Mom, are you—positive you want—this? *Positive?*"

Here was reprieve, a chance to take it back, to stop escaping, justifying, varnishing, destroying. To stop seeking what I hadn't earned. To take the best I had and try to make it into something better. Instead I nodded. As if reversing our positions, I pleaded like a child: "Yes, please, Pete—please."

The grin returned full force. "Sure, it's okay. Anything you do is okay with me, you know that, Mom. Can I go now?"

When I was by myself once more there came a growing sense of relief. It nibbled at the shame Pete's trust had brought me until gradually there was the feeling that what I was going to do was actually inevitable and what was inevitable, greater than I, must in the end be right. Certainly this marriage was proven wrong. Wrong for everyone. It was no marriage at all, so obviously all parties to it would be benefited by supplanting it with something vital. The process of uprooting was painful beyond belief but in the end, all would benefit. Take Si; why, Si would find such freedom, such peace, and as for my sons, surely their love and trust had nothing to do with whom I was married to; Pete had just proved that!

Lulling myself, hypnotizing myself, I heard Pete's voice outside the window. Obviously he'd sidetracked his packing so now would be a good time to recheck the things he was planning to take to school. He wouldn't be returning to this

73

house, now that Si and I were separating, and imagine the countless odds and ends to be given away, thrown away.

I had crossed the room to open the door when it was flung open violently. It was Alan. Alan, tall and dark, stood before me. Lips twisted in scorn, eyes blazing, he reached behind him and slammed the door shut.

In a voice I wouldn't have recognized, he said: "You— you—"

I stiffened. "What, Alan—what?"

"Yeah, *what?* What kind of woman are you—who are you? Have you no honor? No decency even?" Before I could speak he stopped me: "No, don't say anything. I know you; you'll twist it into some sugar-coated bunk, something that'll make Si the heel and you the martyr. The truth is, the God's truth is that you're no better than a streetwalker. Worse maybe because you always have to marry them. Whoever's the Dream Guy this time, why can't you just go to bed with him and get it over with? Just change men for a while and quit calling it marriage."

This was unjust.

"That is not true," I cried. "This is—"

"Don't try to snow me," he shouted. "You snowed Pete, poor little bastard, but you can't snow me! Anything you do is okay with him, Pete says—well, it *isn't* okay with me. I despise you. I despise everything about you, and if you do this, if you run out on Si—oh, what *is* it you want? You've got the best guy that ever lived, the best. You've got Si and Pete and me, isn't that your share? If it isn't, just let me tell you one thing—if you do this awful thing, you can subtract me from the list. You won't have *me!* The rest of your whole lifelong you can be sure that your son Alan—this great pet of yours! —isn't your son at all; he's *dead.* The queen's favorite started dying half an hour ago, and the dead just don't give a damn— they're dead, see? So you can—"

74

Whatever he was about to add was never added. His body wheeled and braced itself against the door. The door was mirrored on the inside and as wild sobs shook him, Alan's right fist beat at the mirror, beat at it.

I had frozen but the ghastly racking sounds brought motion back to me. I touched his shoulder. "Alan, Alan," I cried.

He turned violently, thrusting me backwards. Still sobbing, he shouted: "*Shut up.* Oh God, just forever and forever shut—!"

For the first time I was seeing Alan as grown, as a man. And it was to this man I was going to appeal. His anger was childish and unjust and he would get over that, but I realized now that he had a right to the truth about Si and me.

Like the utter fool I was, like all soap-opera fools, I said: "Alan, in a way, you're right. You called Pete a little bastard and in a way that's true. In a way you're both bastards because neither of my marriages has been a marriage at all. When anyone marries for the wrong reasons, how else can it turn out?"

Beginning to feel reasonable as I had with Silas, I continued: "Take your father. I told myself I loved your father but actually, unconsciously, what I was doing, Alan, was running from my father, in rebellion to him. Then when you came out of it of course it made all the rest, the part you don't know, completely worth it. Then Si, certainly I believed this right, more than right because, like you, I knew how good Si was— *is*. But here again I was running from my father. In both it was escape, not marriage. Marriage is fulfillment, two halves meeting to form the perfect, the one perfect whole. No, wait!"

Alan was looking through me, beyond me, with a boredom so abysmal that it was more terrible than hate. For one fleeting instant there came the belief that he had meant what he said, that he was forcing me to choose between him and Jim Hatch. But this could not be—yet suppose, suppose it was? Suppose he meant precisely that? No, such a choice was unreasoning. There was no need for it. Once Alan knew Jim, with a little understanding from all of us—

Floundering on, I said: "Wait, Alan. When you know this man—"

"When I know him?" he flung at me. "Don't kid yourself! I'll never—"

"Oh, yes, you will. And when you see us together, you'll see a marriage that is a marriage, and you'll see a whole woman instead of half a woman. And a whole mother, not some fumbling half-thing, using her sons to compensate her own lack. What a liar I've been! What a cheap gimcrack of a woman—you may be right that I've been no better than a streetwalker because few streetwalkers would attempt to dignify a state that can't be dignified. Oh, Alan, at last I've found someone who can make me whole, who can give me dignity!"

"*Dignity?*" he repeated scornfully. "Why, you poor weak sap, you are throwing away your last shred of dignity. Do it, do whatever you want, you always have. But don't try to drag me with you. For once you're going to eat your cake and *not* have it, because I don't seem to care for any new fathers. I'll stick to Si, thank you. And this is for all time—you'd better believe it!"

Before I could search for some other footlight to shine on Jim and me, Alan had gone. The door had opened and closed and I was alone. For one second I saw him, saw both my sons and their rights as compared to Jim's and my rights. Struck dumb, I stood there. Suppose what Alan had said was true? About throwing away the last shred of dignity, for instance? But how—how could it be true? How could a right marriage be wrong? How could happiness breed unhappiness? It couldn't! This was as absurd as to say he despised me, or —or that he would not be with me.

Gazing at the closed door I saw the mirror smudged with

76

fist marks. A smudge that might have been tears had merged into the fist marks. Because Alan was so much taller than I, these smudges formed a dirty halo above my reflected head. The rest of me looked the same, a too-thin woman in English tweeds, her favorite suit, a golden-brown mixture just right for autumn. At the elbows were patches of golden-brown leather and around the patches the tweed had begun to wear thin. The woman was inordinately proud of this; it was her one article of clothing worn often enough to wear thin.

Gradually through the open window she was aware of children's voices. There was the sound of a baseball hitting a bat, then Peter's voice. He must be coaching someone on how to pitch for she heard him say: "No, not that way. Aw, you're no good!"

She stared at herself in the mirror. Her lips moved.

"Me too," they said.

Liz, crazy-to-go, crazy-to-stay. Too unstable to do either with undivided heart. Ashamed yet goaded. Her mind a rat race; shame racing willfulness; now shame ahead, now willfulness ahead.

The truth is, it was I yet not I who took that train for Reno. Who wept the whole six straight weeks, who phoned Jim Hatch to say I never, never could go through with it; who cried out in agony when he replied: "Great. That's your business."

CHAPTER SIX

Exit Silas, making two down.

Enter Jim, making one to go.

Husband No. 3, Dr. James Culpepper Hatch, was a surgeon, divorced, no children, and fancy-free, so free of fancies as to be without them. Should it have been blood which ran in his veins, each corpuscle was dedicated to surgery and any woman who presumed herself even a runner-up was headed for a fall, and fell. In fashioning Jim, nature played a kind of trick; he did appear so precisely what the surfeited lady wished to order: hard to get, with looks and intellect and style thrown in.

His particular field was brain surgery and in every aspect he carried it to a fine art. If, a frightened patient, you walked into Jim's office, you might not like him but at once you were able to relax because instinctively you trusted him. You trusted him as you trust any perfect mechanism. Here was someone who was safe the way a bridge is safe, a skyscraper, a vault.

A strong surface attraction made you want to know him as a person, and a barrier, equally strong, kept you back. In time you might come to feel that the attraction was a form of cheating as with a painting that looks authentic only to turn out an extremely clever imitation. His knowledge of the brain, of brain surgery, was authentic however. And this you somehow knew. Certainly other surgeons knew it. Time and again Jim Hatch saved lives by a hair, saved minds from wandering off into limbo, by brilliant diagnoses, by still more brilliant surgery.

A dispassionate man. A man concerned with humans solely as objects for his own gifted hands to dissect. A machine rather, a perfect machine, perfectly functioning.

I met Jim, if pickups are meetings, in a 1937 haze of gin. The meeting took place in a small restaurant I don't remember ever going into, filled with people I don't remember ever seeing.

This is typical of all working alcoholics; their contacts are, to put it mildly, unpredictable. All that could be called predictable in my drinking was the pattern. One cocktail, one single cocktail, spelled eventual drunkenness; drunkenness spelled tomorrow's abasement and hangover, and each bout had three separate rounds. The time and duration varied but never the number; three by anybody's count.

First round, the "fun" round, minked, primed and cocky as a penguin, I'd be on the town; man or men in tow. Gloriously on the button, we'd hit the high spots, 21, the Stork, occasionally Leon & Eddie's. Food was under glass and left there. "Food? God, No!"

You can see why I never hooked a fat man for long. I do recall one very pixie fat man. He was around just once, I think, crying: "Food, food!" and ordering it and being told, "We gotta go," before it came. He didn't last the night; no woman can compete with food. The love of victuals equals the love of liquor except that no one rapes a girl or robs a bank because he eats too much.

My second round was timed according to state of nerves and stomach; it might arrive in one hour, might be four to five. This was ever the mournful round, the deep soul stuff, the let's-talk-about-me-and-you; you being a gent of course.

The deep soul stuff leads to secluded corners, to spots "away

79

from it all." Dependent upon powers of navigation, "away from it all" may be the end of the bar, a victoria in Central Park, or another dump exactly like the one you left. Rarely, it might even lead back to your own home for the mere novelty of it.

One time, sometime, someone and I, the name was Dick, I think, were somewhere, the Colony, I think. Anyhow it was elegant and I was plotzed. This I do not think, I *know*. Arrayed to kill, I luckily was killing, and not only Dick, a brace or so of others. But it was Dick who had the lovely soul, an exquisitely sorrowing soul to match my own. We said very little, danced in silence, and then the urge to comfort, the need to share our sorrows forced us out into the bright, bright night. I cannot hope to tell you by what route we got there but we ended riding back and forth, in the stale, stinking cabin of the Fort Lee Ferry, he in tails and top hat, I in silver lamé and chinchilla.

The third round was the throat-cutter. This was the expensive round, the one costing flowers, first editions, donations to pet charities. Apologies by phone, wire, carrier pigeon. However that would be next day, not tonight. Tonight, should you have the insufferable audacity to balk me, one sleekly timed, machete phrase will slit your throat from thar to thar. Seldom, yet now and then, I even slit my own; the Terrible Me Department.

The alcoholic's world is eye level and down; liquor glass level and down. There's a saying, I wish I knew by whom, that no man can earn a sunset or deserve a star—this is completely beautiful, and true. All those guzzling years I never saw one sunset, never saw one star, looked at them and did not see them. No unfolding leaves. No flowers beyond the ones with tinfoil stems.

Across the rim of a martini glass was how I first saw Jim. Reflected in the mirror of the bar was what appeared to me a fine, a particularly engaging group—the Lord knows why and I bet He does, at that. I belonged to the table-hopping drunks.

A species committed to the theory that the ones you don't know are ten times more entrancing than the ones you came with. A form of madness this, which fills your nights with entrancers almost none of whom you meet again or hope to.

So it was not Jim alone I picked up, it was his entire table: "Hi, pets, move over. I'm Liz Addams."

There's every reason to believe the name was enunciated to sound like Liz, the queen of England; liquor made a first-class snit of me, one thing I really wasn't. *"In vino veritas,"* my eye! Don't fall for that; in wine—in booze—are lies and lies and bigger lies; *this is why the drunk is drunk,* to bypass *truth.* The true alcoholic is the perfectionist and, since he and life are not remotely perfect, he cannot bear it and escapes in grog.

I recall Jim's table as an oblong of admiring faces with one obstinate exception. Jim was not admiring, not bedazzled by the condescending charmer from across the tracks. Nose to the ceiling, his eyes said: "What's the smell?"

That must have done it. I suppose it can be said that the complicated botch which lead to the Power and the Glory stemmed from a male unimpressed by a female used to impressing. Up to now I hadn't especially singled him out. Now I did. Especially.

It seems peculiarly essential to give an accurate description of husband No. 3, as accurate as can be about the one who accompanied me to hell. After all, here is the guy who squeezed me into choosing between barred windows and no barred windows. Also here is the one in three I find no conceivable excuse for having married.

Randall Trowbridge? Yes.

Silas Addams? Yes.

James C. Hatch? *No!*

Jim was younger than I, an item which I well know could be enlightening and doesn't happen to be because as a matter of fact he was a thousand years older. Born old. Older than the oldest glacier. Deep-frozen. Typed, jelled, rubber gone from the elastic. Any human without hope is washed up and Jim was not merely without hope, he was hopelessly indifferent to hope. You sensed this and disowned your senses.

As early as that first evening he said: "If I had the power to pull the lever that would exterminate the human race I'd pull it."

And Liz, what was her response?

Jug-happy Liz beamed: "You *would?*"

Sic transit gloria; or thus do dames get theirs.

Now's the time to lick the chops; the charmer is charming up the wrong pilaster.

In appearance, Jim was oddly arresting. Height and weight were average but he carried himself with an authority, with such a fine combination of dash and conservatism that he stood out among far more imposing men. He was considered disgustingly good-looking and was. The features, one by one, were right, were excellent, yet somehow in the all-together they were as improbable as sunrises on colored postcards; hair too black a black, eyes too bold a blue, teeth too white and too symmetrical, skin too oddly olive. This plus the glacial manner added up to something that would repel you if you had the wit to sense it.

Though first to last surgery was his idol, Jim Hatch was infatuated with things, whatsoever things were costly and spanking new. I, the surfeited, found this endearing, an instinct that accounts for half the charity of the rich. The rich not only enjoy the luxury of giving, they relish re-valuing what they have in the light of what the have-nots haven't had. I had thought of jewels as adjuncts to a costume. Through Jim's eyes I saw them, or could see that he did, as objects of monetary value. Eyeing my wrist I'd murmur: "Mercy me (or, for Christ's sake, as the case might be) you mean to say that bracelet would have supported your family for a whole year?" We were both impressed.

Jim was frank, delightfully so, about the fine glow trappings brought him. Up to leaving home for college he'd had only hand-me-downs, hand-me-down clothes, hand-me-down toys, hand-me-down books, and as he said, he'd had a belly full. Now he wanted lots of everything, gleaming convertibles, the thickest steaks, wardrobes packed with custom suits. Who could blame him? And he did have them, often ordering more just to prove he could. But things not for sale—ah.

A person may be under the illusion of having run the gamut of snobs, snobs going up, going down, going nowhere, but until he comes upon the snob with the contemptuous soul, he is a rank amateur. These are scarce, thank God. So scarce as not to be readily identified.

James Hatch bought what he could buy and things he could not buy, he scoffed at; scoffed to the point where you felt naïve for having valued them. It was not done crudely. It was done casually, in cold amusement. How many drinks must I have gulped to aid me in deciding he couldn't have meant what he did mean?

We are motoring to Montauk at the tip of Long Island. I say: "This always reminds me of parts of France. You know, I lived there, Jim. I adore every last poplar."

He turns his head. "So? I hate to disillusion you but of all countries, France tops the list in decadence, Greedy, filthy sensualists."

It hurts like a blow. "Oh, I didn't know you knew France. Have you lived there, Jim?"

No, of course he hasn't lived there. He hasn't even been there. He doesn't need to.

We pass a public school. The doors open to disgorge a hundred yelling boys and girls. I say: "I never did go to public school—I've always thought I missed a lot."

He laughs shortly: "I should say so! The worst public school is better than the *best* private school."

We dance on the St. Regis roof. The music is waltz music.

I say: "Slow heavy chords sometimes make me think of Whitman. I adore Walt Whitman, Jim."

He lifts an eyebrow: "Really? Do you usually go for queers?"

We are in the Grand Central, waiting for Pete's train from Boston. I'm terribly excited, thrilled at seeing Pete. In order to make Jim a part of this, I say: "Wouldn't it be marvelous if Pete would take up medicine? Where ought he to go? Father always said Harvard had the finest medical school."

We move toward the gate as Jim says: "He did, did he? Well, I suppose Haw-vard's fine if you like surgeons who crook their little fingers."

Innumerable examples.

Mankind, for instance. Not that it kept me awake nights but somehow I did believe most people did intend to do right.

Hogwash. Look at history, look at today, said Jim.

And God, for instance. I speculated a lot about that. I felt there simply *had* to be Something—

Jeers. He'd had plenty of that junk as a kid!

Snob of snobs. Spitter on whatever qualities, whatever opportunities, whatever tastes he does not have. Destroyer of ideals you do have. The lowest in iconoclasm.

His was a locked personality, its compartments unrelated, some containing valuables, some containing trash. Weird incongruities, apparently never examined nor affecting nor disturbing one another. Here was shrewdness, occasionally wisdom, yet an arrogant stupidity when it concerned your intelligence, even your memory of facts he himself had given you. Hard yet childishly sentimental over some slight past favor. Wary yet wildly lavishly bold. Honest yet straddling an ingrown war to win. A lone wolf yet capable of compromise. Cold, icy cold, yet hot with ruthless vehemence.

The heat was not real heat however. It was synthetic, a

burning like the burning of dry ice, which became an affront once you'd learned that it affected you but not Jim Hatch.

Vanity was the one consistent trait. I never saw Jim Hatch get by a mirror yet I never mentioned it. There are some habits so embarrassing you must pretend you do not see them. I must say however that as time went by, as I picked out his clothes, suggested this, suggested that, the vision in the mirror did grow handsomer and handsomer.

So far as I could tell this vanity was not interested in admiration other than his own. I would watch him, I spent years watching him, first because his approach inevitably brought a certain excitement and later because any woman knowing herself unloved automatically acquires the habit of watching.

We are to meet for lunch. Say, at some club Jim couldn't have imagined belonging to before our marriage. The foyer is abuzz with ostentatiously unostentatious men and women; casual couples, the women in tiny hats and mammoth jewels and little black numbers whipped up by whichever couturières are charging the most for little black numbers.

Jim enters. He stands by the door, bold blue eyes seek above, beyond, through, until they find mine. Upheld by another's social water wings, his poise is magnificent, strictly Beekman Place. Here again is a curious form of hand-me-down, unrecognized by either of us, certainly not by me. Raising a hand in greeting, I get up smiling; in the early days because this attractive gent belongs to me and later because he does not.

Even when it was too late, too late even for the Lord God, the expression in the eyes when they found mine was a caress so personal, so selective, that the heart hoped again. And his public kiss, long, long after private kisses were undreamt of, was like posting property: This Woman Is Mine No Trespassing. Possessive, fervent, and at the same time utterly devoid of feeling—where *did* he learn the trick?

I wait while he strides to me, receive the kiss, watch his swift survey of me.

"Nice outfit," he approves. "All set? I see the captain's ready—we'll have cocktails at the table."

Hand-me-downs. A la Beekman.

Unless you are pure unadulterated dope, your mind finally insists upon identifying tricks as tricks. Remembrance of last night and what was said or not said, done or not done, presents itself in such vivid contrast and yet—yet hours have elapsed, so maybe—your mind knows but your lips cannot be sure.

Slipping your arm through his, you run the gamut of the foyer as every little black number manages to look at him and he never looks at one. Always, in all places, Jim drew all types of women, disdaining all. This is unfathomable unless in their heart of hearts women despise the easy nincompoops men have let us make of them.

(Oh, what, what *is* the matter with you men! Can't you see, can't you understand that, liking to sleep with you or not liking, we females so crave to respect you!)

No, Jim was sheer trickster, the sex Houdini wriggling out of emotional possibilities so neatly as to kid himself. Out in front, the wife is part of the act, back in the wings she is a pest, the fifth wheel. I see now that the act was the result of fear. In public where he was safe he endeavored to atone for what he was both unable and unwilling to express in private. An unconscious plea to accept a substitute replete with trimmings and thereby free him from further obligation. As though he said: "See—how can you doubt my devotion? The whole world is witness."

This is like satisfying one's appetite by looking at colored photographs of roast beef rather than by eating roast beef. This kept me dangling, it also made a heel of me for asking more. Titillated, I lived on hope and on the envy of other women: "How Jim adores you! He never *sees* another woman."

It worked for quite a while. It takes time to appreciate that the man who hates women hates *all* women.

Naturally it must be the humiliation of humiliations to be hitched to the public rover-boy, one of the glancing guys with eyes like bees in a flower bed. Awful. On the other hand you'd better pause before the male who totally rejects the female except as partner in a social act. Awful too, and not so normal. You wonder. If he cannot get by a mirror is it logical that he discards constant wholesale admiration?

You wonder. He *is* a marrier so there has to be some need in such men even if it only expresses itself sadistically; titbits to foster confidence, indifference to blight it. But he does marry, so should you muff it, some day somewhere some upturned face is bound to register. (And if you feel this, lady, you'd be right!)

Try as I will I cannot produce much in relation to Jim and me that isn't extreme. We were extreme people. I, marital eager beaver, chasing dreams as blatant as a soap ad; Jim, frozen, locked, making like his own conception of a man. As I review the mess, obviously it is hard to see the man as I first saw him, or thought I did. What was he before I was added? Jim-without-Liz? It's nigh impossible to separate the two because the moment one and one made two, I added on, making them more than two. I added Sam to Jim.

Here was the closest to Sam I'd ever had a crack at; a challenge to sink the teeth into. A tough self-made hombre whose emotional inertia was too provocative to ignore, too tempting to withstand. I'd acquired the habit of conquest and Jim was a rough customer; pushovers weren't "fun." Adding Sam, I went on to add half-baked dreams, thereby managing to conjure up someone who never was. Liz Addams *earned* Jim Hatch. He was her upside-down cake.

Had I let Jim be Jim, had I married whatever he was instead

87

of an unreasonable facsimile of same, might not the farce have been caught in time? A little less rosy nonsense, a little honesty, more guts, conviction, self-respect? Especially if I had nipped buds in time, but then even today I'm no bud-nipper; raise hell at climaxes, yes indeed, but register a mild complaint, no. Therefore I cannot think what the outcome might have been had I not allowed buds to grow and thicken until great branches darkened our lives beyond repair.

And this is the least of what I cannot think. I cannot even imagine how Liz ever came to trap the woman-hater in the first place. A riddle which has been inspected with tweezers and remains a riddle. Rooted deep in Jim was a perennial resentment of everything Liz stood for and perhaps his hostile curiosity overrode his conscious will. Once he said she was a feather in his cap; this is about it. Kansas boy makes good. Good for him!

I have two friends, Sue and Tony Webb, long-suffering friends—and who were not—who, on the garment of my life, are like stout hooks and eyes. Without them I'd have fallen apart much sooner. These two are the ones who tell me that the day I promised to cleave only unto, for the third time, I came near to being beautiful; me, not Schiaparelli's best. Me, not those carloads of bronze orchids and bronze gladioli, not the Webbs' own crowded drawing room, but me, the bride.

Why, sure. Liz always has nice weddings, always makes a nice bride, always picks nice bridegrooms; one in cutaway, two in morning coats—styles change. Photographs tell the tale.

Let's see, here's the Liz in pearls and ivory satin, misty and bemused; here's the Liz in diamonds and smoky velvet, grave and very sure, and here's the Liz in gobs of jewels and suave honey-colored crepe, sleekly sophisticated and just a wee might drunk.

In picture number one, the groom adores. In picture number two, they each adore. In picture number three, the bride adores—no, this isn't completely accurate. In number three, the doctor's confoundment amounts to inverted adoration: Sue's and Tony's drawing room in Oyster Bay, Long Island, is one hell of a way from Kansas.

Confounded, the surgeon forgets himself; he unbends long enough to tell the Webbs: "Liz is the one woman on earth who can hold me."

Hold him to what? I wonder.

They say I was almost beautiful as if here at last was the true Liz. As if her real self had finally cashed in, as if here indeed was the permanent green pasture. The bride herself would have wagered every cent Sam left. Only an Almighty could have dreamed that ten years to the day would find her taking the road David Boothe had taken. Via small pink pills instead of gas.

The one bramble in the pasture is Alan. Pete is in the wedding pictures but the elder son is missing. Alan despises his mother, despises her and will not relent. And this cuts deep. Were it not for Jim's love and Pete and drink and sleeping pills, his mother could not endure it. Surely—oh, surely Alan will relent when the new home they are building in Westchester has been finished! His mother has done everything, has all but gotten to her knees. Has written, wired, phoned. Has gone to his college town to weep and supplicate: *Alan—Alan, please understand! Please—this home—wherever I am—must be your home!*

Recently I came upon a phrase: "Don't try to please, give pleasure." Don't *try*, and not to *please*, but *give*, and *pleasure!* A universe of difference, the same as between being *in* love and *loving*. The former is self, the latter is without self. As I see back to all the years of trying to please, of self-doubt shrieking for credit and approval, of the hurt when they were not forthcoming, I am amazed, astounded beyond measure, that even God Himself could keep me from going mad. Making a cult of making a hit. Running in circles—see me, see you. In place of living a life which by its very joy and decency *gives* pleasure.

Were it possible to map a marriage, the first two to three years of this one would appear as curlicued mountains rising to peaks of seeming ecstasy. It is the period in which the partners act out their own interpretation of what they think the other wants. Both wear masks, try feverishly never to be caught without them.

Jim is good at this, better than Liz. The surgeon is accustomed to masks, accustomed to hiding Heaven knows what!

Liz is good, but she is prone to switch too often, too hastily. Should this mask not bring applause, let's see—what was it he seemed to like yesterday? What did I do last week to please him? Think now. Think what it was that made him want to marry me.

This marriage is polygamous. Pretense is ever with them; pretense walks with them on the golf course, dances with them on dance floors, makes a fifth at bridge, divides them in cars, crowds them in bed.

It is in bed that the wife is having an experience she hasn't had before; a husband, the man "with rights" who isn't overly intent on taking advantage of his rights. Here is the union she has dreamed of, companionship "without all that nuisance."

Man bites dog. Headlines: Woman No Likee Sex Wed To Man No Likee Women. Pretty pair, a pair to frighten Freud.

The subject is skirted. Postponed, say. The man yawns: "*Terrible* day—got to get some sleep. Tell you what—tomorrow's Saturday. I'll take the day off. We'll drive somewhere, eh?"

The man is trying; there's no doubt that he tries, by the process of substitution. And no doubt that the woman tries overmuch. She is beginning to cling; she who never clings!

In spite of sleeping pills, she is beginning to lie awake. To listen to the quiet breathing, fretting, wondering.

This is most unheard of, most unsettling. Desire is the yardstick by which male love is measured; no desire, no love. The relief at being free of all that nuisance is no match for the terror of not being wanted. Growing a little frantic, now and again she goes so far as to reach out an arm to touch the figure in the next bed.

"Jim—" she whispers, "Jim darling, you do love me—?"

Instantly his mask slips into place. "Why, Liz, you *know*. Let's get some sleep—get set for tomorrow." He is asleep.

Imitations of emotions are the saddest hand-me-downs of all. And if successful, the most dangerous. As time goes by, those who know this pair could easily believe the wife the capricious fly-by-night and the husband the stern realist, but I'm not so sure.

Liz, the wife, has flown by night indeed, yet eventually, no matter how she's worked and worked to pretend that this or this or this was the lasting truth, eventually when she came to see that it was not the truth, she said so. In Jim's case, life outside the operating room, whatever his skillful hands could not cut into, was closed and pigeonholed. His outside world was a world furnished in his own limitations yet always presented as the real McCoy. Had he said: "To *hell* with sex," and stuck to it, it would have been legitimate, but he did not.

She was a rainbow chaser. He, a substituter.

Liz may not have recognized a true rainbow, as with Silas, but in time she did come to recognize a *phony* rainbow. Whereas Jim settled for the painted backdrop of a rainbow. To live as a sister would have been possible, quite possible, pleasant even, but then, *call it sister*.

But this the man will not allow. Tomorrow and tomorrow and tomorrow and meanwhile the ardent look, the fervent kiss—see, these are the *motions* of a tender love, see the pretty backdrop?

Sex in marriage cannot be bypassed or indefinitely postponed any more than constipation can be bypassed and indefinitely postponed. Sex is far from perfect but it's here to stay. To call brass, gold, or imply that, given time, brass will become gold, is uglier than rape and a damnsight more deceitful.

It is not that this woman feels a need of sex. Her need is to be needed and she is not being needed. Night upon night she lies awake, uneasy thoughts swirling, until at last the pink pills bring heavenly oblivion.

CHAPTER SEVEN

The middle section of the marriage map would depict a mountainous background. In the foreground are abrupt downgrades into country unlike any known country. An unaccountable land, now lush and tropical, now drear and bleak, where one would wander deeply troubled by the sudden inconsistencies. A few of the roads are broadly, blackly inked, the road of war, for instance, yet even these show no positive destination. The rest are single threads, meandering off to nothing.

It was during this period that the masks slipped and eventually were shelved. Jim Hatch had grown weary of pretense. Surgery was his life and beyond rare instances he no longer bothered to fake a personal life. There were rare instances though, lush ones. The most idyllic and therefore the most unreal were four months spent in Mexico; Medicine had competition there.

Looking back, I sometimes wonder if it really happened. Could it have been a joyous dream? Perhaps. Perhaps, afterwards, all oases seem like dreams. The fact that we in the States were at war and Mexico was not, contributed greatly to the sense of gay release. It was as though school unexpectedly had let kids out to watch a transient circus.

Jim-in-Mexico—it has to be hyphenated—was Jim, the relaxed, the debonair, the heretofore unseen. Four feet across the border and lightheartedness enveloped us, clicked on like a light switch. We laughed at inconveniences, at plumbing which didn't work and bugs which did. We laughed and lazed and danced and Jim drank more as I drank less. Mexico is a land where one needs no special occasion to celebrate, a land for happy people where even brawls end up in laughter.

Arm in arm we went to bull fights, adoring the bulls, enraged by the stuffed picadors. We went to Xochimilco, dodged beggars, waded in fat, purple violets, learned to plead in garbled Spanish: "Hey—no mas La Paloma!" Poor tired La Paloma trapped by Latin music makers to enrapture the unwary tourist.

We drove south to Cuernavaca and further south to Acapulco. Those were the days when you made your road as you went along, watching in the rear vision mirror to see it close in again as though nothing but a burro had ever come this way. The rocky road to Paradise; a last turn left, a last turn right, and there it is!

Oh, Acapulco, before Hollywood found you—and moved in to leap from crag to crag! May God force the world into bankruptcy before the almighty buck ruins all the corners of the earth.

Acapulco has two heavenly beaches which then were silently empty and now are Coney Island. It was once a jutting strip of land where natives fished to live and now is a tawdry glitter strip like Sunset and Vine. The natives were friendly and wonderingly big-eyed and now are obese and insolent and the eyes are big with greed.

We stayed at a hotel that was not a hotel in a room that was not a room. The office was a tiny desk under a banana tree in an enormous patio; our room was two walls and a concrete slab clinging to a cliff. The slab went as far west as the cliffs went, its two walls on the land side, sky and sea the other walls. No yard, no roof. The yard was the Pacific Ocean, the roof was giant stars and giant cantaloupe moon and noonday sun filtered through giant palms, and afternoon sun filtered through giant bougainvillea.

Naturally it's not there now. On its site looms a horrid pile of pink cement and red tiles and acres and acres of white tin blinds to keep out the winds and keep out the gulls that used to glide to landings in Jim's and my room. The gulls that strutted and pecked our feet and ate our cocktail olives and dropped drops very like the anchovy stuffing in the olives.

Jim acquired no Spanish and had use for none. A shrug, a lofty eyebrow, a palm upturned accompanied by the curled lip, and pointing, constant pointing. His sole concession was Spanish endings to English words. Whenever ships disgorged dressed-up, self-conscious tourists, Jim would motion, to a waiter, to a bartender. "Look, los sons o'bitchos. Los bastardos americanos." And the waiter, the bartender, would look and agree and laugh his head off.

Being the type I was I'd memorized one sentence, very correct, very *español*. "I'm very sorry" seemed wise to know in anybody's language, and no one had to drop a hat to make me spring it: "*Lo siento mucho, señor.*" (*Señora, señorita.*) My success proved overwhelming, but why not—hadn't I been weaned on languages? It was weeks before the hotel manager said gently: "*Señora* 'atch, forgeeve—do not use that until you *keel* somebody."

Not un*less*, un*til*.

Gentle fatalists. Polite hearts. The enraptured glances had been quenched mirth. I'd nudge someone, passed in front of someone, and been prostrating myself with grief—"*lo siento mucho, amigos!*"

We'd planned to stay two months and lingered three, stayed three and switched to four. Snap a finger, that's how

95

fast it went. Lazy sunlit days, lazy starlit nights. Easy lazy tempo, easy lazy love. I'll skip those late afternoon siestas with naught to do but sleep when one isn't sleepy. I'll skip the nights with naught to do but brush stars off the bed and listen to the radio mingling with the crash of surf.

Let it suffice that the man is a man and the woman is dumbfounded. The lost is found. The dead is risen. The two whom the Book said were joined are joined indeed.

Was this really true, Liz? Was it really?

Yes, it was true.

This—and magic little things.

I am sitting in the Lincoln Continental. The top is down and, in brief halter and bathing shorts, I fry. Between newly awakened breasts, the sweat forms to slowly trickle. My seat and legs stick fast to black upholstery blotched with salt. We are returning from the beach called the "afternoon" beach, the one where there are long unbroken breakers, where big diving birds, cormorants, maybe, swoop for fish. Jim has suddenly remembered something he cannot live without, toothpaste, maybe. Anyhow, I sit and fry.

All at once—in Mexico whatever comes, comes all at once —I am conscious of even more noise, more confusion. People call to one another, point, start running, singly and in groups. I manage to rouse myself to the point of turning my head when there comes a shrill piercing whistle, a cop's whistle— someone is hurt. But, no, the crowd is doubled up with glee.

Unsticking my body inch by inch, I pull upright. By standing on the broiled seat I see over the heads of the crowd and there, in the center of the town's main intersection, on a wooden crate, stands the pride of Medicine, the surgeon in chief. The lean mahogany gringo, nearly naked, is directing traffic with gestures worthy of New York's own. The crowd applauds. Straight from nowhere streams the inevitable brass band; it forms and blares, the whistle toots and the crowd cries: *"Ole, ole!"*

But won't they think Jim drunk?

No, no—not they! They know; it is that at the moment the señor *feels* like a cop and so becomes one—the proper thing to do.

When he wishes to get down they refuse to let him walk but hoist him to their shoulders in triumph. As they approach the car, I bow solemnly and say: "*Magnifico, señor 'atch.*"

Jim slides to the ground and returns the bow. "*Gracias. Viva Mexico!*"

"*Viva Mexico!*" we shout.

It is nothing. It is everything.

Sunday nights we eat at the sidewalk café on the Plaza. As everywhere in the Latin world, Sunday is the big night. In the middle of the baked Plaza stands a scabby bandstand where the band booms. Circling the outer edge of the Plaza is a wide walk where the boys march clockwise and the girls march counterclockwise. Boys leer, girls titter, and onlookers nod and remember.

Hubbub. Turmoil. The stink of tamales and cheap perfume. Chatter like the chatter of two thousand parrots. Magenta, orange, lemon yellow, acid green. Sombreros, mantillas, greased shiny hair. Dogs bark as dogs cannot bark. Two thousand dogs, two thousand parrots. Waves of sound, of smell, of colors. Orderly pandemonium is the Plaza on Sunday night.

The bandstand boys give a last blare and quit to sweat to drink to sweat again. Out from a doorway appear three *mariachis*, the strolling band. Fiddle, drum, accordion, an impossible combination. They head for the sidewalk café and give us—*La Paloma!* "La weary dove," as Jim would say.

He stops them midway.

"*No mas Paloma,*" he calls.

The mariachis stop, blink, and await our choice.

Jim finishes his wine, wipes his mouth and stands. He goes to the drummer. "Here, give," he says.

The drummer's eyes are brown pansies and as he recalls the traffic cop, the pansies crinkle. "*Si, señor?*"

They bow.

Jim takes the rough sticks from the rough hands and ruffles the drum experimentally. The drum is old and battered but it is good, and we congratulate ourselves that this is so.

For Jim to be a drummer is as inconsistent as a woman I once knew. A heavy rawboned woman, face devoid of make-up, suits sternly mannish. The downstairs of her house was the same, no nonsense, but at first glimpse of her bedroom I stood astonished. It was swathed in organdy. Organdy petti-coats on bed and dressing table, clouds of frilly organdy at the windows, crisscrossed and looped back and dripping on the carpet. When I turned, astonished, she grinned sheepishly.

"I know," she said. "I have an organdy heart."

In some minute corner of Jim's heart, he is a drummer. At night clubs he drums on tables. In homes where they've hired a piano player he invariably finds a matchbox which, to the horror of the hostess, he beats on the piano top, backbeating the rhythm.

Now he is testing the drum further. The first beats are slow and steady, gradually growing stronger and mightier and then not so mighty. He ceases altogether and begins over. Wetting his lips there comes a whistle, clear and true, to the throbbing backbeat of the drum.

The tune soars. It is *Give My Regards to Broadway* and Jim gives it the business, trills and heavy emphasis: "Give My Re-gards to Broadway, Remember Me to Her-ald Square."

The crowd is entranced, the hush a vibrant hush. I look around and see that the natives have taken this gringo to their hearts. The whistling drummer in white linen suit and blue checked shirt is as admirable as the whistling cop in blue breechcloth.

Rehearsing the tune once more, Jim cries: "Okay, you guys —take it!"

We beam expectantly.

The fiddle beams, the accordion beams, yet both remain silent.

Tucking the drumsticks, one behind each ear, Jim reaches politely for the fiddle. I sit up straight; I've never heard of his playing fiddle. The crowd is as disturbed as I. I feel a tense ripple and fear he may have gone too far; to whistle is one matter, to play fiddle something else. I feel them think, gringos never know when to stop—a pity, too. This one was *muy simpatico*.

This one readjusts the stick behind his left ear. He raises the fiddle to position and softly, tenderly develops the strain of *Give My Regards to Broadway*. The listeners recognize it and there is a rustling sigh like the sighing of palm trees.

The owner of the fiddle sighs. Cocking his head, he listens, while the tune is played through three times, maybe four. He nods. "A—ha," he grunts. Reaching politely for the fiddle he plays back the tune, three times, maybe four, slowly, cautiously, his eyes on Jim.

The accordion gives a tentative note, stops, attends, tries again, grows surer. Surer and off key. For encouragement the gringo beats the drum straight and finally backbeats. Satisfied at last, he lifts a right arm.

Bringing it down hard like a train signalman, he shouts: "Boys, that's it!" And never was Herald Square remembered in such off-key fervency. The palm fronds sway, the crowd sways, sweat glistens. The leftover *mariachi*, the drummer, is not one whit disgruntled. Small gourds are whipped from the back pockets of striped pants to join in madly; this is now a four piece band and worth more centavos.

Then comes the split timing when the crowd perceives that the band is ready for the road and parts to let it pass. I stay put and for an hour I hear Jim but do not see him and this is good. Around the Plaza Broadway is being given thunderous regards and this is wonderful.

Wonderful?—hell, it's *heaven*.

Like most tourists we started with a guide but soon we ourselves have become guides and he the *turisto*. We settle his gambling losses, shield him from yesterday's love, sober him up mornings, tuck him in nights. Nacho is *muy* naughty, a rascal whom we have grown to love very much. *Mucho* much.

Nacho is in his middle twenties, Alan's age, with, oddly, gray eyes like Alan's. Both are flyers, Nacho a commercial pilot, awaiting transfer, Alan a bomber pilot somewhere in the Pacific. This I had to learn from Pete. I have known it quite a while and like other mothers have almost grown accustomed to it. I am not able to pretend that Nacho is Alan any more than I pretend that Mexico's peace is anything but a phony peace, yet in a fashion, Nacho is a comfort. He is young and has gray eyes and is a flyer who deigns to speak to me. My elder son has not spoken to me since I married Jim Hatch. He does not, will not, write, which spares me the agony of other mothers, an agony I would gladly share. And so, as Nacho's mother is dead and my son is dead to me, I have become a *mama mexicana*. Quite a job too.

One afternoon late—one is forever late in Mexico—Jim and I go lazily down long outside steps to a bar hollowed in the cliffs. We face the sea and the west sun blinds us. From high above we hear the weird cries of the diving boys, natives who dive to death and sometimes find it in the shallow whirlpools two hundred feet below.

Hand in hand we descend, I in violet slacks and lime silk tunic, Jim in vivid yellow pants and orange shirt. A damn attractive couple, and we think so too; the Hatches, *mañana* kids.

Halfway my eye catches an utterly extraordinary sight. Four humans are squatting in the blazing sun and are blazingly incongruous together. I squeeze Jim's hand. "What on earth?"

There's a railed platform, a sort of unroofed pavilion from which to view the divers, a place to rest when climbing the steep staircase which runs from sea to cliff. The divers come this way and not many others. Now a peculiar foursome crouches there, one girl, three men. The girl is American as is one of the men. The other two are Nacho and a diver in a scarlet G-string.

We recognize the diver: Tarzan, the boldest of them all. A strutting character with magnificent chocolate muscles and kinky hair who smirks and brags.

We see Nacho's head move rapidly from side to side, watch his lips form words, feel the tension in the mobile figures. Obviously Nacho is in command and whatever brings these four together, it is giving him the bang of a life already full of bangs.

"Come on," Jim says.

"But, sweet—?"

"Come on. You'll get into the act later. Nacho'll be itching to report."

The cool dimness of the deserted bar welcomes us. We order tequila Collins and wait; Jim wholly relaxes, I am curiously uneasy. What can Americans, particularly a girl, be doing in secret confab with Tarzan? I don't know why I know it's secret but I do know. A kind of furtiveness and also the blinding heat of the place they have chosen.

Jim laughs at my impatience.

"Women," he mutters.

I make a face. "All right. But, darling, there is skulduggery. Why the huddle? Why that nice girl and that nice man?"

"They want to buy Tarzan," Jim suggests. "Want to cage him and ship him to the Bronx zoo."

This makes me grin; Tarzan would make a lovely ape.

Our Collins are about finished when we hear the sound of flying footsteps. "Three Collins," Jim tells the bartender.

He's right. It is Nacho, bursting with importance.

"What?" I cry.

Arms fly skyward. "Ah—hah, what indeed!"

The bartender steps from behind the bar to chop ice. Nacho reaches to grab the bar towel and makes passes as if the bartender were a bull. On the instant, the bartender *is* a bull. He charges in fine style; in equally fine style Nacho deflects the charges, feet hugging the tiled floor, torso swiveling in timed elegance.

"Stop it!" I say.

At once the bull becomes the bartender, the matador, the breathless kid with a tale to tell.

Here is the tale. The gestures will have to be imagined.

The Americans are Texans. On their honeymoon.

"But too little honey," Nacho says.

They have a *big* car. (Nacho is a car-lover.)

"Not so beeg as the Leen-*coln*, but beeg, very beeg; a Chrysler."

The car has a trailer.

"Oh—you should see! Long, *most* long—like the millionaire's yacht."

The trailer is parked on the beach up the bay from the afternoon beach.

"Fine for the honeymoon—I think *I* try it."

Jim laughs. "Whose wife?"

The Texans have been there a month.

"And *now*—you *hear!*" (Nacho is a ham.) "The wife she fall for—*Tarzan*. They swim in the night waters of the bay, maybe two times, maybe many, and now she say to husband: 'You go home. *I* stay. I, Tarzan's girl'—ho, *ha*, can you imagine!"

Jim laughs. I do not laugh. I wish to vomit.

"No," I say, "*no*."

I start to get up and immediately Jim pulls me back. "You

stay where you are and mind your own business," he tells me.

I twist aside. "This *is* my business. It's any woman's business. Jim, I have—"

We hear a sound and in the arched doorway stand the girl and the diving boy. Jim tastes his drink and complains of too much sugar, Nacho waves a knowing hand, and I—I die a little.

The most tortured mind could not conjure up more mismated companions. The total of what these two can ever have in common is that their eyes blink in unison at the dimness of the bar. It occurs to me that the girl may be moronic. This is the kindest thought to have, but no, below the broad brow the china blue eyes are bright though they do appear stupefied like those of an insect caught in cobwebs.

Tender is the word my mind picks; spring rain, a wobbly kitten, wisps of cloud separated from the main cloud. She is young and very trim, her wash dress as clean and smooth and yellow as her hair. Yet, if she is what she looks—how, why?

As they walk the length of the room, my gaze cannot bear to move to Tarzan but it does so, hypnotized. The tight wire hair, the cave man's torso, the loose dangling arms, the splay-feet, and in between, the bulging G-string thrust forward arrogantly as if it were a box of medals.

Staring fascinated, one would think I'd never seen the creature and actually I never have. In its entirety, yes, but not in relation to something else, not as the jungle in relation to civilization. This could be in a zoo, its hairline an ape's hairline, its nose flat and mushy like an ape's, its eyes cunning and embarrassingly close together. The same eyes which I have seen observe women, unclothe them and slide on, telegraphing their lewd message to the coarse mouth and on down to the scarlet G-string.

At a table apart from us they sit opposite one another; Beauty and the Beast. The horror of the combination is not remotely that she is white and he, black. Color has nothing to do with this; this is a matter of evolution. Two animals, one white, one black, can be at the selfsame stage of breeding. Or one, the black, may be a splendid prize-winning animal and the white, a throwback, wild, stunted, not adaptable. God in Heaven—this can *not* be! With my entire being I know I must go to this girl. Must unstick the baby eyes and make her understand that this very instant will decree a lifetime. This was life's crossroad. No matter where other roads might lead, this will lead to certain degradation. She must see, be *made* to see that lust bridges no gaps, that while the body can outshout the soul and mind, the soul and mind live on to learn in misery what they have let lust do.

Oh, Jim—let *go* of me!

I watch two hands reach across the table, meet and lie clasped. No words have been spoken and I know precisely why; it is not merely that they do not speak each other's language, it is that they never can.

The back of my mind hears Jim and Nacho.

"And what does the husband say?" Jim is asking.

"Ho—*that* one. He is chicken. I, the interpreter, ask why he does not chain the wife and he say: 'I desire only the happiness of the wife'!"

Nacho's lips curl contemptuously. "*Happiness?* You shall hear what the happiness will be; I *tell* you! Tarzan will use her in what ways he likes, then grow tired of the easy one, and say to the *amigos*: 'You take, *por nada.*' After the friends take, and the friends' friends, come the tourists. And the tourists are not *por nada*—they pay, you bet."

Jim says, "Where will they live?"

"Tarzan and the little one? Where Tarzan live, the thatched hut with the dirt floor and mama and papa and brothers and sisters and the chickens and the pigs and the million flies and the charcoal fire that smoke all day, all night. It will stink, I tell you!"

"You stink. Both of you," I say. "Here is a crime against God, and you *sit—I will not!*"

Jim moves quickly. The fingers which grip my arm are steel.

"You *will*," he states. "This is not our country. Nor our laws. Would you like to disappear some night—end up with your throat slashed?"

I try to pull free. "If necessary—I'm no Joan of Arc but there are some things more vital than living, and this is one of them! I may not affect her in the slightest, but, Jim, can't you see I have to try? For my *own* sake—good God, Jim!"

His fingers tighten. A steel arm circles my shoulders.

"Stay where you are. Stay completely out of this. That's right, isn't it, Nacho?"

Nacho has lost interest. He shrugs. "Maybe not right, señor, but wise, most wise. The diving boys have many followers." A forefinger slips across his neck from ear to ear.

Chairs scrape the tiles. As the girl and Tarzan stand, I try to stand, but Jim holds me back. Nacho turns to smile at my distress, a smile half sad, half cynical. "See, señora 'atch, the fates have taken care; they go and it is better—may I have one more tequila, please? The excitement brings the thirst."

An arm, one human arm is all that holds me back as I sit and watch them pass.

I knew then and know better now that I should have tried if I was forced to tear the place apart and yet—oh, my excuse is no excuse and no amount of rationalization can make it one! To myself I said that nothing, nothing in the world was so important as the wonderful oneness of Jim and me; nothing must be allowed to spoil it.

And then it was spoiled anyway—*because of this?*

CHAPTER EIGHT

The spoiling began on a day as perfect as all others. Afterwards this seemed unfair. If man be the bigshot of earth, nature should contrive to warn him. The sun should sulk, tides should reverse themselves, gulls refuse to fly, dogs weep. It was exactly the same however. No one, nothing to point out that hell was around the bend, that in fact this specific phone call was a call from hell.

Jim was always getting New York calls; this one was disrupting only in that it meant leaving Acapulco. Though, with Jim and I the way we were, what difference could it make whether we were here or home? A lot was at stake, at least to him. An enormously rich and influential patient was ill, facing a critical operation, and if we liked to eat, we'd best hit the road. Fine by me—what wasn't?

Also it was well into April and April is muggy in Acapulco. Also I'd been toiling at a naval hospital and my leave was long up and I was feeling guilty. Also, always and always, there was Alan. Weeks, months, years, had passed with no direct word from Alan but surely one bright day there'd have to be a letter, wouldn't there? And mail in Mexico was mail in limbo.

Pete as well as Alan was in the Pacific. He had volunteered the moment he was of age. But Pete was all right. Even in the First Marine Division, Peter Addams would be all right. More immediate was the thought of our servantless house; there'd be dust to here. Our handsome house which now for the first time was going to be a home.

No, all things considered, it was time to head north.

Flinging our clothes into bags, doling out hundreds of pesos in well-earned tips, Jim and Nacho and I kissed paradise goodbye.

The mugginess had made us decide not to leave till after sundown. But it was late, much later, for the hotel owner had arranged a sendoff, a dinner of seven courses with wine and more wine, toasts and more toasts.

"Oh, amigos, adios! Gracias—gracias. Goodbye, goodbye."

We waved ourselves out of sight.

"Jim," I cried, "they really love us."

"And our pesos—"

"No—not that. Such lovely hearts!"

"Such lovely pesos."

Nacho smirked. "Si, the luv-ly pesos."

They laughed at my response: "Disgusting, you two, commercial."

The road out followed the line of the "afternoon" beach. The moon was a thick pink-yellow crescent and as the waves broke, the foam seemed yellow. We left the beach and started up the winding road, up, up. At the crest, we stopped and looked back to sigh forlornly at the beauty left behind.

I kissed my hand. "Goodbye, Hornos, we will come again soon!"

Then down, down, we went. Down and around, and around, making a new road as we went.

Chilled beer from the thermos. Spanish songs, American songs. Jokes with the point obscured. Reminiscences of him

107

and her, of these and those—remember? At Chilpancingo the thermos was refilled. Near Iguala we tangled with a midnight torch parade. At Taxco we got a little drunk—drunker —at Berta's. Bewitching journey.

Even at dawn Mexico City was grubbily sophisticated. We three brown gods were rapidly reduced to tramps in faded slacks and rumpled shirttail. We were welcomed however. All hotel night clerks recognized Acapulco gringos.

"Ah, Acapulco, *mucho color?*" the night clerk asked.

"*Mucho* needa bath," Jim told him.

Quick showers. Quick change of clothing. Quick breakfast in the room while Nacho saw to oiling and greasing the car. We were driving straight through. Should the plenty fancy patient die before Jim returned to operate, the surgeon's practice and the professional reputation that he had so carefully nurtured would suffer.

Nacho waited at the curb, a hand caressing the car. Nacho loved us but adored the Continental.

I hugged him to me. "Wicked *nino*, promise never to forget us! We'll be back next year—"

(Next year? Next lifetime!)

At the start there was flavor to the trip home but little by little it was like a tall Collins with watered gin and masses of melting ice. I don't recall how far we'd gotten, the border, I think, when I realized Jim was play-acting. Playing Casanova too frequently and too determinedly, as though he was hoping to build up a surplus. As though a car could last four times as long if its batteries were charged once a day for four days.

Then this too petered out. Remarks like this began: "I feel great, but I see you're bushed—ought to get more sleep."

Or, at bedtime, no reference at all, whereas at breakfast: "You sure were tired last night. I wanted to wake you and didn't have the heart."

It appeared to be a matter of geography. Below the border

our relationship was richly flavored but once across the border there was increasingly that flat taste of melted ice. If only Jim had known or cared, the physical adjustment was the least of the joys of Acapulco. It had been the comfortableness of being natural, the exchange of foolishness and then again, no need of any exchange at all. Those were the joys. To be loved is far sweeter than to be made love to. No male will ever believe this and so, one by one, Jim's doors were closing, slammed by misunderstanding, sealed with self-consciousness.

Whoever told men that it was sex that kept the little woman purring? Not women, surely. Yet the cockeyed theory still persists and no male is immune to it till, well, till eighty. If a man, any man, should be asked what he would most like to be and he were honest—which most men are—and he happened to think of it—which most men wouldn't—he'd say: "A stud." (On a numerical basis, to hell with proficiency!) And yet, down deep inside, *he wouldn't mean it.*

The sex subject was bolexed up a billion years ago. A billion years ago a guy on all fours with wads of fur said to another guy on all fours: "Dolls is quieter when they got kids, so give 'em kids."

There it started.

Then one day sometime later a doll on all fours with wads of fur said to another doll on all fours: "When guys got kids, they stick around, so give 'em kids."

Now since shoes are so expensive, the human stands on two feet instead of four. Since there are drugstores in every block he owns a razor regulating fur but the thought process remains the same: keep 'em quiet; keep 'em home.

There be those who wallow in sex, not in the talk of it but in the doing it. This I know, who should know better? Nevertheless and notwithstanding, one half of the adultery, assignation, fornication, and yes, copulation, could be indefinitely postponed if mankind would quit showing off. If the male didn't have to prove prowess and the female didn't have to prove seductiveness. Can-do and come-on, dunked in sportsmanship, account for more tragedies, two-legged and industrial, than all the glands since Eden.

Jim Hatch was not thus handicapped. Prior to Acapulco there'd been lack of prowess and lack of sportsmanship; a free and empty state to which he now returned. Our at-oneness had been merely a climatic hiatus. A surprise entertainment between the acts of a poorly written play.

I could not grasp it. I neither understood it nor was willing to admit it. From Houston to Macon to Richmond to New York I busily invented alibis, not for the loss of passion, but for the loss of that sweet ease. We were naturally on edge, I told myself. After those lazy days, the long grinding days were murder; we were exhausted—but then, why didn't we say so? Why were we pretending, why self-conscious?

Confused, alarmed, I took to sleeping pills again. And Jim drank less and I drank more for, as I assured myself, Jim had problems while I—what problems did I have?

I dropped him and his toothbrush at the Biltmore. Jim was the city slicker now, and beautiful. A dark brown slicker in gray flannels and buttoned-down shirt. No hat though—

"Darling, you're beautiful—but where's your hat? Don't doctors have to wear hats?"

Never mind. He'd buy one.

Never mind anything. He'd see me later.

"I'll find all I need at the hospital. A boy'll pick up anything else. God's sake, go on, I'll see you."

It was ten days before I saw him. Ten days of raising hell with the gardener for neglect, of rounding up house cleaners, of hasty phone conversations with Jim. Certainly he missed me. Yes, the rich patient was going to pull through but he thought he'd better stick around in case of later complications. Certainly he was anxious to get home—I didn't think he enjoyed this, did I?

"Of course I think you enjoy it," I laughed. "But you eat, don't you? Why can't we meet for dinner?"

Well—all right.

"Make it day after tomorrow. At seven. No, not the room, the Biltmore lobby—see you."

At the preparations I went through you'd have thought it was I who'd cheated the undertaker. Hair, nails, the works. New hat, new dress, new gloves, new bag; gun-metal linen with just the right amount of white piqué to flaunt my gorgeous tan.

Jim was a clothes-observer, mine after his. That evening, after the long kiss, he looked me over: "Nice effect, sophisticated. Christ, I'm tired, let's grab a bite."

At dinner it seemed as though we were more at ease. The conversation centered on the big operation, which was entirely natural. I listened hard, glad that things were shaping the way Jim wanted them. The patient's family and all his bigshot business associates were anxious to show Jim their gratitude. Particularly the wife.

"How old, darling?" I asked. "And little or big or what?"

He chewed steak. "Who?"

I laughed. "The wife."

"Don't know her proportions—haven't noticed."

I remember laughing, saying: "I can believe that. You might notice her clothes but never herself—is she rich, too, darling?"

"Hell, yes," Jim snorted.

I let the subject slip back to medical niceties, and afterwards regretted it. Regretted it bitterly.

A week later he phoned again. He was still sticking around, but it wouldn't be long now, thank God. He was done in, had worked like a galley slave.

"You and me both," I told him. "In case you're interested, I'm back slaving at the Naval Hospital. When will you make it home?"

"Soon. Sunday, I guess. See you."

I sighed happily. "I sure hope so—bye, love."

Sunday came, and Jim. But he was not my love and no amount of rationalizing made him so; he was the old indifferent pre-Acapulco Jim. What with this and the shambles at the Naval Hospital, I went a little mad, I think. As summer passed and the hospital emergency ward was knee-deep in burned and broken flyers, my heart would come to a full stop until I'd scanned each name tag. There'd been no word from Alan. Letter upon letter from Pete and not a line from Alan. Every casualty was Alan and this of itself was mad, for Alan was army and these were navy and not even the government was that mixed up.

The motive behind my job had been a kind of atonement to my elder son. No volunteer job, this, of books and lollipops and floating veil. It was a penance of blood and guts for the son I'd failed, *realized* I had failed! And while it wasn't much, it was still the worst, the very worst I'd been able to find.

Whom I married, how much I drank, the sort of person I was, might not be a son's business and again it might. That depended upon how one had started out and I had started out with Alan as my soul's most beloved only to ditch him and move on. The fact that I had not meant to, had never for one moment intended to ditch him was beside the point; he felt I had. Or said he did.

And for what? For what greener pastures? A measly quarter acre; four months at a Mexican seaside!

The now-Jim bore no more resemblance to that Jim than a firefly resembles a floodlight. The now-Jim was afraid, painfully afraid—why? If Nacho's name was so much as mentioned, he froze. Life was a process of walking on eggs. Only last night he'd turned a kiss on the nose into a hint for something more—"*Christ*," he said, "aren't you *ever* satisfied?"

Satisfied? You! You who'd spent a lifetime trying to keep *out of bed.*

Toward the end of that summer of '44 word came from Alan. A flimsy envelope with a single flimsy sheet. My fingers shook so in opening it that the sheet tore but not the part with the writing. There was very little writing. A few meager sentences marred by blots and dashes, their meaning garbled, often incoherent, yet somehow managing to be both piteous and scornful at the same time.

He wrote that he was tired of life. Life was scarcely worth all this killing. It was a—a blot here—*slaughterhouse.* It was a slaughterhouse. Life and his mother had betrayed him—*she with all her husbands and her drinking!* If Pete made it back, tell him hello—Pete was a good boy. Pete and he might see each other and again they might not. As for her, she wasn't to bother answering—he didn't want to waste one minute of her great happiness. Anyway, who knew where he'd be?

That was all.

Month followed month. The flimsy note became shredded from folding and unfolding. Whatever sense it had made grew distorted from reading between the lines. There appeared to be some sort of threat between the lines and this shredded the heart exactly as the note was shredded. I tried desperately to think of Alan, the little boy, of Alan going off to school, off to college, and occasionally I could.

There'd been the matter of eating between meals; cookies, candy, soda pop; this was forbidden, about the only thing that was. I could see the curly-headed figure in the yellow wash suit. The mouth is quivering but the eyes look straight into mine; Alan is painfully honest.

"What is it, lamb?" I ask.

"Alan has to be punished," he says.

"Why? What has Alan done?" I ask.

The mouth works. "He—he stole a *cookie.*"

I hold out my arms. "Why?" I ask.

He flies to me. I feel the small body brace itself.

"Cause—cause the cookie *had pink frosting.*"

I have to scold him and do, but now, in retrospect, I wonder if it was pink frosting or a form of self-flagellation, the willingness to be punished to get attention.

I see a boy in dark blue shorts and blue flannel blazer. He is twelve, going away to school in Massachusetts. Driving there, he says: "Mom, come in with me, won't you? Promise you won't leave me and drive off."

In retrospect I wonder if this wasn't unnatural. Pete was the opposite; couldn't wait to get me off the school grounds.

And I see a wonderfully good-looking college boy, tall, hard, strong. The captain of the track team yet strangely, he has missed the main meet. He is sorry his team lost but something else came up, a girl, a party, some other kind of meet. This shocks me and still shocks me. What did I take from Alan or never give to him that could make it possible for him to do such a thing? I knew only too well, and yet I did not know.

Somewhere in the flimsy letter must be an answer but I am too torn to find it. It is too late. And then, after guilt-laden months of silence, I got the telegram: "The War Department regrets to inform—"

Missing. Dreadful, dreadful word. A word which permits no surcease, which dangles hope at the end of a long string to be swallowed and yanked up, swallowed and yanked up, like the tube of a stomach pump. *Missing;* death is preferable—no, no, *not* preferable!

Alan, where are you? Oh, Alan, are you—*dead?*

The third and last section of the marriage map of Liz and Jim Hatch would depict a crowded bleakness very like a series of dark bayous. A bleakness more pronounced because of the lush period which preceded it.

The relapse of this marriage was sheer torture. To glimpse

a dream come true and then have it snatched back was intolerable to the woman I was. A woman forever clutching the exception in the insane conviction that it could be made the rule.

This third section of the map shows no life, no color. A transition shocking in the extreme; from rich-hued bougainvillea, warmth, action, radiant greens and blues, to dead slate-gray.

No animal could live in such a place. No bird would dare to build a nest in these barren trees. Nor would a human come here who knew of any other way. But one does come here; a frantic woman frantically pitying herself wanders hour on end in this gray place. A woman who has lost her head. Aimless, bruised, outraged, a foolish woman. Mourning a lost son, she bends under the whole guilt. Mourning a lost love, she refuses to admit that it was never love.

An extremity of ego, of willful pride, has caused this and even now it will not let her go. Scarred with futility, ego still compels her, dictating hours of weeping, hours of stupid drunken laughter. The man is now the focal point of all derision. His cold indifference goads her into threatening the very thing he secretly desires.

"Who in hell are you?" she jeers. "Jesus, I'll divorce you— I'll fix you!"

It is entirely natural that in this period the man should grow to hate the woman. Her presence is a permanent reminder of his innate lack of even the wish to enter into the most rudimentary of partnerships. The man remembers Acapulco as vividly as she does and retreats further and further, believing it is passion she cries for. His eyelids droop from the impact of so many scenes, of so much charm gone sour. The feather in the hat is now a goddam nuisance.

The months roll by, a year, with no news of Alan. The woman is sick, sick from self, from nothing to be true to. Her blood thins, the heart hammers, the guts tangle. And yet some of the strength of her father is in this woman and it is well that it is, since this frenzied butting against reality is drawing her mind dangerously close to derangement. Grief, pride, undiscipline, drink, barbituates are splendid shoot-the-shoots to windows thick with wire mesh. Oh, sad, sad places! That whitewashed land of human wrecks trying to exist without God, the Rehabilitator.

It is the loneliness that is hardest to endure; the aloneness. The strangest element in the state of Liz Hatch is that no one suspects her misery. Jim does not see her at all and the world continues to see her as it always has, the favorite daughter of the gods. To friends and to those addicted to the social columns she is to be envied as ever.

They see a change, yes, but the change is surely temporary, a matter of war work. Liz is hipped on war, forever ramming marines and sailors down your throat. You meet her everywhere of course, the club, dinners, theaters, cocktail parties, and she is just as chic, just as devastating to men, just as—But she is using people, not for herself this time, for others, for her wounded pets. Her approach is painfully direct.

"You've got that big swimming pool," she'll say. "I don't know how you get servants but you have them—I want to use them. I want to bring, say, forty boys out. Part ambulatory, part on stretchers. Roast a hog, will you? And gallons of cold beer—the business."

"But, Liz, we can't this week. We—"

"The hell you can't. Every drop of water in your swimming pool, every brick in your damn house is there because these boys bled to keep it there, so open up, baby. Open up!"

The social columns loved it and you'd better love it. The Salvation Army was the Salvation Army but Liz Hatch was Liz Hatch. You never quite dared buck her; you were afraid of her but you thought she was wonderful too.

Being "wonderful" was a social must, a habit the woman has acquired from years of not knowing herself and therefore having to play chameleon. All things to all. At the ring of a doorbell she will sweep despair from eyes and lips and mind and gaily stand erect and one would swear that this is Liz, born Burns.

Were Alan here, *he* might suspect, but Alan is not here. The war is over and Pete safe in China, whereas—somewhere in the Pacific a body with other bodies may be banging against coral reefs, the difference being that those other bodies would not choose to be there.

Oh, *Alan*, I too am *missing*. The War Department *presumes* you dead, but I—I will *not* presume! I've spent my life presuming, presuming you knew my love for you, presuming you would forgive—oh, my son, *is* it too late? Is it really too late to remedy at least in part the damage I have done?

The weeks drag by and Pete is coming home. Perhaps *Pete* —surely he is mature enough to sense the forest she is in. To think it odd for instance that she and Jim have separate rooms, separate lives.

Pete will be greatly changed. War changes all men. Either it blasts them as sand blasts a windshield or it strengthens and refines as gold is strengthened and refined. Nearly four years at the Naval Base have taught the woman that there is no middle ground.

The day Pete flew in from Pendleton she knew in an instant that she was right. Here was one of the strengthened ones; beyond the sad thinness and a drawn quality, there was a shining something, a grave awareness. The eyes were worn, and the lines around them, over-wise. The harsh planes of the young face were incongruously stern; nevertheless she sensed a taut ripening. So. So she had not spawned a stockbroker after all!

Late that first night, with Jim asleep in the room beyond, Pete came to stand at the foot of her bed.

"Hi, Mom," he grinned. "See you still read late—aren't you kind of peaked?"

It was not the old grin. The old grin used to include all of him, a puppy wriggling, and while this one was open and friendly, it wasn't all of him.

She dropped her book.

"I still have all my bad habits," she told him. "Haven't changed, but you—you've changed, Pete. Want to talk about it?"

This is something else she's learned; men do want to talk war, want to desperately, only not to sniveling, oh-you-poor-boy varieties.

"Suppose you wonder if I was scared?"

She smiled. "Not a bit. I already know. If you say you weren't, you're a liar or a damn carrot, one or the other. Sit down."

He pushed aside a pile of books and magazines. "Then I'm a damn carrot, because honestly I don't believe I was. Not the way most guys were. I was too mad."

"Mad? About what?"

"What people do to each other. You know the cliché—man's inhumanity to man—only it isn't a cliché; it's true."

She felt an inner quickening.

"Where's it going to take you?"

"Back to Yale. To start over."

She ran impatient fingers through her short blond hair.

"That's out," she said. "They won't spit on you, not with all this G-I stuff. Gosh, Pete, how could you manage to flunk three subjects in one short year?"

"Crazy for the Marines, crazy is right. But you wait. I'll get in all right. I have to; the place you flubbed is the place to begin again."

"Pete, what's back of this?" she asked. "What sparked it?"

The answer rocked her.

"You did."

"I?"

"Yeah. I was around three, I think. Alan and I—"

She stiffened. "Leave Alan out."

"I can't leave Alan out, Mom. Alan's part of us."

"Leave him out," she repeated.

The quiet eyes rebuked her.

"No," he said sternly, "to leave him out is to kill him off! Alan isn't dead. You wait; he'll be back. He'll be back and I'll go to Yale. That's for sure."

"All right—you were three years old. Go on."

"Let's see, it was March, I think. Anyhow it was muddy and I was covered with it. The cook, Nettie, I think, had just scrubbed the kitchen. I clomped in the back door, tracking mud everywhere and the sorer she got, the more I tracked. I was having myself a ball when you heard the ruckus and came down and, brother, did you let me have it! You got the mop and pail and said: 'Okay, buster, hop to it.' It was murder, Mom. I had to scrub every inch of that big floor, blubbering all the time about how I hated it. And do you know what you said?"

"Hardly," she laughed.

"Well, you bet I do. You said: 'Who doesn't hate it? I'm certain Nettie does, and now maybe you'll see why. If you've got to bully people, bully the rich. They can get the hell out.'"

She laughed again. "It's still the truth," she said.

Pete laughed with her. "Well, that's where I first began to find out that every last human being, from the top to the very bottom, has rights. Isn't that what it was all about?"

Yes, she told him, that was what the floor-scrubbing was all about. And what the war had been about; man's individual rights.

Looking past him at his reflection in a dark window she felt proud; a new type of pride. Warm, valid.

"How nice, Pete. Thanks. Your dad and I'll give you all the help we can. You'll need it!"

"Yeah, I will." He hesitated. Then all at once he smiled,

all of him, exactly as he used to. He looked a little shy and very young and very dear.

"Mom, I'm going to have a lot of help. I—I found someone out there, the Big One."

"The *big* one?" she repeated, puzzled.

"God," he blurted. "Plenty of guys found Him. I guess out there you either did or you didn't." Then he seemed to stop himself, as if he had said enough for now. "Gosh, but you look young, Mom. How come?"

Young. A bitter sob climbed in her throat. Tensing, she held it back, held her voice steady.

"Oh—by getting drunk, I imagine. By sleeping pills and marrying every few years or so. Run on to bed, Pete. I'm tired. We'll talk tomorrow. You and I can do quite a bit of talking."

CHAPTER NINE

That night after she'd finally gotten to sleep she had the same dream she'd been having off and on ever since going to work at the Naval Hospital. It was a dream where her arms kept reaching out, reaching out, to enclose boys in uniform. In the beginning the arms were only about twice as long as normal but they'd grown longer and longer until, huddled inside them, were hundreds, thousands of boys.

During one of their long talks she told Pete about it and he thought it was a fine dream. He said the time would come when it wouldn't be a dream, it would be reality. One day she'd find herself giving all she had, heart and mind and soul as well as arms, to aid others. Pete was wrong though. It was a great idea but it was too late, way too late. Mind and heart and soul, whatever it was, were too tired, too bruised.

These next weeks netted several fine bull sessions. Pete had intelligence. Moreover he was sound, something she'd never been. Yesterday he'd taken a car and driven to New Haven and after their conversations she was sure he'd manage to sell himself to the dean. This was a dedicated boy. If Liz Hatch knew anything at all it was that Peter Addams would turn out to be whatever he planned to be. He had hold of this new thing, the Big One as he called it, and now he no longer needed her or anyone else. Which was good. It cleared the decks for a plan she'd been fooling around with for quite some time.

It was Thursday. Thursday evening. Having left yesterday, in all probability Pete would be back tomorrow—well, good luck, boy. You're quite a lad!

Next week was Thanksgiving. Thanksgiving 1946. Count your blessings, hear ye, hear ye! Alan is now presumed dead, so this could be counted a blessing, couldn't it? Pete was proving a blessing. And the wholesale slaughter was over, over till some Joe, Stalin or otherwise, discovered himself slipping.

Thou shalt not kill, Joe. Take it easy; to coin a phrase, death is so final. All deaths.

Death of love; Si's. Check that off.

Death of trust; Alan's. Check.

Death of faith; in one's self. Check.

Faith? Yes, faith. A kind of tremulous, half-baked notion that back on a top shelf was the person you'd like to be, a person to be counted on for honor and stability and seeing the other fellow's point of view.

Jim's for example. What were you trying to do to Jim? Make him into a call boy?

("Let's live in Honolulu, Jim. I adore the smell of ginger.")

("Let's stay in Mexico, Jim. You're so cute in Mexico.")

You'd wanted a man who didn't push and got one and had been pushing ever since. Now look at you! Falling apart, literally.

You're out on the well-known limb, Liz. However, bedecked, bejeweled, be-elegant, you can push the Junior League but you can't push Jim. Howl divorce once more, just once more, and see where it lands you!

The very thought of divorce, another divorce, a third one, was repellent beyond any thoughts except ones of Alan. Anything but this, anything. To walk out on life would be duck soup by comparison. What with Sam and David and Alan, there'd been a lot of practice at dying; one step and *pouff*.

Death was two things. The death of others was guilt, a heavy terrible bag of guilt. The death of yourself was sleep and sleep was one hell of a temptation; the famous last pasture. Pastures were your dish—quite the dame for switching pastures, eh?

Well, what else is there?

Oh, not much. Nothing but what you've never tried.

And what's that?

Starting over—

Starting over? Good God, I'm pushing fifty!

So what? You're the Brain, remember? Get this, Liz; it's failure you're afraid of. Right?

Right.

But is it failure? Or *admission* of failure? There's a whale of difference.

It's—well, all right, it's admission.

Right. Then don't kid yourself that suicide isn't a noisier admission than divorce ever could be. Suicide is a scream from the housetops—

From the *graveyard*.

Okay, the graveyard. Whereas to start over, to go all the way back, stay off the pills, off the bottle—*Wow, I couldn't do that!*

Then page the undertaker.

No, wait. How about the old dog and new tricks?

How about *no* tricks? No tricks this time, play it straight. Give only what you know you've got; a mind, an interest in people, a desire to help.

Hold it; there's the first hooker. *Help*, sure, but how? Jim says I want to help everybody—*my way.*

That could be true, but if you started over, you'd start over

123

in that too. The works. From scratch. Say you were going to help Jim *his* way, what would his way be?

Ho, medicine! Medicine! For Jim's money, a home is a place to recuperate, a wife is a sounding board.

Well, isn't a wife who's a sounding board better than a corpse.

Not to Jim.

Are you so sure? Have you tried recently? Take a crack at it—what have you got to lose?

The woman, divided against herself, felt her heart hammer and the palms of her hands break out in sweat. Hope fluttered. Jim was downstairs in his study; what if—what if it were possible to start over? Her heart remembered the old days when even if other things had not been compatible, they had at least discussed surgery for hours on end, when he had said what a help it was to get a lay point of view. She knew so many of his patients and quite a number had been friends she'd introduced him to. Her personal knowledge of them had helped him to ease the shock of a dangerous operation.

Sighing deeply, the woman walked to the long glass wall of her bedroom and stood staring down at the terrace. There was a pale moon. In memory it seemed as though half of life's decisions had been made under a moon. She switched off the lights and saw that a light snow had fallen, and that in the moonlight the giant tree trunks were arranging and rearranging themselves in geometric patterns on the terrace.

Downstairs, a band of light showed below the study door. Amazing how much courage it took to open that door; the knob slipped in her wet hand. But once she'd wiped it with her flannel robe the knob turned easily.

Jim had not heard her. Standing there in the shadow, she stood looking at him, wondering how to begin, when suddenly his head jerked upwards. It startled her, making her hand fly to her mouth.

"What do you want? What is it now?" he asked wearily.

Hope swooped back into its secret hiding place. The too blue eyes were icy and the manner so defensive that it was necessary to wet her lips, to crease them into a smile.

Her voice needlessly loud, she said: "Oh, I—I heard you earlier on the phone and I—Jim, I've know Buff Parker for ages and—and I do know she's a sensible woman. She won't get hysterical if Jerry has to have an operation."

The study was tomblike.

The answer was slow in coming but when it did come it expressed amusement. "Thanks," Jim said, "but aren't you taking up medicine a little late?"

She held the smile, creased it deeper. "Well, I don't know —you used to ask me about people. And Buff Parker—"

He broke in: "What I used to do scarcely applies in any way, shape or form. When you leave, please leave the door open, it's close in here."

She didn't move. "I—I felt—"

"When don't you?" he asked. "Get back to your wailing wall. Take up where you left off and let me decide about hysterical relatives."

More ill at ease than she could ever recall being, still she did not move. It was to be expected that her legs should tremble but what was the matter with her mind? It used to be clear and quick.

No tricks, she thought. Play it straight.

"I wasn't weeping, Jim. I was upstairs on the chaise, thinking, sorting out. Seeing what I've been trying to do to you, to us. To almost everybody." Words were coming faster now. "I'm beginning to realize how self-centered—one-tracked— I've been and, realizing this made me want to ask you if we couldn't go back and start over."

At sight of the boredoom in his face, she hurried: "Oh, I don't mean back to what we once thought we had, not that.

A new basis, brand-new. If—Jim, I'd like the chance to make this lovely house into a real home, and—and myself into a *real* wife."

His laugh was like paper tearing.

"I thought we'd get around to the real wife angle—forget it. I'd think even you would accept by now that no man can be argued into bed."

A great wave of anger drenched her, sweeping away the good intentions.

"You—you're the one to forget it! Why, you're so damned apologetic that every word you utter, every gesture, is suspect. I'll admit that at first I did take it for granted you'd be interested in sex—read it in a book, I suppose—but since you aren't—and I'm not—since we're both running in the same direction, why don't we *both* relax and use beds to sleep in? I understand it's been done before."

When he was about to answer she said quickly: "No, wait. Jim, we could make a go of it if we really tried. You and I have a hell of a lot on the ball. Couldn't we try being friends, two decent civilized people living in the same house, considerate of one another? If we had friendship, what else would we truly need?"

The cold eyes were emotionless.

"I couldn't guess your needs," he said. "Who could? But I do know a little about mine and what I need is a divorce. Through the years, every time a leaf has dropped, you've yacked divorce, divorce! Okay, I agree. The sooner, the better."

Anger was snuffed out. And hope and courage. She forced herself to try once again however.

"Jim, I'd hoped—"

"Don't," he said. "Get lost. Go off and die. As long as you get going I won't give a damn how!"

Trembling, shrinking from the vast dislike which encircled her, the woman's gaze left his. Her hands were working at the soft yellow robe and after some time her lips moved.

"It seems like—like an awful waste," she said.

The moon was higher now. It flooded the glass-walled bedroom, giving it a ghostly beauty. It was odd about moons. When you were happy, there wasn't anything lovelier, when you were not, a moon was a dull lonely ache. A longing to be released; let me go, *let me go*. A hurt.

And houses. Houses felt hurt too, could die of it.

In the moonlight the woman lay on her bed and wondered what would become of this house. It had been such a part of her, so much real emotion had gone into the building of it, that suddenly it was important in a way it had not been since the contractor left. Even at this date she could recapture some of what she'd felt in all the different stages of its construction. The annoyance at the several false starts up to the final rightness of the accepted plans.

She was able to see again the raw stakes marking the foundations, the slow rise of brick walls with the great gaps for windows, and at last the second story brushed by the giant trees. She'd put great stress on not sacrificing a single tree. The virgin forest and, beyond it, the surrounding acres of ever-changing fields must be made to appear part of the house itself. And through the use of windows this had been accomplished.

Wherever feasible there were windows. Literal walls of windows, broad and continuous so that from the inside nature seemed almost a clever extension of the décor. A mirrored wall in the living room, centering an enormous fireplace, also contributed to the illusion of endless space and movement.

The furnishings, the draperies, rugs and materials, were the result of months of search. They must be related subtly to the outside and yet, as she often said, not be too subtle to compete with the job God had done. And what was obviously God's favorite color had been used throughout.

Carpeting, walls and materials all were green, varying in its seasonal shades from the tender meadow limes of spring up

127

through the dancing greens of summer to the ripened gold of the wheat fields. The scheme had turned out exactly as she'd planned, making the house larger than it actually was, making each room a complement and a continuation of the outdoors.

And now the house was dying. Its graciousness was empty, as devoid of meaning as the smile on the photograph of someone you do not remember. Assurance, pride, illusions had gone out of it and on this November night the woman who lay alone was endeavoring to face the reasons why.

The task had been a clumsy halting one. Her adult life had been spent in running from what she did not choose to face. If there'd been any rejecting to be done she was the one who did it and until tonight there'd been no real need to change. Tonight however the man long asleep in a room beyond had found words at last which despite her ingenuity she was not able to juggle into some wishful interpretation of her own.

He had left no loophole. Even she could not misunderstand. Their life together had ended and if this was so she too had reached the end. To those who felt they knew her this would be incredible but they knew only what she had permitted them to know. They could not know for instance that her own estimate of herself was so battered that the thought of starting over was both senseless and intolerable.

Her conscience had been right. The job would mean going back and starting from scratch and with Sam gone and Alan gone, what incentive was there? A time came when right or wrong a person grew frayed from failure and from a constant pretending that you had not failed. As you got older your supply of whitewash seemed to dwindle.

During the hours just passed, many of the steps that had led her here had been inspected with unaccustomed realism. She'd recognized with shock that the broad sleek highway down which she'd traveled was no highway at all. It wasn't even a road but rather an unmarked trail, devoid of purpose, of responsibility, and like most trails it had reached a dead end.

Her use of life had been a senseless waste of good material. This she saw and was willing to accept but she wasn't willing to start over. The acknowledgment had brought with it no resources from which to pay the piper and no true desire to pay. A lifetime of winning had stunted her capacity to lose.

A horrible aloneness filled her. In final desperation there arose the thought of God and she clutched the thought, meanwhile casting about for any prayer she might have learned. There were no prayers, not even the little one Hannah had taught her. There was nothing but automatic scraps:

IF I SHOULD DIE BEFORE I WAKE

GIVE US THIS DAY OUR DAILY BREAD

HE LEADS ME BESIDE THE STILL WATERS

Her mouth twisted. It would be fine, she thought, to be beside still waters. While not for a moment did she believe this would be her destination, she did, in a way, believe in God, in a God. Quite often she had planned to call on Him, to leave cards as it were, but God wasn't too socially au *fait*, and outside of that one long-ago minister, she'd never gotten around to it. It wouldn't be gallant now to ask help from Someone you'd ignored.

If there was a God, at least He was going to catch her sober. Jim could be thanked for that. Jim had expected her to go and grab the bottle and so, for laughs, she hadn't and was glad. There was some slight ray of satisfaction in this and in the fact that she would leave no weepy notes. No corn, for once.

Moving her head, the woman looked at the illumined face of a clock nearby. It was very late. The time alloted for thinking was running short and had been wasted. Hours ago—weeks really—she'd known almost certainly what she was going to do.

All right, let's go, she said under her breath.

The moonlight made the yellow-tiled bathroom seem miles away across the blue-green carpet. Slowly she got up from the bed and, not to make a sound, guided herself with exaggerated caution from familiar object to familiar object. First the carved bedpost which held the quilted canopy, then the lowboy with the fabulous Chia Ching period bowls she'd found in Pekin, then the Queen Anne secretary, then finally the chaise longue with its quilted covering to match the canopy.

At last, her fingers reaching in, she touched the cool tiles and flipped on the light.

Adjoining the bath, through a wide archway was a jonquil-yellow dressing room. Thick plate-glass doors fronted a solid line of closets and so it was difficult to overlook the row on row of dresses on their satin hangers, the long shelves for hats and shoes, the special cedar closet which held her furs.

Her eyes slid off the array and yet Liz Hatch could not keep from wondering who would get it all. Oh, what difference did it make! Since the house had lost its meaning it did not matter what became of it or the contents of the closets or her jewels or any of it. All she would require was a spectator's sport outfit to walk beside still waters.

Partway to the medicine cabinet, the glib irreverence provoked a belated and surprising reaction. Sensibilities that had been numbed were sparked alive, causing the woman to lean against a wall, breathing in sharp gusts of unexpected fear.

She waited. After a time the intrusion passed and she was able to walk to the mirrored cabinet. Inside was the small square amber bottle but when she took it out a new fear swept her: *suppose there were not enough.* She was so careful to keep the supply up that this one contingency had not occurred to her.

Shaking the bottle, she thought, What will I do if there's

not enough? Instantly there came a wave of nausea and then the capsules pinged reassuringly and her insides unknotted.

On a glass shelf beneath the cabinet was a line of mono-grammed containers for creams and lotions and these had to be pushed aside. After this had been done the amber bottle was uncapped and tipped with caution. She must count the pills. And carefully. Without fear.

It was odd how steady her fingers were. Particularly when in the glare of tonight's self-probing she had seen that fear was the one consistent element in all she knew about herself. Every angle of fear. A to-hell-with-it bravado, yes, but no courage. Yet now, at this awesome moment she was quite objective. This proved—*what* did it prove? Here was one act there was no need to rationalize.

Freed from the habit of alibiing herself the woman's attention returned to the bottle. She tipped it further, watching a last capsule slither out to roll lopsided across the shelf, completing the pink mound.

The mound did not look large enough. So in a measured solitary fashion she counted one by one and there were not enough, only fourteen. To be certain she recounted, lining the pills in a pink parade, and this time there were only thirteen.

This upset her terribly. The meager supply coupled with an inability to count seemed to augur failure and again her insides knotted and her hands began to shake. She was searching the cabinet frantically when all at once her expression changed.

Why, thirteen would do! *Thirteen was her lucky number.*

The thirteenth—a Friday, too—was the date of her first solo flight. When she'd picked that date even the very youngest pilots had protested.

Keith, her instructor, a darling slat of a kid, said: "Solo on the thirteenth? You're bats. You'll never make it."

She'd made it all right, all right; three pretty take-offs, three pretty landings. And after sundown, in the middle of a snowstorm. Keith had stood, wet and shivering in the snow, and when she taxied over, he grinned: "Congratulations. You owe me a drink, Liz. Two drinks. One for the thirteenth, one for pneumonia."

It was when she had gone to pick up her drink that she had discovered she was shaky. She'd thought she was wonderful but now her hands were like the morning after. She'd had to bend over and suction and they'd kidded her unmercifully.

The getting a pilot's license however had some point to it; it wasn't running away, the opposite. It came about because of an awful fear of flying, a phobia that had begun to affect her life and the life of others. Pete was in prep school and one short vacation he'd asked to fly to New York and she roared to high heaven. So instead of losing an hour or two of his precious time he'd lost almost a whole day. That did it. He was sweet about it of course, Pete being Pete, but it made a heel out of her.

And this had preyed on her until, a few months later, she went to the Westchester Airport and gave herself up. Scared silly, she'd walked into the Flight Office crammed with legs and leather jackets.

"I'm here to learn to fly," she'd announced.

There was total silence, as dense as the smoke. As far as the leather jackets were concerned, she was Mrs. Methuselah; what would an old hag want with a pilot's license?

Come to think of it, this too was a solo flight. Very solo. And she would make this the way she'd made the other. Remarshaling her thoughts the woman pulled them back to tonight. She raised her head to look outside; the moonlight had faded. It was getting on toward dawn.

Okay, let's go, she said to herself.

One by one, with infinite care, she picked up the capsules.

Each was picked up and counted as if it were a pearl dropped from a strand. After all had been accounted for, she wedged them down into a tightly cupped hand and turned on a tap, waiting for the water to run cold. Waiting, her reflection in the mirror caught her. She was nonplused to find that her mouth had settled into the copy of a grin, and then right away, she got the joke. The absurdity of caring whether the water was cold or not.

An ability to grin at such a time egged her on to attempt an even more ambitious show of sportsmanship. Filling a glass she lifted it in a toast to her reflection, thinking, you *bet*— why not do this right! It isn't every day one goes about committing suicide.

On the instant, pretense crumbled. The cheap headline words hit her straight between the eyes. Her conscious mind scuttled, now here, now there, frantically ducking further realism, until at last it found refuge in the childhood memory of another mirror.

This one was long and wide and in it she could see a frightened child, with her father tall behind her. The father's face was stern. He was endeavoring to explain to the child why her hair had disappeared, why the little head was so revoltingly slick and naked. But the gray eyes would not meet his. She kept pulling back. Finally the man shook her.

"Stop this," he said. "Look at me. You've been sick and the sickness made your hair fall out. It'll come back, I tell you, but this isn't the important thing. The important thing, Liz Burns, is for you to learn right here and now that there'll be plenty of times in life when you can't bury your head and you can't run away. This is one of them."

Gradually the figures blanked and with them any hope of sportsmanship. Liz Hatch leaned against the basin, sick with the nausea of what she was about to do. Panic, a searing indecision, tore at her.

Fighting for control, she leaned there and eventually the rasping sobs abated and there was an awareness of her surroundings. The water had been left running, it was spraying the soft yellow robe and when she noticed this, it somehow angered her. As if in spite, she gripped the glass and filled it to overflowing; then stooping quickly, she sucked the pills into her mouth.

The pills had coagulated in the tight hot hand. It was necessary to fill the glass again but at last the bitter mass was down. The woman was on her way. Once more she had chosen a trail that was not meant for use if there was any other way to go.

CHAPTER TEN

Here for a space the story must be seen through Pete's eyes. What he himself saw and heard and felt, added to what Jim told him later. A large portion of all we ever learn about ourselves is hearsay and one's acceptance or rejection depends solely upon the trustworthiness of the observer. Pete is worthy of trust, so while part of this is hearsay, it is also the truth.

As I, Pete's mother, was walking through the Valley of the Shadow, Pete came and found me and started after me. He had returned from New Haven, jubilant, bursting with the news that the dean at Yale had agreed to take him back. Running through the garage into the house, he called: "Mom, Mom."

There wasn't the slightest premonition of anything amiss. The Lincoln was in the garage and though the downstairs was empty this didn't mean a thing as no one could ever predict his mother's sleeping hours. Reading as late as she did, it was entirely possible that even now after lunch she was still asleep. Or she might be in her dressing room. If she were, and the bedroom door closed, she wouldn't be able to hear him.

He ran upstairs, crying: "Hey, Mom!"

The bedroom door was closed. For a moment he stood

listening and then tiptoed up the hall and opened the door. The room was flooded with sunshine, warm and bright, and it was perfectly quiet. Now, for the first time, there came a sense of something wrong. An instinct, the identical hair-bristling he'd had when scouting in Okinawa.

The bathroom lights were on and this wasn't like his mother; she'd spend a hundred bucks on a hat the size of a matchbox but she was nuts on electricity. And anyway she slept so badly, she couldn't have missed seeing them once her reading lamp was off. One of the canopied beds was untouched, as smooth as it had been since his return from the Pacific. The other, the one she slept in, couldn't be seen from the doorway. She must certainly be very sound asleep. She must have taken more of those sleeping pills than usual; he did wish she'd lay off that stuff.

He moved toward the bed, and the first thing that caught his attention was an arm which didn't look like an arm. It was standing straight up, stiff and detached very like those spare arms and legs in museums. Dangling from it was a hand which looked as if it might have tried to signal and gotten tired. As he came nearer he saw that the arm was braced against the headboard while the rest of his mother lay on its side, twisted, sort of grotesque, like one of those dolls made of rags.

He moved swiftly now. He felt the face, felt the stiff hand and they felt too cool, too cool and dry with all that hot sun on them. He'd been around death and near-death so often and remembered what he'd seen a corpsman do. Lifting his hand sideways, with fingers opened and tight together Pete struck the face as hard as he could right above the nose. It didn't move. The face should have cried out in agony but not a muscle quivered.

He tried nothing further, he knew that too. When you didn't know, it was strictly for the doc. Not Jim. Jim was a surgeon and Jim's office was in New York. Who was the local

136

doctor? Was he the same they'd had before? What—what was his name?

And a hospital. The Westchester? No, All Angels, that was the name; they'd have all the gadgets. Stomach pumps, pulmotors, transfusions. They'd send an ambulance. An ambulance was the first step.

Going to the bedside table he looked up the number of All Angels Hospital. It seemed hours before it answered and hours longer before he was connected with what was called Emergency. At last he got it.

"Emergency speaking," a voice informed him.

"About time," Pete said, "my mother is dying. She could be dead already."

When the voice heard the address, it said that was pretty far out in the country.

"Then you better hurry," Pete said.

The word *hurry* brought back the doctor's name; Murray. Dr. Neil Murray. It was right. There were the name and number in the green leather book by the telephone.

The doctor was in his office, had just come in, and yes, Pete had done right in calling the hospital. He'd call All Angels and confirm it, and then go there and wait. Had Pete called Jim? Somebody should—would he do it?

He would, right away.

"Good boy," Dr. Murray said. "Take it easy, Pete. We do wonders these days."

"That's right," Pete said. "I've seen 'em."

The switchboard operator at the offices of James C. Hatch, M.D., sounded hurt that anyone should expect to speak to Dr. Hatch without appointment. She was sorry but Dr. Hatch was with a patient.

Pete's mouth dried with sudden fury.

"Don't give me that crap," he said. "I'm his wife's son. Get him."

137

After a shocked silence there was one more long delay. Staring down at his mother's crumpled body, Pete decided he didn't like Jim much. He'd stood up for him to Alan but he didn't really like him. Jim was too big for his pants. He wasn't half the noise Pete's own father was and twice as hard to get in touch with. Some of the blame of what had happened was Jim's—it wasn't all his mother's. A small part of it could go to Alan and, yes, part to his own father and probably to himself too, but Jim Hatch was no bluebird.

"Good afternoon," a woman's voice said.

Pete's wrath boiled over.

"No, it's *not* good!" he shouted. "Look; I'm Peter Addams and I want James Hatch and want him quick—on *the double, madam.*"

"Oh—Peter," the voice smiled. "This is Miss Resnichek. How are you, Peter? I'm afraid you can't speak to Dr. Hatch right now. He's busy. He withdrew some papers from the safety deposit box this morning and I believe he's reading a will."

Pete held onto himself; no point in chewing Miss Resnichek.

"Look," he said, "this is more important than any will you ever heard of except the Will of God—get him, will you?"

Miss Resnichek was not a fool. Almost immediately he heard Jim's voice: "Hi, Pete. How's tricks?"

"Jim, listen—this is going to be a shock. It's about Mother."

The wires hummed emptily. Then finally Jim answered: "Shoot. What seems to be the trouble?"

Later, several years later when Pete was able to gain Jim's confidence, one of the things he told Pete was that he had gone to the joint safety deposit box that morning and withdrawn Liz's will. He was just curious about it. He had just started to read it when Pete's call came. Written at the top of the sheet were these words:

*I, Elizabeth Burns Hatch, being of
sound mind and body,*

Throughout the entire conversation those words had stared up at him: *I, Elizabeth Burns Hatch, being of sound mind and body—*

When Pete had asked the next question Jim was staring back at the words.

"It'll be a shock. Can you take it, Jim?" Pete asked.

Looking at the words, Jim said: "I can take a lot."

"Here goes then: I got back from New Haven and—and *found* her. She's *drugged*, Jim. I called the—"

Jim laughed. "Did you say drunk? Or drugged?"

Pete's voice rose. "This isn't exactly a joke, Dr. Hatch. Your wife, my mother, is drugged; *out*. Dr. Murray is on his way to All Angels. The ambulance should be here any minute —I'll go along with her. See you at the hospital. Hold everything."

Jim cleared his throat. "No, Pete; I won't be there."

"You—*what?*"

Jim cleared his throat again.

"I said, I won't be there. I've got an office full of patients. I'm busy."

Pete's stomach turned over. He couldn't have made himself clear. "*Jim*," he cried, "I think Mom is—*is going to die!* She—"

"Oh, I understood," Jim said. "That's *her* business. She's got her job and I've got mine—and I can't ditch mine. Goodbye, boy. Thanks."

Pete gazed down at his mother. When he was able to speak, it was barely a whisper.

"You mean—you honestly mean—? Why, *you could rot in hell for this!*"

139

"That may be true," Jim answered. "It probably is. Good-bye."

Pete found his voice. "*Well*," he shouted, "*well, now I understand why she did it!*"

"Yes, now you understand," Jim said.

Later Jim told how he'd gone on sitting there, how his hand reached for a pencil and began doodling around and through the phrase *sound mind and body*. The tendons in the back of his neck had cramped into knots and one eyelid was twitching. He'd taken a handkerchief and rubbed the eye and in doing this he saw that the backs of his hands were glistening so he rubbed them too. Then the library door opened. Miss Resnichek stood there.

"What do you want?" he'd asked.

She was looking at him oddly. "You were expecting Dr. Houston. He's here with his report. Shall I put him in your office?"

A second wind came to him. He'd felt himself stiffen.

"Do that," he told her. "And, Miss Resnichek, break all appointments for today. No matter *who* calls—no matter *who* —you don't know how to reach me. Is that quite clear?"

It was, Miss Resnichek nodded.

For Pete to get all this out of Jim required infinite patience, infinite courage, but, being Pete, he did it, and was the one person alive who could have so far as I know. I, Pete's mother, am amazed at the depth of Jim's confidence in my son. Distrusting me, and rightly, he trusted my son and the trust was not misplaced. What follows was never told me until a short while ago, until Pete was thoroughly convinced of the change in his mother. Thoroughly convinced that if Jim's side of the story was ever told it would only be told in the hope of serving Almighty God.

And this, this alone, *is* my hope.

The story could have been one-sided. It could have been

solely from my point of view but, since "none of us liveth to himself," what Jim thought and felt is as much a part of what happened to me as my own thoughts and feelings. Jim's side was true as he saw it, so, if this story is to help others like us, it must include his viewpoint, as well as mine.

When the narrative switches from Liz the woman, to Pete the son, to Jim the man, and back again, it is the way life goes; three of all the myriads of threads which pieced together go to make up that which a person was and now is.

That evening, a Friday, it was after dinner that Jim Hatch decided to drive from his office in New York to Westchester. He would do the usual. He had no thought of going to the hospital. For all he knew his wife could be dead but she had forfeited his respect long ago. Yet because he had a home he had decided to go to it. The Hutchison River Parkway was taking him there and the Parkway runs directly below All Angels Hospital. Naturally he was aware of this and, without intending to, as he rounded the curve he glanced upwards.

The winged hospital was ablaze with light. In the November mist, the wings stood out like giant signboards, converging. Dropping his eyes, Jim watched the road when suddenly out of the mist, loomed an apalling thought: *suicide was an act of violence!* For him of all people to have forgotten this was staggering. He left the Parkway at its next exit and turned back up a hill to the pile of yellow brick.

It was snowing a little. High above was a group of thick-bunched clouds from which a few wisps of snow fluttered down in a halfhearted attempt to freshen up the day's grime. This annoyed Jim. His new postwar convertible would be splotched. Driving past the large parking space, he braked in a section marked: For Staff Only. Visiting hours must be over; there was an acre of lined empty stalls, nevertheless it was characteristic of Jim to assume official status. After he had locked the car doors, he turned back to retest them and then satisfied, walked through the parking space and up the steps to the main entrance.

Through swinging doors was a lobby of doubtful marble. A receiving desk was to the left, an information desk to the right and in between, huddled nakedly, were a series of plaster of Paris saints. At their dirt-stained feet semicircles of red glass containers with flickering candles were attempting hopelessly to humanize the antiseptic neon glare.

Even to the healthy the saints were ominous. They were heroic-sized and as the eye became accustomed it was impossible to imagine what solace they would bring or who had conjured up such vulgar dime-store splendor. The eyes distended condescendingly, the lips pursed inanely and, in the too-short arms, stuck with scotch tape, were wads of dirty cotton flowers as improbable as the saints themselves.

Jim looked away in disgust and yet the votive candles reaffirmed the rightness of his decision to come here. Their significance was undeniable; money for appeasement—God, how could he have been so careless! Feeling for his checkbook he went to the information desk and asked for the Mother Superior.

Jim had not forgotten the furor caused by Liz's divorce from Silas. The publicity had half amused, half impressed him:

NEW YORK SOCIALITE GETS RENO DIVORCE
ASKS NO ALIMONY SHARES CUSTODY OF SON
WITH WELL-KNOWN CLUBMAN AND INVESTMENT
BANKER

It would require a boxcar of votive candles to keep Liz's most recent dramatic bid from the reporters. If he was lucky he could stop it before it hit the sheriff's office.

The eighth floor of All Angels Hospital was normally reserved for surgical cases and therefore was apt to be less noisy.

Here the student nurses lowered their voices and the attendants were careful not to clatter the metal trays.

Opposite the elevators were four wards with seven beds apiece. The beds were never empty. Either you died and were whisked out from behind protecting screens or you went home and someone else moved in. Private rooms were not available on short notice and Dr. Murray, Liz's doctor, had not gotten one but what difference could it make? It was touch and go whether anything would ever make a difference to Liz Hatch again. It still was anybody's bet.

In this particular ward six of the beds were unscreened. The patients had been made ready for the night and while occasionally a groan came from one of them, for the most part they were quiet, their attention riveted on the activity around the seventh bed.

It stood at the far end. Curtained off by screens on metal standards, it had become as private as sleazy cretonne could make it. The six patients, their senses heightened by pain and boredom, were well aware that some disheartening battle was being waged behind those screens.

Within the cubicle the space was extremely limited. Barely room for the bed, the doctor, the two black-garbed nuns, and the suspended glass container from which a rubber tube hung down to run along the mattress and end in the figure on the bed. One of the nuns stood at the foot of the bed, her fingers moving firmly up and down a string of wooden beads as her keen eyes observed the patient's face. The second nun watched the contents of the glass jar, counting the slow even plops of glucose into the rubber tube. Cautious not to brush against the tube, she turned to face the doctor.

"The glucose is running low," she warned. "Shall we send for more?"

The doctor sighed. The sigh was audible. It reached outside the curtains to Pete Addams who had been waiting there

143

hour on hour. He tensed, listening for the doctor's answer.

A moment passed. Then the doctor said: "Sister, I can't get the pupils to react to light. But at that we're lucky—the breathing is better."

Pete relaxed somewhat. In the middle of a deep breath he held it so as to overhear the nun's reply.

"Good," she said. "Will we want more glucose?"

"No, let's wait. We mustn't overload the heart. But watch that pulse, Sister. For God's sake, watch that *pulse*."

The nun gave a soft chuckle and in the dim light beyond, Pete smiled with her.

"Yes, Doctor," she said. "We'll watch it for His sake."

Right, Pete thought.

A student nurse came down the aisle between the beds. She nodded to Pete. In a low tone she said: "Sister. Sister Agnes."

One of the nuns pushed aside a screen and slipped out.

"Yes, Ann, what is it?"

"The patient's husband, Dr. Hatch. He's finally come," the girl told her. "The Mother was with him but she's gone. He wants Dr. Murray."

Pete moved to look past the girl out into the bright corridor. He wondered what he ought to do and while he was wondering, the nun said: "The doctor won't want to leave now; I'll attend to it. Where is Dr. Hatch?"

There was Dr. Hatch. Pete saw him near the elevators, a heavy camel's hair coat over one arm.

"There," the nurse pointed. "That's him in the swell chalk stripe."

The nun smiled, hitched the rosary to a hook projecting from her stout leather belt and walked through the ward, Pete close behind her.

"I'll attend to it," she repeated. "You may go, Ann. Thank you."

Pete did not go beyond the door. He stayed there, looking from the nun to Jim and back again. These nuns were great. He didn't know anything about religion but he did know that according to Catholics, suicide was a mortal sin. They figured your life belonged to God and it was up to Him whether it was long or short and yet in spite of their belief there hadn't been the slightest suggestion of holier-than-thou. He'd watched for it and there wasn't any.

The sister's starched headdress creaked slightly as she left Pete and went to where Jim was. She certainly must be asking herself what kind of man this was, must be thinking it very strange he hadn't showed before. Well, *wasn't it?* He knew Jim hadn't seen him yet and he wished they *never* had to see each other.

He heard the nun say: "Dr. Hatch?"

Jim looked trapped.

"Yes," he said.

"Yes," the nun repeated. "Dr. Hatch, Doctor Murray won't want to leave the patient. Her condition is very serious. Is there anything I can do?"

Jim was staring down at the plain lined features.

"I don't imagine so," he answered. "The Mother Superior advised my coming here. I'm trying to find out what I'm supposed to do."

The words seemed to Pete to have an undercurrent of meanness. The guy's a real bastard, Pete thought, a fish-blooded bastard. He was ready to step forward when the nun answered.

"*Do?*" she repeated. The single word was a reproof. "*Do? I* should think you're supposed to help us save your wife!"

Having decided to knock Jim's block off, hospital or no hospital, Pete happened to notice Jim's eyes, Jim's lips. They were frightened. Frightened and hurt and full of pain. He'd never seen a more confused face and the sister must be seeing it too because her manner changed abruptly.

"Come. Get that campstool over there," she pointed. "As you'll see we don't have much room. Come, follow me."

I'm stuck, Pete thought.

Okay, so I'm stuck—he said to himself. Going to Jim, he held out a hand. "Hello," he said. "I'm sorry about this, Jim. For you as well as Mother."

Jim halted, staring at him, staring at the outstretched hand. Finally his eyes dropped and he gripped the hand.

"Thanks," he said. "I won't forget this, Pete."

Picking up the stool, he went past Pete to the entrance to the ward. The sister had gone ahead and when Jim hesitated, six pair of eyes turned to look at him, seeming to turn in unison as though they were porcelain eyes on some sliding display in an optometrist's window. As Jim moved down the ward, the eyes moved down the ward.

Pete followed and even he could not bear the thought of what this scrutiny must be doing to its object. The procession; the sister, Jim, the eyes, Pete, went the length of the room and at last the sister separated the screens.

"Here," she gestured.

Pete stayed outside. He turned to face the window he had been facing hour after hour. Just as he was turning he saw Jim look at him and then edge in behind the flimsy screens. Then he heard Dr. Murray's voice. It was louder than it had been at any time.

"Well, so you finally made it?" Dr. Murray said.

Waiting for what he knew would be a defensive answer, Pete was aware of his own mixed state. Love for his mother, a giving, unquestioning love, had been, till recently, his one sure love. It wasn't a blind love, merely unquestioning, and it didn't question now. But now, interwoven with this was his love of God, a greater, stronger, over-all love, especially for those whom others had harmed. His feeling for Liz, his mother, had never included pity. Somehow he'd always thought of

146

her as being strong enough in every way to be whatever she truly wanted to be.

He still thought this. What she had done to herself hadn't changed this feeling one particle. Who was he to know why or how she had come to such a terrible decision? Any person, his mother, anyone, must suffer beyond conception to come to this, to be able to part with the most wonderful of gifts. And it was so pitiful because, in seeking oblivion, you wouldn't find oblivion; you'd only find yourself having to begin again, *this* time, *separated from God.*

As for Jim, well, maybe Jim was warped in a way. He didn't know. Nobody except herself could really harm Liz but people could harm Jim because he didn't seem to have the stuff to stop them. Not that Jim gave in, no; it was more that he didn't seem to give at all. Or *take.* He didn't seem capable of either giving or taking, whereas his mother, well, she could do both in a big way. Nothing could ever have harmed her if she hadn't allowed it.

Oddly, in spite of a great many things she'd done which he didn't admire and didn't respect, Pete did admire her and did respect her. He guessed the reason for this was that all his life, *always,* he'd known what she was like inside. With Jim, well, you just couldn't be sure.

He heard Jim's voice.

"Yes," he was saying, "I finally made it. Sorry to miss the first act."

Oh, *no,* Pete thought. You poor stinker, you don't *mean* that. That sounded awful—and you didn't even mean it!

Jim was clearing his throat in the nervous way he had.

"I'm a busy man," he went on. "I don't find time for theatrics of any type. Particularly not in a hospital."

Behind Pete someone snickered faintly. After that it was quiet. The quietness inside the cubicle must be crowding them, must be pushing them against the curtains. Pete could guess Dr. Murray's expression, the expressions of the nuns. They'd be blank-faced, at least the nuns would be. He knew how the doc was feeling; shocked, ready to sock Jim. Pete had felt that way himself but now—now he was mixed up. Really mixed.

Jim would probably be looking down at that figure on the bed. He'd almost have to. If you didn't look at Dr. Murray and didn't look at the nuns there wasn't any other place to look. And that figure was so motionless, so flat it didn't seem real. It hardly made any bulge at all. Unless it had moved, and Pete didn't suppose it had, the hands would be turned palm upward in the strangest fashion. Lax and still as though they'd never reached for anything.

Above the turned back sheet the face would be gray, the mouth hanging open, pulling the features down, making the cheekbones even higher than they were.

It could be anyone. Or no one. It could be a dummy.

Pete felt his eyes overflow.

No! It *wasn't* a dummy—*it was his mother.* And she was *breathing.* Dr. Murray had said so!

She would live. Not for a moment of the long afternoon, of the long, long evening, had Peter Addams ever actually lost faith.

She would live and she would find herself. One day, he couldn't guess how, she would find what he had found. God would show her the self Pete knew about, the real inside self. And then—wouldn't *that* be something! All her charm and loyalty and humor, all her wonderful ability to interest people, to move them—

Jim was the one to be troubled about. Someone really ought to help Jim—he sure needed help. Maybe the time would come when he could get through to Jim. He hoped so.

CHAPTER ELEVEN

The day did come when Pete did get through to Jim. He didn't succeed in helping him any but then, nobody from God to the guy next door can ever really help anyone who doesn't want help. And Jim said he didn't. He was satisfied as he was. Not satisfied exactly but he'd have to let it ride.

They talked together however, at great length. It was then Jim told his thoughts and feelings that November night at All Angels Hospital. For the most part what he was thinking and feeling concerned the Liz he'd first encountered ten or more years back; the rest had to do with that night, his reactions to the figure on the bed.

The remark about being a busy man with no time for theatrics hadn't represented in the slightest the churning which had gone on inside him. Pete was right about that; the remark was wholly defensive. No sooner was it out than he'd have given a great deal to take it back. The expressions in the eyes of the nuns and Doctor Murray had forced him to look away. And it was then he saw Liz. There was no other place to look.

His immediate sensation had been identical to Pete's. The rigid hump barely disturbing the blankets could have been anyone or no one; it could have been a dummy. One of the dummies he so often saw on the operating table. This anonymity had been a relief, and if he'd left then, if he'd walked out of the hospital, he might have spared himself a lot of anguish. But he didn't. He stayed, allowing his gaze to follow the familiar rubber tubing up the side of the mattress, up the wrist and forearm to where it ended in a vein.

His gaze had continued on up to the firm chin, now curiously slack, on up to the pale nostrils and the closed eyelids. Here the sense of anonymity left him, here was the feature which, for him, made the face unlike all other faces. Above the eyelids were those flaring eyebrows. They were dark, dark brown, and of itself this was unusual with the light hair and the gray eyes, but it was the shape of the eyebrows and her manner of using them that intrigued him. He'd always told Liz they were dead giveaways. Thermometers, he'd called them. Even in sleep, one was arched, the other level. Tonight, for the first time, they were uncommunicating and unresponsive.

A surge of emotion swept over him. Legs trembling a little, he sat down on the creaky campstool. When Dr. Murray spoke to him he didn't answer for he was attempting to relate the emotion to the figure before him. However he wished, and he did greatly wish to drag his eyes away, they kept going back, drawn by some dormant need to recapture the magic this woman had once had for him. He'd thought it dead. Perhaps it was dead but obviously the memory was not.

The magic had been so far from allure as to be unrelated to it. What was it then? Color? Warmth? Yes, warmth, a warmth which drew you to her as the smell of food draws the hungry, as the glow of lighted windows draws the lonely. Before this warmth encircled you, you hadn't missed the lack of it, but afterwards, without it, you felt yourself halved and empty. You'd been cold and dark and then you were warm and light and this made the coldness and darkness harder to take. There weren't words for what she could do to you. Whatever it was it had been bigger and finer than Jim's own solitary, long-considered plans for himself. Plans which not for a moment included the sharing of self, nor any interests beyond those of Medicine. And then surgery.

This had changed almost at once. Almost immediately Jim had become a person possessed and now, in memory, he very gradually was beginning to be possessed again.

Did Pete know the circumstances of their meeting?

The place was just a place and the people with him were just people. His personal life was practically nonexistent, a matter of eating and sleeping in order to function at his profession. His earlier marriage had never been permitted to interfere and since he hadn't ever imagined anyone like Liz, he hadn't expected his plans to be sidetracked. From the moment he saw her, though, he'd felt that here was someone who was going to interrupt his life. People always said Jim didn't notice women and this was true, but he had noticed Liz.

She was standing at the bar at the end of the room. He'd been watching her and had gotten an impression of both forthrightness and impermanency; she was there and was enjoying it but she would move on. A grown child, eager and aimless. As he watched, her face lighted and she smiled and the smile changed her whole face and the face of the whole world. Pete knew that smile. He knew how tough it was to put into words the quickening it gave others.

How could anyone describe her? How could you say what it was that made Liz stand out wherever she went? Certainly it wasn't beauty. Personality? Yes, of course, yet personality had become so loused up that the word had lost meaning. Magnetism was closer. An aliveness which probably all humans were intended to have and hadn't attained. It was so powerful that it had pulsed across the room and alerted Jim like fingers on his wrist.

She'd turned and their eyes met and locked and something dark in Jim was lighted and the light went out to meet her, even before she came to where he was. He knew then and always had known that it was he who sought her. Unsureness seeking sureness. The unwelcomed seeking the welcomer. The taker longing to be given to. In her, you felt no aloofness, no pride, but rather a proudness. And this proudness seemed to be for others while the welcome was for you alone.

At the table he'd realized she'd been drinking too much. Why was this, he wondered. Why would anyone like her need to drink? You yourself were so certain that with such ease, you would never need a crutch of any description. It seemed ridiculous.

Now of course he knew what he couldn't know then; liquor wasn't a crutch for Liz, it was an exit. A quick flight to a world of her own making. Liz could walk without crutches, walk truer, faster than anyone, but she couldn't wait to walk, she must fly. It wasn't that this world was too much for her; it was that it wasn't enough. This was the main reason why he hadn't tried to stop her drinking. Whatever Liz was searching for, and kept on searching for, was as surely beyond him as she herself was beyond him. There'd been a time when she could have changed him but never a time when he could have changed her. In this unceasing, indeterminate quest of hers, Liz was no man's to change, to hold, even to follow.

The first evening was a daze. Jim had felt somehow freed, as though he'd emerged from a tunnel he hadn't thought of as a tunnel. Like coming from a low cramped space onto an open one where he could breathe and stand erect.

The next memory was very clear, one of a few weeks later. In place of the woman on the bed there was the image of a woman by an open door. This was in a house in Westchester. Liz had arranged it, had asked them to invite him.

The hostess phoned him. "Si Addams is out of town, he

almost always is," she told him. "I'm desperate for extra men. Do come. Liz promised you would."

She was entirely safe in promising. He'd seen her only twice since that first evening and would have walked to Westchester if he had to. However he had barely stepped inside the house before he regretted coming. This was beyond his depth. He knew it and the Chinese houseboy who took his hat and coat seemed to Jim to know it.

On either side room after room stretched out, elegant and formal. Between him and the host who came to greet him ran a great hall lined with lighted cabinets; he didn't know then that they were called *vitrines*. Inside these on mirrored shelves were miniatures framed in jewels, rare snuffboxes, ancient ivories, collections of small carved figures. He didn't know then that the figures were called figurines and had been carved from jade and quartz and alexandrite.

Nor had he the least conception of the worth of the objects nor that the rug he walked on had been walked on by Marie Antoinette. Nor that the tapestry, *petit point*, it was, on the row of stiff unsat-on chairs had fabulous museum value. All he did know was that his cherished dinner jacket—tux, he called it—was too long, too stylish, and his shirt too stiffly starched.

He'd felt a fool to have come at all. The temptation to see Liz in her own environment had tripped his better judgment; big-name patients and hospital board members were one thing to the rising young surgeon, their personal lives another. For the first time it occurred to Jim that there might be more to this than money. If so, could it be acquired or was it always "an accident of birth"?

Meeting the other guests, he discovered that Liz was not there yet. He had a cocktail and then a second and then some redhead had sidled up to ask if he was interested in oriental figurines; there was a famous collection in the hall. His interest in figurines approximated his interest in the redhead but afterwards he was glad he'd feigned interest. This was how he managed to see Liz the moment she arrived.

In All Angels Hospital, staring down at the lifeless, tangled hair, Jim was seeing it only as it had been that night. The woman on the bed wasn't Liz; Liz was leaning against a doorjamb, hair bright and blown, with here and there a glint of snow in it. Eyebrows flaring, mouth parted in a broad grin, she was informing the hall that it was just possible she was a little drunk. And, oh yes, she'd brushed a shrub and had snow in her hair and would like a bath towel. One of the small ones, please.

"Hi, my lovelies," she added.

Behind Jim a man chuckled. Who but Liz Addams would blow in in a million dollars' worth of furs and jewels and demand a bath towel?

Why not, Jim thought. Why was this noteworthy? Naturally she would ask for whatever she wanted. It was beyond imagination to think of Liz Addams as other than direct, anywhere, any time. What the man was really saying was that being natural came as natural to her as having furs and jewels. As Jim stood there, thinking this, she spotted him.

"Jim—how nice!" she called. "Wait for me. Wait till I get prettied."

Wait for her? He'd have waited all night. Even in these surroundings.

So this was where she belonged. Each word, each gesture attested to it and yet for some curious reason he had the feeling that she belonged everywhere and nowhere, depending upon group rules. When rules started to bind and limit her, she probably would cut through them and with the drinking this could be very dangerous. The result would be either tragedy or glory, no half measures.

But how could it be tragedy? Wasn't unpretentiousness an

advanced form of honesty and wasn't honesty the ultimate ideal toward which all ideals groped? In Liz this was carried to such an extent that outside of the costly get-up, she might easily have been a neighbor woman in Kansas. Here was a universal quality which had astounded him then and still did; was Pete so accustomed to it that he couldn't understand what Jim meant? He had seen it time and again; the ability to represent, and even combine, people totally alien to one another without any apparent adjustment and no condescension. It must be what was called "class" in Kansas. If so, it was a class with damn few entries.

Look, for instance, at the way she was going up the hall, talking and laughing, arm in arm with the Chinese maid. Who else could do this without, at best, some show of condescension or exhibitionism? What this woman had was a genius for people, a great gift even when half used, even dulled by liquor. Perhaps her waste of it was the element which marked her for tragedy. Jim's medical mind abhorred waste. To see a tremendous talent submerged in alcohol, unvalued, unrecognized, offered to fools, amounted to a sacrilege. God alone knew what could be made of such a gift in place of wasting it collecting people as others collect rocks or stamps or old guns. Naturally any talent was lessened and warped, or not, in exact ratio to its use. Nothing remained static.

As Jim's eyes had followed Liz and the tiny maid, no bigger than a kitten, he expected her to go into a private room to fix her hair but she didn't do that. The maid had taken the furs and was handing her a small green object and then others got in between and he lost sight of her.

He'd moved quickly and there she was, standing alone in the center of the living room, head down, drying her hair in front of everyone. He didn't suppose Pete could believe what a shock this was. Pete had been brought up to do what came natural whereas Jim's mother would no more have done such a thing than spit on the rug.

Without realizing it the guests had formed a ring around her and when she'd dried the hair she ran her fingers through it and tossed back her head and the hair was wild and gleaming and strange-colored; the color of sun-dried rope. The dress she wore was identical in color, yards and yards of floating chiffon. As they'd watched, she proceeded to twist the small green towel about her head, turban fashion, and then, like a woman in a dream, she began to dance. A funny, drifting little dance round and round the crowded room.

It was as if she were alone. Back and forth she swayed and twirled and the emerald bracelets slid up and down her arms and the dress trailed out behind like puffs of smoke. A string orchestra which had been playing chamber music came to life and caught her rhythm and never, never had he seen such a sight.

At the finish she had danced straight to Jim. The gray eyes were laughing up at him and he was prouder than in all his life.

Eyes laughing, lips serious, she said: "Want to know who I am? A houri—watch your spelling, boys! It starts with H."

It was a performance which, from anyone else, would have been forced; that god-awful glandular bounce that freezes your teeth, but with Liz there was none of this. The gaiety was an outpouring demanding nothing in return. An extra motor, extra power, reaching out and recharging you, making you come alive as she was alive. Instead of subtracting from you, it added to you. Suddenly you could believe yourself capable of things you hadn't imagined.

Through the years Jim had watched her do this very thing to so many, not even knowing that she did it.

Taxi drivers: "The Ritz, please. God, how can you be so pleasant in weather like this! I adore taxi drivers; you're a species of yellow-painted saints."

Waiters: "Evening, Leon, double martini—wait; how's Dottie's eye? Still on the beam?"

(This is the first you'd heard that Leon's daughter had a walleye and Liz had paid to have it straightened.)

Clerks; had Pete ever stood by and watched her in a store?

Clerks stopped being what they were, stopped being mediocre men and women with sore feet, and became whatever Liz saw in them. She herself hadn't the vaguest notion that the wan girl who sold her stockings had received Liz Hatch in return, that part of Liz which considered all people important. The girl had no notion either. Five minutes before she was bored stiff and unappreciated. Now she isn't. Something has occurred to make her important to herself, to the store.

Used to this sudden blossoming in others, Liz took it for granted. If only she could have stood behind herself, have appreciated how people responded automatically, she might not have wasted her gift. Christ, what couldn't she have done if she'd cared enough!

Waste. To conceive and give birth to kinship only to run away, to refuse to nurse what she'd given birth to, or acknowledge any responsibility for it. Could it be she did loathe herself as she so often said she did? It was incredible and yet, if not, why would she force such suffering on herself and on those who hoped to love her? Anguish from drink, from guilt. Days and years of terrible remorse. What did she ask that wasn't already hers?

"God—how *could* I have said that!"

"God—how can I *bear* myself!"

"God—I *hate* life!"

If you felt this, why didn't you do something about it? Why didn't you let go and adapt yourself? Jim didn't get it, for while Jim Hatch didn't enjoy himself or anything he represented, he did accept what he was. And leave it at that, leave it without regrets. To be at peace with himself was a state he'd never expected. All that was essential was not to test himself beyond his obligations as Liz was forever doing. Striving, straining, suffering. Seeking a goal she couldn't name, a goal which in all probability didn't exist. Even if it did exist she wasn't going to find it because by now the search had become tortuous and misdirected and unsustained.

The world was full of dreamers. Nuts who chased rainbows at midnight. Fiddlers who reached for notes not on the fiddle. Neurotics who rejected what there was in the mad hope of something better, who turned today into a year from tomorrow.

When Jim had finally gotten it through his head that Liz Addams thought she was in love with him, it stunned him. It was some time before he could analyze what it was she believed she'd found in him. It was her father. She was reading her father into him; that was the secret.

She would make remarks like this: "Darling, you're so like Dad! The farm background, the struggle, the courage. And your wonderful frankness and sternness and, yes, your faults, too; impatience, crudity, brusqueness. But above all, *strong*, Jim. Strong the way he was—guts!"

Liz had taken soil which looked familiar, had planted seeds of her own choosing, and then, when they didn't sprout, had blamed everyone but herself. Sam Burns was evidently the most vital man she'd ever known and what she was hoping to do was to duplicate him. It amounted to a desire for someone stronger than herself to worship. Well, he wasn't Sam and so he'd lost her. She had walked out, out and back into a fantasy life which now might be ending in this. In self-destruction.

In re-experiencing those earlier impacts Jim had been so far from All Angels Hospital that it had come as a terrible shock to feel someone trying to edge past him. His body tightened and his eyes blinked. Then he saw that the sisters had gone and Dr. Murray was peering down at him.

Clearing his throat, Jim said: "Did you say something, Murray?"

The doctor pushed a screen aside. "Yes. I'd like to know if you're going to be here. She's improved some. If you're going to stick around I'll get a bite to eat. I suppose you've had your dinner?" he added.

The old high wall enclosed Jim.

"Sure, go ahead," he yawned. "Naturally I've had dinner. Hours ago."

"Naturally," the doctor stressed the word in irony. "By the way, Hatch, I understand Pete phoned you. I understand you knew about this the same time I did."

The door in the wall banged shut.

"That is correct," Jim answered. "I knew about it but I also knew my wife. I knew that whatever she took it wouldn't be quite enough. She's a split-second timer."

"Is that so?" the doctor asked. "Well, it may be the first time, Hatch, but you came damn close to being wrong. And she's not out of the woods yet. Sister Agnes will be on the ward but if some other patient needs her, I wish you'd keep an eye on Liz; that is, if it won't overburden you. And don't play God. If anything happens, any change, press the buzzer. We don't share your optimism. Women in middle age don't snap out of a thing like this so easy. You're a doctor, you should know."

"Where's Pete?" Jim asked.

Dr. Murray had stepped out of the cubicle. Now he turned back. "For the love of God, the kid's gone to get some food! Is that okay? He's worn out doing your job but he'll be back, Hatch. Keep your head—we'll all be back."

Jim grinned. "Sure, sure," he said.

So, except for a nurse outside the curtains, he was to be alone with Liz. Hearing the retreating footsteps, he realized that now for the first time he was free to look at her un-

159

observed. Or not look. Greatly as he preferred not to look, a force more powerful than his will compelled him. He moved to examine the closed face and thought, how unlike the one he had been picturing.

Yes, she was middle-aged. This had never occurred to him but of course it was so. There was a slight sense of embarrassment at catching her off base this way until memory promptly reminded him that Liz didn't give a damn about age. It was what you were, not how long you'd been it.

No, Liz didn't bother with junk like that. He'd wondered if it was because the only qualities she really admired, ideals, stability, brains, courage, were apt to improve with age. Or it could be a form of conceit. As tortured as she was she still was so sure of herself that maybe she'd decided that Liz Hatch could afford to ignore certain facts that drove other women crazy. Whatever the cause it was one hell of a relief.

Nor did she hedge about her drinking. At least not till lately. That night at the Westchester party she'd volunteered she was a dame who loved her liquor.

"Me and martinis are like this," she said, crossing two fingers.

He remembered her stopping one of the Chinese boys.

"Hi, Tai," she said, "two martinis, please. One with an olive for my right hand, and one with an onion for my left. Nice big ones."

It sounded silly when you said it back to yourself but it didn't sound silly then. The boy had grinned from ear to ear.

After she had the cocktails, she settled back. "Now I'm all set," she said. "Let's talk about you, Jim. Where did you come from? Where were you born?"

Easy. Direct and easy. Maybe Pete wasn't old enough yet to know how seldom people asked exactly what they wanted to ask. Where Jim hailed from it wasn't considered proper to ask personal questions yet with Liz you knew right away that her questions weren't nosy. She was honestly interested and the simplest method had been to ask.

He recalled how very much he'd hoped that his answers would sound as natural as her questions. He wanted them to because of a wild hope that had just begun to take root. A hope that if this woman would give him time he might eventually catch onto how she did things. Might, might even catch up!

That night, easy-like, he'd found himself describing his home, the bleak house in the northern part of Kansas. His family, too, the Hatches; about how silent Ma was and how Pa quoted Scripture to settle everything from drought to an ingrown toenail. There were two sisters, one married to a schoolteacher and one who'd died around the time he went to college.

Naturally it was college that made the big change in his life. He'd worked his way through of course but when he started to get new ideas, he got, well, kind of ashamed of the house and of Ma's rough hands and Pa with that awful Scripture. Now he was ashamed of being ashamed.

"Don't be," Liz said. "The inner cringe that comes from comparisons is part of growth, stacking the new against the old. We outgrow shame of others. I had a wonderful father and yet I can remember writhing when he used to swear in front of friends. It's being ashamed of yourself one doesn't outgrow, at least I haven't. Take your mother's rough hands— look at mine, Jim! Look at them."

The bitterness of her tone astonished him. He'd examined the hands holding the cocktail glasses and had seen that they were broad and capable.

"What's wrong with them?" he asked.

"Wrong? What are they good for? Good to hold glasses, to thumb my nose when the world doesn't agree with me! Jim, these hands have never done one damn thing. Never ironed a handkerchief. Never darned a sock, never—"

"They could," he interrupted. "You could teach them."

"Me?" she scoffed. "I can't put on nail polish. I've tried and the result was Lady Macbeth, no less. No, Jim, I'm soft all the way through and, for God's sake, let me be ashamed of it! Now, back to you. After college, where did you go to medical school?"

He didn't hear the question the first time she asked it. Maybe if he'd never heard it or never answered it, he wouldn't have been sitting in All Angels Hospital. The reason he didn't hear it was that his thoughts were on her. If your hands were soft you were lucky and that was all there was to it. Any other attitude was morbid, sheer waste of that great "accident of birth." While money wasn't the works, it greased the works. And when you added honesty and breeding and that extra motor, *ashamed*, my God!

CHAPTER TWELVE

She was repeating her question. "After college, where did you go to medical school?"

The details of the situation that followed were burned into Jim's memory. The din in that huge cream-colored living room was almost tangible. He'd barely heard Liz. As he leaned forward to answer, he'd wondered if these people drank their dinner. He was hungry.

"Kansas!" he shouted. *"Kansas has a good Medical School."*

Hardly had he opened his mouth when one of those unaccountable stillnesses caught the room; a freak of timing which found him yelling into absolute silence. If this hadn't occurred it was possible that he and Liz might never have married, but it did occur.

There wasn't a sound. Looking up he'd found everyone staring at him and felt himself grow red. This angered him as he'd said nothing to be embarrassed about; why were they staring? Then a great beefy character had let out a snort.

"Kan-sas," he snorted, "well, well. Whadda y'mean they've got a *good* Medical School? A hick, eh? Jee-sus, I'm sick of hicks!"

If a common housefly had been able to exist in so rarefied

an atmosphere its buzz would have sounded like a jet bomber. The faces around him were horrified but they were also amused. Jim saw their eyes rating him the way a new kid at school is rated, especially a new kid who wears the wrong clothes. Now that they'd heard where he came from he could feel them speculating as to how he happened to be among them; the hick in the sanctum.

Feeling rather than hearing a faint titter spread from group to group, Jim sat coiled, hands clenched. He was out of his element and hated himself for having allowed it; this might be more than he could handle. Should he duck this or should he let Potbelly have it? For a minute he was lost, lost in a cream-puff jungle. What outraged him was that before their veneer had slipped, he'd been looking up to these people.

But the minute passed and Jim found himself. He came out fighting.

Nodding his head slightly, he said: "Okay, bigshot, I'm a hick. But when one of your kids needs an operation, drop by—I make my living off guys like you. And you usually lose that Harvard accent on your way to the operating room."

There was no amusement now. A sense of distaste showed on the faces; the jungle protecting its own. Jim waited, guard up, and then for no reason he turned to Liz. She was a Cream Puff too and yet already a voice was telling him that she was not, that she belonged to no group.

"That all right with you?" he asked offhandedly.

Her reply was instantaneous: "A machine gun would have been better."

They'd smiled at each other. Finally she leaned over to speak directly at him as though they were alone at a small table in some crowded night club.

"Jim, these charming folk are new to you; delightful, aren't they? Lovely, gracious people."

Having slowly appraised the lovely people she returned to

him, speaking in her low clear voice: "Skip 'em, Jim. Let the jerks keep their eastern colleges; their precious *alma maters* and *alma* papas and dog-eared Emily Posts are all they've got. These aren't men, really. They're near-men, *hyphenated*. Yale-men, Princeton-men, club-men. Then there's the double hyphen; men-about-town; that's extra fancy. You get that working nights."

She lit a cigarette. Waving the empty cocktail glasses she beckoned a servant. The room had been transformed into a plush theater in which a hushed audience was hanging on the actors' every word.

After the glasses had been filled, the leading lady cocked a quizzical eyebrow and continued: "Know something, Kansas? What these V.I.P.'s have needed is less of daddy's dough and more of what you've got, more *guts*."

She laughed aloud. "Want to know something else? I wouldn't be a bit surprised if one foggy morning Liz came out of the gin to find herself in love with one Jim Hatch. I could use a man with guts—I never had one!"

She had one after that.

After that there was a cord between them and the cord got tighter and tighter. Jim's whole life began to change; the street he lived on, the apartment furnishings, clothes, his manner of speech. For instance Pete would think it odd but, never in his life had he spoken the word love, as applied to himself. Never until Liz showed him it didn't belittle a man to say: "I love you."

The remarkable part was how smoothly the changes had come about. So gradual that at the time Jim thought he thought of them himself; home-town boy makes good. Joke, eh?

He hadn't minded any of it, the contrary. There'd been no feeling of being inferior. He was proud of her, so anxious to be whatever Liz wanted that it never entered his mind to resent what she had that he didn't have. The only feeling that might be called resentment was due to her coming between him and his profession.

Medicine was Jim's god. The mere act of walking into the operating room gave him a sure sense of being somebody. This confidence in himself was a bullet-proof vest and he wished to God he'd stayed inside it, but he hadn't. The two of them were in each other's blood stream the way a transfusion is. Nobody could have stopped it and nobody did. Not even Alan. Certainly not Silas.

It was almost a year before he'd met Silas. By then they each knew plenty about the other, though you'd never have guessed it. Neither batted an eye. One thing you could say for Silas, he kept his emotions to himself—if he had any. Jim liked Si, liked him fine, but what did liking have to do with the cord between himself and Liz? And anyway, Si had had a front-row seat for years and half the time the seat was empty. It was Jim's turn now.

The first year or so was a merry-go-round with Liz on every horse. It was so new and spun so fast that a lot of it was blurred. The memories crowded each other like a gallery filled with portrait after portrait of the same woman. Sometimes the portraits merged and sometimes they stayed separate and clear, frames and all.

One very clear one was of Liz at the top of the spiral staircase in the Addams' house in Jersey. Dressed in black satin with practically no top except some lace and a long wide necklace of fresh gardenias, she was sitting on the floor playing mumblety-peg with Pete and another kid. Even before he got up the stairs he'd sensed the vibration of that extra motor.

Jim had on his brand-new dinner jacket. When she saw him, she said: "*Pretty* you! Prettiest man in town!"

The word pretty is one word men hate, and of course she knew it. All the same when she said it, you sort of sneakingly liked it; a compliment wrapped in amusement. You could take it or leave it and you took it. You straightened your tie and your shoulders and felt damn dashing. There was no one could build you up as she could and no one who could take you down as fast, but then, Pete knew that, who didn't?

Another memory was at a ritzy farm in Connecticut. A number of guests were standing about and Liz, the usual cocktail in each hand, was surrounded by men. She was wearing a gold dress, dull gold like her hair. As Jim moved up he'd heard a man betting that there was one thing she couldn't do.

"Bet you five hundred you can't milk a cow," he said.

Memory flipped a page and there was Liz in a barn, winning that bet, gold cloth spread out all around her. Later he'd asked where on earth she learned to milk.

"Sam taught me," she said. "In Scotland, one summer. Know anybody needs five hundred?"

Memory's pictures of their wedding and wedding trip would be lighted forever by their own special spotlights. Liz in the observation car approaching San Francisco; at sea on the deck of the *Lurline*, the morning the ship had rounded Diamond Head. From somewhere close by, there was music and many voices singing.

He had looked down and found that Liz was trembling and great tears had poured down her face.

"Are you sick?" he asked.

"Oh no," she sobbed. "No, no—I'm healed! I have come home."

"*Aloha,* Mrs. Hatch," the steward had said, and dropped a lei of white camellias and some waxy lemon-yellow flowers called ginger across her shoulders.

"*Aloha,* Jim."

"*Aloha,* Liz."

The two years that followed the wedding trip were almost complete. At least he had thought so. Except for Alan. Had

Pete ever felt that Alan might be the one human being Liz really loved?

No, Pete didn't feel so. Love had different levels. Love was in proportion to the need of the one loved.

Well, he could be right; Jim didn't know. At any rate, outside of Alan, those years had seemed complete. But after then, while some memories were wonderful, any God's quantity were not; the drunken Liz, the cruel Liz. The mind's eye carried plenty of these.

When Jim told Pete about Liz and her war job, his respect was obvious. It faded now however. His eyes were ice as he said: "And then, in between, came Acapulco."

Acapulco, the Indian summer, the swan song, the symbol of things which were and are no more. Greatly as he disliked mentioning sex in connection with Pete's mother, he almost had to, in passing. Passing was the word. The last gasp of whatever had remained.

That period in Mexico had been nearer perfection than any relationship Jim had ever experienced. Neither one of them had appeared to be trying to prove anything, which was always one of their greatest obstacles. Liz wanted you to be somebody else and then would proceed to treat you as though you already were but this wasn't the case in Mexico. Jim didn't have to be Sam. He didn't have to be Silas, or like or unlike anybody; Christ, what a relief! If only she'd settled for this, for what he could do when he could do it, and let it go at that, but no, the exception must become the rule.

The easy, comfortable periods of their life together had never been the rule no matter what they'd pretended. The truth was, he suspected, that the emotion between them just wasn't strong enough and rooted deep enough to survive on its own.

One spring Jim had transplanted a flat of snapdragons and the result was about the same. The ones he left in the box till they got well started, warm and close together, were swell later on, bloomed straight through the fall. But the ones that were separated too soon only yellowed and dried up.

He'd been terribly unwilling to admit to himself that his sex desire was so slight as to amount to indifference; no man cared to do this. He'd believed that with Liz it would last, at least outlast Acapulco, and it might have. It might have come back if she'd taken the trouble she did when they were first married. Instead of turning on him and belittling him, if she'd encouraged him as she used to, well, who knows?

It was sex that had started Jim's feeling inferior, made him realize he wasn't going to be able to top Liz in anything but medicine. It snowballed. The more he was ridiculed the more out of step he felt in other matters. If ever a flick of desire did work in him, she would nip it fast with remarks like: "You don't mean the great lover has time to waste? My, my, patients must be falling off!"

Right after Mexico was when she'd ripped away the last gangplank. He'd always made a point of greeting her with a kiss wherever they met—felt it somehow proved something—but this time she said: "Why bother, Jim. We've got such a pretty brother and sister act, why gum it up?"

That did it. As long as they'd hung onto this one intimacy, there was hope for them. As long as they embraced anywhere at all, the private lack could be ignored, but this fixed it. He'd *hated* her, hated her for bringing it into the open. Then, as he'd realized what a thorough job she'd been doing of ramming him down her friends' throats, he hated her for that too. The hick, the interloper, accepted solely for his wife's sake. He saw how all along she'd been cushioning him, bridging the gap from Kansas to Westchester.

Differences in caste were queer business. Customs recognizable to those born in the caste, unrecognizable by others. And the lingo. And the maze of subtleties, of shaded meanings.

To one born to it, all of the rules were learned to be for-gotten but the interloper better not take chances. He better stick to how-do-you-do, instead of Hi, if he'd been used to saying, pleased-to-meet-you. He better stick to dinner jacket, instead of black tie, if he'd been used to saying, Tuxedo. And the attitude toward servants, the waiting to be waited on, the strict politeness to them but offhand as hell with the hosts.

Liz said none of it mattered, that the thing to be was your-self, yet he was discovering that when he was himself, she felt the need to explain him.

She would say: "Jim doesn't mean that. He's kidding."

And: "Jim missed lunch; he's starved. Would you mind terribly if I asked for a sandwich?"

And: "Jim doesn't want to leave, darling, but he has to be at the hospital early."

You bet Jim had to be at the hospital early. And late. This was the one place he could top her.

Sitting in the night quiet of All Angels Jim had at last confessed to himself that his only love was medicine. Liz had hexed him into hoping otherwise but it hadn't lasted because it never was so. He didn't want to be involved with people personally and never had; all he'd ever wanted was to be a damn good surgeon or whatever he started out to be. Since he was a kid in patched pants this and this alone was all he'd wanted; to be the best there was at the job he had.

Well, while he wasn't the best, he was damn good and so, whether Liz lived or didn't live, nothing ever again was going to interfere with his profession. Maybe this wasn't the right way to live but it was his way. Somewhere along the line his personal life had jumped the track and living or dying wouldn't change it. Once and for all he finally accepted this.

If Pete cared to hear the worst, Jim had honestly hoped his mother *would* die. There was a reason for this; it was—it was because, God, *what would it be like if she lived?*

He just couldn't bear to think of what it might be *now!*
Trying to leave life would have to change your life and already
she was much too much for him. She would have been for
any man at this point. Her death would be a dreadful waste,
but dreadful or not, he couldn't bring himself to face the up-
heaval, the misery, the remorse. That eternal search, never satisfied, never ceasing, what form would it take now?

No, dead or alive, it was all over. He was tired. Tired of
trying to make the grade, of sneers, of drunkenness; tired of
being hitched to a woman who wouldn't settle. He'd had
enough.

There was no further reason to consider this woman; she
herself had cut the cord. She'd sold a bill of goods and then
tried to skip town and if she was going to get away with it, it
probably would be better all around.

And anyway he was bushed; tomorrow was another day.
He'd call the nurse and tell her he was leaving. As he started
to get up however, Jim had stopped midway; in the pallid
light he saw that the figure on the bed had shifted slightly.
The head seemed to have changed position and the eyes were
open. Jim stared and the gray eyes stared back. There was no
awareness in them, no expression at all. The face was as pale
and as lax as ever but the eyes were open.

Jim was hypnotized. He was a doctor and he must do what
Murray had ordered but—but suppose he ignored it? Suppose
he didn't ring for the nurse? Pulling aside a curtain, he saw
the nun; she was standing where Pete had stood, by the window, and was fingering her beads.

He sat back and the curtain fell into place. Sitting perfectly
still, he waited. Then abruptly the campstool creaked as Jim
leaned forward to press the buzzer.

CHAPTER THIRTEEN

In the flow of eternal time there is one certain period in which time seems to rest, to hold its breath before mustering forces for the reversal from dark to light, from ebb to flow. It is then that mankind is prone to slip most easily out from this phase of life over into the next phase. This is not a break, an hiatus, but rather a slender swaying bridge between what is here and what is somewhere else.

The heartbeat is at its lowest then and yet, should man be awake, it is then he is most apt to recognize each man's aloneness; a state of drained clarity tremblingly near to the buried, the unknown. It was during this period that I, Liz Hatch, returned from the Valley of the Shadow.

The journey had been an unmenaced one. If along the path the shadows took frightening forms, my conscious mind has not retained them, nor was the awakening either fearful or exultant. I had slipped out and now I had come back and whatever lay between had been for me, at least, untroubling. The one implicit feeling was a sense of freedom, of being in all ways unencumbered as though my windows had been washed, as though some part of me were left behind. A part old and hard and heavy.

With the loss of it I felt clean and light as in a pleasant

dream yet I knew it was not a dream. My mind was sharply clear; it too was washed and unencumbered. And it was waiting. What it waited for I had not the remotest preconception, and still the sense of expectancy was very strong.

When I try to tell the circumstances of what happened—and this is often, for people everywhere are searching—almost without exception I bang up against a wall of can-believe, cannot-believe. Perhaps the results can be believed but not the circumstances. Or the other way around. Man-made requirements have so fuzzed man's need that whatever comes must come as it does or not come at all. I understand. I was like this myself. Unless blueprint words are found, the entire structure tumbles. Yet why should this be so?

There are so many, many things there are no words for. What words account for preference? Synonyms, yes; choice, liking, precedence, but what of the state itself? Why is one newcomer a friend, the other an utter stranger? Why is this painting beautiful and that grotesque? Quite simply, why do you like blue and I like green? There are myriads of causes, but none which describe the preference itself.

There are no words for intuition. "I have a hunch," we say. A bolt from the blue, a warning, a premonition, a certain something—Right. A certain something.

And so words for this are hard to find. I had run from life in fear and guilt and desperation, judging it intolerable, and I returned to it in expectant quietness. Many reasons for the guilt and desperation I understood too well and the quietness I did not understand and yet I was giving up to it, accepting as I had never accepted before.

Outside the quietness were concrete objects which were slow to register. It was the glass container that served to locate me. I'd seen hundreds at the Naval Hospital, still as my eyes checked it off, I'm sure I didn't realize that the long tube ended in me. It did orient me however; I was in a hospital. No matter how peculiar and closely curtained the space it was somewhere in a hospital.

A faint light was beyond the curtains, so far beyond that it was more the suggestion of light than light. And there was no sound at all. The world in which I lay was a very private world and I was quite alone. And then, all at once, I was not alone.

Throughout the whole of existence there are a few, a very few things which are true and which one accepts as true and this was one of them. I was not alone. Something was here that had not been here before, it was not a person and not the memory of anyone or anything. What it was I didn't know, merely that it was.

There was no increase in light. No sound. No motion. No scent. Though in a fashion I cannot explain it was all of these, the source of these. Lying utterly still, I waited. Unable to accept, I was now accepting, letting myself be claimed, letting this something mount and permeate and cover the self I'd been as the tide rises to cover what was formerly dry and bare. What it was or where it came from I did not know nor was there a need to know.

Why should this be strange? Why is it strange to accept help one cannot account for? All one needs for the acceptance of help is the certain knowledge that one needs help.

Suppose I am lost and know it, as I had known it for a long, long time. Suppose I am terribly, terribly lost and suddenly someone beautifully strong comes and carries me to safety, will I say: "First let me see your I.D. card?" Suppose my car is stranded and a great tow truck appears, will I say: "Wait, who are you? What is your address? Exactly how did you know I needed help?"

No, I wouldn't say this. Later, as I looked back, I might ponder and try to guess but at the time, if I knew I was stranded, I would be grateful to be found.

Acceptance is based on awareness of need. And the more desperate the need, the fuller the acceptance; I have found no other explanation. Giving names to things does not explain them. Solving things with figures does not solve them so long as one has started with the Unknown X.

A seed; what is a seed? A gene; what is a gene? The atom; what is the atom? And Truth. And Trust. And Love. And Hope. And Personality. And Beauty. And Compassion. What are these?

Beyond mere labels there are no words to tell what these are or where they come from, and so it is supremely foolish to discard a thing because there are not words to fit it.

Suppose someone was born blind; then how would you describe a snowcapped mountain in full moonlight? An eagle flying? Suppose someone has never had the sense of smell; then how would you describe the scent of pine? Of sea and jasmine and fresh cut grass and burning leaves? Of rain in spring? Suppose someone was born deaf; then how would you describe the music from a great organ? A train whistling in the dark? A small child singing to himself?

There are no words. And this thing that came into my private world was all of these, and more, much more. The source of these. It was true and, at the same time, truth. And truth is what one recognizes and so has little need to hear, or it is what one doesn't recognize and so cannot or will not hear.

This was truth itself and I breathed it into me. The part of man which no man knows stretched out its hands and groped and touched its source and intermingled and flowed back into the place it came from. The soul of me was very, very small, a midget soul, yet, having retained a fraction of its total, it was alive. And so, as it came home, slowly, by infinitesimal degrees, the one who was I started to become more than I.

And now, in tremulous fulfillment, I knew what This was,

knew and began to tremble. As the plant knows where the light is, I knew.

This was the Father.

My heart trembled. Trembled and swelled until it seemed that it would burst.

How could I, Liz Hatch, know this? How could I identify the truth of Truth? I cannot answer. I think and think and know that it is so and cannot answer. Behind this, leading up to it, were years of searching and searching and finding what was not-true, and maybe this is a portion of the answer. Maybe finding enough not-truths and never settling for not-truths, brings Truth a little nearer.

The air was radiant with a gladness to burst the heart. An outpouring, drenching and cradling and upholding the person who was I, yet not I. The scant, leftover shred of me, as yet unspoiled, was going back. Back to the One Who had always waited, only now the barrier between had disappeared.

The barrier had been in me. The Father had been here forever; the Circle starting from and ending in Itself; the Source; the Father with a hundred names and no name. And no name needed. This was the Meaning, the Answer to all there was or ever could be.

There wasn't anything else. I with all my names was nothing except in relationship to This. All past, all present, all future were nothing except in relationship to This. I'd been playing a tiny part on a tiny stage and now I was being linked to the Cosmos, to Him Who held the stars in place. I'd wanted drama and here was drama, incredibly vast, incredibly exciting, of proportions to stagger the imagination.

I could think of only one untarnished word. This word was Glory.

Here was the Glory of the Patient Presence Which had waited since the first beginning.

Wonder came. A vast well of overwhelming wonder into which I sank, released. Immediate with the wonder came the peace, not the timed peace the world knows, but an in-going, an at-oneness. And then, following for one split second, came an actual sense of timelessness. Of a forever.

And I understood. By this I understood that I had been forgiven. That whatever I had been and done, or not been and not done, was forgiven me. Whatever else life held I was being given now a washed page; my tiny soul had all eternity in which to grow.

Surely tears ran down my face but if they did, I did not feel them because they had not sprung from sorrow. That would come, I somehow knew, yet for the moment there was no sorrow, no regret, no guilt. Nor were there fears nor questions.

Wonder and peace and forgiveness was all I had room for. What was to come would come later.

At last, young soul that I was, I fell asleep. When I awoke it was daylight and all about were voices and bustle. Fingers were on my wrist and at the other side of me, someone was speaking. It was Pete.

"How is she, Doctor?" Pete was asking.

The answer boomed: "Great, boy! Good as new, *good as new*."

Within my private world, I smiled. Better, I thought, *better than new*.

On hearing the noises of the world outside mine I'd been loath to open my eyes for what if, *what if the Father were not there?* But He was there. He was the hope in Pete's question. He was the rejoicing in the doctor's answer. He was the peace within me, and the timid yet fierce desire to shout: "Son, I've found Him too!"

I opened my eyes.

"I'm hungry," I said.

My doctor laughed. A glad proud laugh.

"Hungry, eh? So the machinery's begun to function? That's a fine machine you've got there, Liz. If it were taken care of."

I reached for Pete's hand.

"It'll be taken care of," I said.

And it was.

Pete drove me home the next afternoon. It was crisp and clear. Snow had fallen in the night and the countryside was scrubbed and adorned. A mile or so from the hospital was a dumpyard heaped with junk and even it had been softened and made sightly.

But—but *underneath?* I questioned. Underneath was the same old rusting, rotting junk. The first foreboding came; wasn't I like the dumpyard? Wasn't I *exactly* like it? Scrubbed and softened and adorned while underneath lay the rusting, rotting habits of a lifetime?

I was deeply troubled. Here was the first faint hint of having to do in place of being done to; a blurred pin-point glimpse of the terrible never-ending job it was going to be. How could I, a single flickering match, hope to penetrate a world of fog? It would be flying blind, without charts or compass or visibility.

Yesterday when I'd described to Pete the Glory of the Presence of God, our souls had laughed together; the son, serene and sure, eyes steady; the mother, enraptured, made new. It had been true sharing; my initiation into one of the most glorious of mysteries. And had ended in that silence filled with calm certainty.

This had been yesterday, so short a space of time, yet now I cried in despair: "Peter, will we, *can* we ever know what this is all about? *Can* we?"

He understood immediately. "No, not all. Enough, though. Enough to do our part. God is the Derrick, our part is to shift the gears according to Christ's instructions. He left plenty. Just take it easy. One ditch at a time."

One ditch at a time.

He grinned. "Even Jesus did that, remember?"

No, I did not remember. Jesus was a swear word!

Panic nipped me.

"But, Pete, I know nothing! I—I—"

"Maybe that's the best place to start," he said. "But actually it isn't true. Almost every one of us—you especially—knows more than we have any idea. Once on the right track, there are many instructions we recognize. Don't shift to high, stay in second; a ditch at a time."

A ditch—"Pete, could this be the first ditch? This *doubt?*"

"What doubt? Doubt of yourself or Him?"

"No, no, *not* Him! *Me.* What if my battery's too dead to be recharged?"

He laughed out loud. "Your battery's a heck of a way from being dead. It'll take recharging and what's more, the recharging is for free. That is, if it's checked regularly."

"But *gas*, Pete? And carbon?"

"We're expected to supply our own gas. And at varying prices. Sometimes the price comes high, depending upon how far from the Source we've moved. And carbon, well, that's each one's job too. Piston by piston."

Piston by piston.

"And in the meantime, if I start checking, and pay whatever the price of gas is, and keep working at the carbon, my motor will run? A little?"

He laughed again. "And how! Just take it slow, this is a long trip, you know."

"Not for me, it isn't! I'm getting on. I've wasted—"

"Whose timetable are you on; God's or the New York, New Haven and Hartford? Tear up the calendar, Mom. This trip is forever."

Forever?

Why, yes—forever.

I breathed again. "Right. How come you're so wise, Pete? Where did you climb aboard?"

He thought. "I don't know exactly. It started back at

Pearl on the way over. You'd raved about the Islands but all I saw was a gyp joint, everybody gouging everybody else; the smaller you were, the bigger the gouge. I found a Gideon, in Pearl of all places, and read some of it, and thought a lot. I guess China was where I climbed aboard. You know, Mom, the white man has been to China and the East what the Pharisee was to Jesus. It's what we whites have always done, only this was the first time I'd been in on it. Think of the American Indian, the Negro, the Mexican. Think of all the whites on earth gouging all the colored on earth!"

"I have thought of it," I said.

He nodded. "I know. Well, now you see how doubly horrible it is; how it must seem to Him: son gouging son."

We were nearing the house. There was the long driveway and at its end, the white brick house which Jim and I had built, on sand, the phrase came to me. Remembering that it was Sunday and Jim would be here, I waited for fear to claim me, the habit of fear, but it did not.

Disquiet, yes. An embarrassment; what could be more anticlimactic than a suicide and no corpse? Corpus delicti, as Jim would say. Perhaps I should have brought a nurse. My doctor had suggested it; there was no buffer like a nurse, but I hadn't wanted one. I had Pete and—and Something else. My one real fear, not fear so much as anticipation, was to find out if He were in the house as well as at the hospital.

My legs shook a little. "Pete, I'm scared," I said.

This time he misunderstood.

"Don't be," he said. "Jim is more lost than you or I ever were."

This I hadn't thought of. Knew it and hadn't thought of it. Of course Jim was lost, terribly, terribly lost, and hurt. Oh, now I would have Something valid to offer him! Something we could work toward together, so true, so wonderful that It held the stars in place!

As we turned into the driveway, I said: "Have you seen Jim, Pete?"

"Yes. Friday night."

Friday night?

"Oh. Was he at the hospital?"

"Right beside you. We left you with him and one of the nuns. You were better and Dr. Murray and I were starving. After quite a while the floor nurse called to say you were awake."

"But—but I wasn't awake. Not when Jim was there."

"No, but he thought you were. Your eyes were open—"

"Open? They were? I didn't see him."

"Perhaps you never have," Pete said.

"I guess you're right. Perhaps I never have."

Patting my knee as if I were the child and he the parent, he smiled. "Good girl. Well, here we are. Take it easy, Mom."

"He might not be home," I suggested hopefully.

"He's home. The driveway was fresh snow, no tracks at all."

"Sherlock Addams—bright, aren't you?"

"I betcha. Hey, hold it, you're not as strong as you're going to be."

The house glistened. Snow stretched as far as the eye could see. The house itself was of snow, hard-packed, with high above it, the branches of great trees forming a protecting canopy. It was as though I saw it for the first time. The expanse of windows, the blue spruce trimmed in white, the changing scrollwork of the shadows. For a single moment all was quiet with the suspended quietness of nature, dormant, of life and movement from within.

Pete helped me from the car and, taking the small bag he had packed for me, went ahead to try the door. I followed stepstone by stepstone, legs wobbling. Approaching the house I noticed that the screen door was still on and thought, Screens in *November*. And then I thought, living ten miles

181

in the country was your idea. If it's too far out to get anyone but cleaning women, why don't you attend to matters like screens?

Since the beginning of the war we had been unable to find house servants, yet never once had it occurred to Liz Hatch to cook and clean for herself and her husband. Meals were eaten out; cleaning was left to others who had to be lugged out and back four days a week. While the thought of learning to do it was in a class with learning to make a shoe or build a bathroom, the fact that I'd even thought of it was encouraging. Check, I said to myself, a ditch at a time.

Inside the house, the hall was in shadow while beyond in the living room was vivid sunshine. Leaning against a wall, I waited. Waiting, I held my breath, not daring to stir for fear that what I can only call the Glory was not here.

Above me I heard someone moving and then I didn't hear for all about me the air was throbbing. Shaken to my inmost being, I stayed there, praying to pray. Reaching for words from which to make a prayer. The Glory was so wondrously whole, so un-used that it seemed as if the most splendid words should come, yet none came. There were no words, merely the same in-pouring. But it was enough for now.

At last I raised my head. Through joyous tears I saw Jim standing in the living room. He was worn and very pale and seeing his lostness, my joy poured out, trying to include him.

Breathlessly, I cried: "Jim, I've something to tell you!"

He did not look at me, but said: "When don't you?"

Suddenly, quietly, came sorrow; the first slender thread which the weeks and months and years would gradually unravel. Strangely, this sorrow was not for myself alone, it was for Jim as well. For both of us and others like us.

There appeared to be no self-pity in it, and no resentment; none of the usual angry pain at his rejection of me. These seemed to have disappeared as though a wire-recording brush had wiped them out. I was astonished.

For a moment he said nothing further. At last he said: "You've had time to think. Have you made plans?"

Plans?

"Why, no, Jim—"

His face hardened. "What are you waiting for? The house to fall on you?"

Oh—please, please, I thought. And then I was able to sense the bleeding gulf between us and knew it was too much for me. A ditch at a time, Pete had said. This was a gulf.

"Jim, something has happened. I can't explain, I—I can't find words," I stammered.

He gave a harsh laugh. "I never knew you to be short on words, but suit yourself, you will anyway. I'm going out and may or may not be back."

He walked past to the hall closet to get a hat and coat.

"You'd better make plans," he said. "I've had enough."

From upstairs Pete called: "Okay, Mom. Bed's ready. Take it easy."

The air about me was thinner now; the throb fainter. This was frightening. I had dared hope, expected really, that now that the Father had come, He would be there always. And such was the truth but it took weeks to find it out. To find that it was I who left, I who erected the barrier between. Like music on air channels, He was always there and, like a faulty radio, I could interfere, could block Him with my own and the world's static.

Upstairs I asked Pete: "What's wrong? I'm off the beam."

"Tired, Mom. You're doing great, just don't try too hard. This business is largely a matter of letting go. There's a saying: 'Let go, let God.' It'll be tough on anyone of your make-up, but it's the answer. Even Jesus couldn't do a thing without the Father; He said so."

Jesus. Jee-sus—no! Jesus!

I felt sick. "Pete, Pete, I don't know one blessed thing—!"

"You will. You'll know plenty of blessed things."

183

"But you—did you ever get off the beam?"

He laughed. "Certainly, for crying out loud! Everybody does. You better rest. Let go, Mom."

"Here," he added.

In his hand was a small square amber bottle. I stared at it and stared up at him.

"It's—?"

He nodded. "Doc Murray said to give them to you."

I was more moved than I could find words to express.

"Pete, he *trusted* me!"

"Sure. And was righter than he knows—"

"No, no," I cried. "Dump them down the drain!"

"Why? Nothing the matter with a pill when you're on the pill level. If you need rest, take a pill. Don't start heaving mountains, kid."

He placed the bottle on my night table. "There. Hit the sack."

The bottle stayed capped. Throughout the night I would turn to stare at it, fighting it, fighting myself, but it stayed capped while hour after hour I lay open-eyed in the moonlight; *the exact same moon of three nights ago.*

I lay there, thinking. I thought of my father and the Father of all, of my son, Peter, and His Son, Jesus. I thought of the sleeping pills and of the liquor downstairs. The first thought was new and strange and often far, far off and the second was old, old, and very near.

I heard Jim come in and when I thought of him and the bleeding gulf, my heart sank, down, down. And then, all at once, I wondered for the first time if there could be another woman. This thought had never once entered my mind and now it did. Now it hit me full force.

I broke into sweat. Here was one possibility I could not cope with. *Could* not!

Yet—yet, *why* couldn't I? Why couldn't I cope with the selfsame situation I'd forced on Silas Addams!

No! What did that have to do with this? Si was—*Si didn't mind things so much.*

Sweat soaked me. My mouth was dry, my head pounded.

And, because the soil was right, the greatest fear of all planted itself: *Alan.*

Alan, Alan!

The terrors merged until I could not bear it. Sitting up, I threw back the covers, hearing my teeth chatter, feeling the old iron clamp settle across my shoulders.

I reached for my robe. Somehow, as weak as I was, I must manage to get downstairs to a bottle. The thought of another woman and of never seeing Alan were twin terrors too great to endure alone.

"Get Pete," a Voice said.

"No," I cried aloud, "I will not! I will *fight* this—"

"Then, *fight* it," the Voice said.

"I *was*—no, I was not! I was giving in," I whispered.

"Give in to Me," the Voice said.

"You? Who—?"

And then I knew. And my heart trembled and little by little my mind quieted.

CHAPTER FOURTEEN

It would be great to report that the months that followed were spent reclining on a pink cloud. That each morn I measured my wings, adjusted my halo and sat, spreading sweetness and light. That Alan returned safe and softened, that Jim opened his arms and cried: "Oh, gorgeous creature!", that all was well with my world. But such was not the case, and is not.

In bygone days, boy-gets-girl would end when boy got girl. They strode from the church, and *finis;* they'd live happily ever after and that was that. Nowadays, even great-granny knows better; the job has just begun.

It is the same with learning to know God. The fuzz about doves perched on the shoulder, about light streaming through stained glass windows is pure bunk. Any Christian who says otherwise is a saint, and I haven't met one, or his God is a stranger to mine. A Sunday-morning god maybe; the type who permits himself to be wrapped in tissue paper with the white gloves the minute church is over. I don't know that one, never ran into him. My God is a full-time God.

That first year as a Christian was a blind trail up a steep cliff, one climb up, one slip back. The fact that the climb upward was sometimes further than the slip backwards was all that kept me from being where I'd started. Perhaps a more accurate metaphor would be the longest, toughest swim imaginable, from a shore you know to a shore you can't conceive. The shore behind is near and mighty tempting and as the waves slam at you, somebody yells: "Come back. Don't be a sap!"

By God's grace however, somebody else yells: "Good girl, keep going."

In time quite a crowd collected. Some curious, some intent, some helping with all they had, some picking their teeth. Jim picked his teeth. If he gave a hoot one way or the other, he didn't show it and who can blame him? He'd been involved in Liz's shenanigans for many a moon, and here she goes again, whole hog or nothin'.

My guess is that he believed I'd lost a few buttons and still believes so. Neither of us ever referred to it but I did catch him eyeing me in a kind of for-God's-sake-what-next way. The first time I went to church Jim's expression was something I'm not liable to forget. He was in the kitchen in his bathrobe, making coffee, when I whipped past on the run. I who seldom wear a hat, had a hat on.

His jaw dropped. "Where do you think you're going?" he asked.

I was embarrassed. "Church," I blurted and fled.

It was funny about church. Up to that very Sunday morning church had no more to do with God than I'd had to do with God. Church was a building to be tramped through or it was a place where you went for weddings, your own or somebody's, and occasionally for christenings. The latter was considered great stuff in my particular group; a christening was a sop to something or other, and the cocktails afterwards were such fun, so *earned*. If you can believe it, I myself had five godchildren—how careless can parents be!

Up to All Angels Hospital, a church was a church but afterwards it was a compulsion. An automatic unanalyzable must which I can't come close to explaining except to say that I was completely certain that every last person in every church everywhere had had the identical spiritual experience I had had. I truly believed this, why wouldn't I? Otherwise why on earth would you go to church? I took it for granted that here was where to find the ones who really knew God, who were old hands at following Him.

Well, you know what I found. Or don't you?

Right here I wish to state clearly, concisely, and once and for all, that I, Liz Hatch, have no corner on God. Nor does the church I later joined have a corner on God. Not the slightest. There are as many Fathers as there are humans seeking Him; the Father for the rich and for the poor; for the well and for the sick; for the sober and for the drunk; for the joyous and for the wretched; for the good and for the wicked. A limitless supply rolled into One. A Father for everyone who needs Him or can conceive of ever needing Him. There is not however a Father for the hypocrite. The hypocrite manufactures his own father.

And now we'll get on with Liz, the shining, the stumbling Christian.

It was Sunday that I returned from the hospital and Monday I was on the telephone. Our only neighbors were a couple named Patton who lived down the road a mile or so and who I'd been told were once churchgoers. I admired Louise Patton; she was one of the few women I respected. If she happened to know a minister I might respect that minister.

As self-conscious as any rookie I called her number. We spoke of this and that and finally I said: "Louise, I—I wonder if you know a minister? I'd like to talk to one."

She didn't lose a beat. No, for-goodness-sake's. No questions.

"What kind do you want?" she asked. "A go-getter or a man of God?"

A go-getter? A spiritual Kiwanian? Cold chills! Or the cup-balancer, the cocktail-sipper; old frozen-face who knows precisely who's who!

"A man of God," I told her.

"Good," she said, "I've got your man. When young John was killed he was the first person here. No great shakes as a talker, Liz. Shy really. But, what a comfort he was!"

His name was Gordon Rogers. As he stood in the entrance to our glass-walled living room, he reminded me of photographs of Nehru except that he was tall and thin to the point of emaciation. The short gray hair was the same, the young-old features, the enormous burning black eyes. His expression lacked however the decisive bulldog quality of Nehru's. It was kindly and wistful and sensitive and sad: the look of a man who's been passed by and knows it and no longer minds.

The shabby unpressed clerical clothes hung loosely and the frayed collar, worn backwards, stood out almost in line with the ears. The stubbed unpolished shoes were farm shoes, laced over and back on metal hooks, one lace spliced and the knot visible. After we shook hands and sat down, he crossed his legs and I saw hanging from a rumpled green-black sock a tag like a piece of torn garter. This was the Reverend Gordon Rogers, man of God. Not for a moment should he have been prepossessing yet due to his face he was immensely so. It was a face in harmony with some secret inner beauty.

If he was shy, he was not ill at ease. One got the impression that although he enjoyed people his instinct was to be alone. What appeared to be shyness was the result of a constant readjustment having to be made between a real desire for seclusion and an equally real desire to serve humanity.

He daunted me a little. My misgiving did not stem in any particular from a sense of wavering but from abysmal ignorance. There was no doubt whatever that I was going to talk to this man; it was merely that our lives had run along such different lines that it would be difficult to start.

For an instant I tried to guess what on earth we'd ever have talked about before I met the Father. I was quite unable to think of anything. Now however his very detachment was the quality which would make it possible to approach him. My own state was so exploratory that the least glibness, the least overassurance might easily have repelled me. I was stepping over into an unknown dimension and it would not require a virtuoso to advise me. Merely, as Louise had said, a man of God. I had presumed Gordon Rogers would be a mild man but I was to find myself mistaken. Men of God are not mild; how can they be and follow Christ?

He was studying me, smiling a slow questioning smile.

"And so?" he said.

One would have thought we'd talked for hours, that we knew one another intimately and it may be we did. It may be that the full-grown Spirit of God in Gordon Rogers was already recognizing the young Spirit of God in Liz Hatch.

My mind sidestepped his question for an instant.

"Will it be all right to smoke?" I asked.

"Why not?" he smiled. "I'll smoke with you. With so many bigger problems I cannot believe our Lord minds overmuch. This *is* about our Lord, isn't it?"

Our Lord.

"Yes," I nodded, "it's about our—our Lord."

And then I leaned back and became quiet and was able to tell my story. It took a long time for I told him then all I have written in this book up to this page. In many ways it was my initial introduction to my own self, to my assorted selves. The whole story told for the first time with no deliberate coloring, no deletions, no rationalizing of sin but calling sin, sin wherever and whenever I could identify it. Childhood and Sam and my lovely mother were barely mentioned.

This was a résumé of me and what I had done or not done. What had been done to me by others, or not done, did not seem to matter much.

"And so I called you in," I finished, "as I would call in any other specialist. I need help. I'll be starting from scratch."

"Like every newborn," he said.

"Yes. Except that I've got all the nasty mess to unlearn."

"The mess was for this alone; the birth of a soul."

"Feet first," I added, "and so dreadfully resistant."

"Resistant, yes. And very often these turn out to be the strongest. Those who have had to learn the hard way, and alcoholics appear to be in this class, are usually the ones who cling to the path. Not that Christ's path is easy for anyone, don't hope for that. It's hard and steep and can be walked at all only because we do not walk alone. Never again, Mrs. Hatch, will you have to walk alone."

I cannot tell the comfort this was. Although questions poked at me, begging to be answered, I made myself stay quiet. How extraordinary that even now, this soon, I was able to believe him. That even now I was quite certain I would never walk alone.

"Yes, I know that Someone is with and within me," I answered. "All I hope is He'll stick around—no, that isn't right, He's always here; I'm the one who has to stick around. Oh, this is what worries me! I've spent my life running from something to something else; this won't be like that, will it? It's not God I'm suspicious of, it's me."

His lips curved in the kindest smile imaginable.

"Mrs. Hatch, you must remember it was your other self you had a right to suspect, not this self. And God is not 'something else'; God is the ultimate everlasting goal of every single human being whether he perceives it or not. And mostly he does not perceive it until he reaches it."

"Yes, that I believe, but I, how could I have reached it?" I cried. "I know that it is so and yet it's so completely wacky

191

for anyone, especially me, to leap from total confusion to total direction in almost a split second. How? And why *me?*"

" 'I came not to call the righteous, but sinners,' " he said softly.

"Are you quoting someone?" I asked.

"Jesus," he answered. "Jesus sought out sinners and when the Pharisees rebuked Him for this, His answer was that this had been the purpose of His coming here to earth. Today as then, the righteous have a habit of forgetting this. Instead they denounce the sinner and thereby are guilty of the greater sin of denouncing Christ himself. No one can call himself a Christian who does not seek out and welcome sinners. In churches named for St. Paul there are people on their knees who have no remembrance that when Christ appeared to Paul, Paul was on his way to murder Christ's first Christians. You, Mrs. Hatch, recognized the Father because you knew you had sinned and hated it and so were ready. But the leap, as you call it, wasn't split-second. Perhaps the conscious acceptance was, but what our Lord calls 'leaven' had been working inside you only He knows how long."

"Leaven? You mean like yeast?"

"Any inward fermenting which changes and sweetens the whole. You were never satisfied the way you were, were you? You did those things but even as you did them, you hated it, hated what you were doing to yourself and others. Nor did you blame others. The story as you've just told it blames only yourself—"

"And that's the worst part! If I realized I was wrong, I ought to have changed—"

"Haven't you done so?" he asked. "Didn't you seek and haven't you found?"

"Yes!" I nodded.

"Yes," he confirmed. "Your strange wanderings have brought you home. And as you become closer acquainted with our Lord through prayer you will discover what it means to be at home."

"It won't be beer and skittles. I can tell that," I told him. "And how about prayer? It's a foreign language; I've tried and tried and all that comes out is conversation. From me to Him. Or thoughts, just thoughts. All those names confuse me, God, Lord, Jesus, Christ. For my money, He's the *Father*. And don't think I don't appreciate what the dear psychiatrists would say; they'd say—and in one way they'd be right and in another they'd be ridiculous—that my own father dominated me and so this higher domination is being identified with him. This is true but it's not the truth. The truth is that behind my love for my father was always my love for the Father Almighty. Not ever dreaming it, not recognizing Him at all, my love for Him accounts for all other love; the *Source* of love."

"Yes," Gordon Rogers said. "And don't fret about praying. What the Father is concerned with is the feeling behind prayer and what we are *doing* about it."

I smiled. "I'll buy that. Where do I start? What is the first, the very first thing?"

Both fearful and eager, I waited for his answer but in place of answering, he threw the question back at me.

"What would be your opinion?" he asked.

"Oh, I don't know, Gordon—I'm going to call you Gordon, may I? Naturally the first thing would have been the drinking—"

"*Would* have been?"

"Why, of course! Suffering cats, I can't follow the Father if I'm plastered, can I? I'll have troubles enough without that."

He laughed and the laugh was a rich bell tolling.

"And I won't be able to swear either," I went on. "I found that out fast. But that'll be a cinch really because now, 'For

193

God's sake' *means* something. It means, well, it means, for the sake of the Father. So that's out. What comes next?"

I thought a while.

"Oh yes, I forgot sleeping pills—*imagine* it. I *forgot* them! —they're done too. If God can't make me sleep, I'll stay awake, I need to anyway. Now what else?"

The black eyes looked at me. Their expression was closer to mystical than anything I had ever witnessed. I held my breath and at last he said: "This is a true conversion."

The word jarred me.

"I don't like the word *conversion*," I told him. "It's halleluiah, sawdust trail, blood of the Lamb; that junk. It smacks of people with JESUS SAVES on the back of their cars—"

He interrupted. "He does, doesn't He?"

I felt let down. "I don't know. I haven't met Jesus. Only the Father. Anyhow that isn't the point. The point is, all that hoop-de-do is bad taste."

He stopped me cold by asking: "Who's to decide? You?"

"No-o," I stammered. "I should be the last one."

"Every Christian should be the last one," he said. "We are told not to judge and this applies to everybody about everything or it doesn't apply at all. The halleluiah approach doesn't appeal to me either; on the other hand, that is God's affair, not ours. He must reach people wherever they can be reached."

"As he reached me via a dose of sleeping pills."

"Precisely."

He was smiling and I tried to smile back but was too deeply troubled. Here was an example of—

"Quackgrass," I said.

"Quackgrass?"

"Yes. It's everywhere. You can yank and yank and never get the last of it. The roots are too tough, too subterranean —oh, Gordon!"

"Patience," he said.

"Patience?" I howled. "Don't have any—never had any!"

"You will. Go after first things first."

"All right then, what is first?"

Gordon hesitated. It was clear that his hesitation was based on diffidence rather than doubt. I felt that whatever he was going to suggest, it would not be easy.

Finally he said: "With liquor and barbituates out of the way, there is one step which seems clearly indicated. I think you must ask your husband's forgiveness and ask for another chance."

"But I have. The night I took the pills I asked if we couldn't start over. I told you, remember?"

"I remember. But I don't remember anything about forgiveness; it sounded to me like a bargain, and one without benefit of God. You are now a new woman, Liz. Your reason for asking will be a new reason. Last week your pride asked that you stay together, now it will be a desire to love those who despitefully use you and to make amends if humanly possible. Can you do this?"

My insides squirmed. It sounded horrible.

"Yes, I can do it," I said. "I won't like it but I can do it."

"And will you be ready for the answer?"

"Answer?"

"Either way. Suppose the answer is, no? Suppose you bank all on love, God's kind of love, and still are refused?"

Then that would be final. The last chip down. If I went to Jim, not in pride, but in love, I would have to accept his decision because no longer could I insult or quarrel or stand on any rights. This quiet man had put his finger on the test of tests. Could even the Father hold me up sufficiently to abide the exchange from hope to no hope?

Holding my mind on the possibility of Jim's lasting refusal, pressing it there like salt on a wound, I waited, facing it the best I could. At last I said: "I guess so."

Gordon sighed. "Liz, I suspect you're going to be the same sort of Christian you were a pagan; all the way."

"That's me," I agreed. "Never anything halfway, so be sure you start me off right, and don't ever sugar-coat it. I'll do what you say about Jim; it'll be simply ghastly but I'll do it. Now, what else? I'm so very far behind I've got to hurry."

"No, don't hurry. It isn't you or I who decides what is to be done and when and how. Take it day by day or better, hour by hour. Let yourself be guided. You have a Bible, don't you?"

I was ashamed. "No-o. I'll get one right away. I'm sorry, I—"

"Don't be sorry. You've never felt the need for one. It's better not to have a Bible than to have one and not use it."

"Well, I'll buy one and I'll use it," I told him. "I'm going to buy two books, the Bible and *The Joy of Cooking*."

I'd never heard anyone laugh harder. After he'd wiped his eyes and blown his nose, he said: "Why *The Joy of Cooking*?"

"Because I can see I'm going to have to do every last thing I've always looked down on others for doing. I don't mean servants; that's their business. I mean when you don't have servants. I can't cook, can't sew, can't wash, can't iron, can't do one damn—one darn thing nine-tenths of the women in the world take as a matter of course. Gordon, you just don't know what a snit I've been!"

"I'm getting a fair idea," he laughed. "But no haircloth shirts—"

"Oh, no, not that—just learn or bust trying."

"Good. Now the Bible and *The Joy of Cooking* and how about church? Will you want to go to church?"

Here was the must. The thing I had to do and could not get along without!

"More than anything," I said. "I can't explain except that all those people can help me so. Think of all they know that I never heard of! May I come to your church?"

He flushed. "Don't expect too much of people. I'd be glad if you'd come; I only hope you won't be disappointed. It's a very small church with very, oh, very few in the congregation."

"The Father will be there, won't He?" I asked. "I won't care about the people beyond their showing me how to get to know Him better."

He appeared to be about to answer this. Instead he stood up and held out a hand.

"It's been a wonderful afternoon, wonderful. Thank you. I must make a call before dark."

As we walked outside to his ancient battered sedan, he told me where the church was. There were services Sunday morning at eight and eleven; the eight o'clock was the Eucharist.

"The Eucharist?" I asked.

"The Holy Sacrament. There's no sermon at the early service. Merely Holy Communion."

I shook my head. "I haven't the least idea what that really signifies. My church experience consisted of college chapel and since it was obligatory, naturally I never paid attention. Does Communion mean those tiny glasses and tiny white things?"

"Liz—" His laugh was wonderful to hear. "Your honesty, your down-to-earthness is going to startle any church you go to. No, Communion doesn't mean the tiny glasses and tiny white things; it means, well, the meaning will become clear later. It was our Lord's last supper—"

"Oh, da Vinci. I've seen it thousands of times—" And then I curdled. "Oh, you mean *Jesus, His* last supper—not the *painting* of it! Oh, how can anyone be such a damn fool!"

He swung around so violently I was forced to step back.

"Liz Hatch, don't ever say that! I have never seen greater humility."

Utterly astounded, I cried: "I? Why, I haven't an ounce of it! I'm the biggest blowhard, the biggest show-off—"

"And *admit* it!" he broke in fiercely. "If sins admitted, if shame and guilt honestly acknowledged are not humility, what are they?"

As he spoke, he flung the long gaunt arms straight out from his sides and, in the setting sun, the shadow behind him formed a cross. I saw the cross both as the chance shadow it was and as a symbol; what I was not yet prepared to see was that behind each man, awakened or unawakened, looms the crucifixion of himself.

The arms dropped and Gordon said again: "Do not ever say that! Never, never run yourself down, nor the steps which have brought you to God, the Father. Those were the steps which showed you that His Kingdom is not of this world; 'when the half-gods go, the gods arrive.' You've possessed all that the world values and have found there is no truth in the material, in *half*-gods. You're one of those who has left her nets to follow Him—*how dare you belittle yourself!* Selfishness, drink, drugs, husbands, suicide, how else do you think you were made ready to feel His Presence? It was you who found the Father, *you*. Not some *good* woman, not some respectable Sunday-school teacher, but you, a *sinner*. Did either of your parents find Him? Have any of your husbands found him? Or your friends? No! So who are you to poke fun at this woman who walked with bleeding feet, self-inflicted though they may have been, along the road leading to our Lord? Who are you to judge her harshly, to call her fool when Almighty God does not!"

I stared, struck dumb, tears flowing down my face.

The man was transfigured. Then slowly, little by little, he was a man again, a lank figure in a shabby suit and unpolished boots. Only the eyes continued to glow.

"I will see you Sunday," he said gently.

Letting out my breath, I replied: "Yes, Sunday."

The ancient car coughed, roared, shuddered and roared

again. At last it settled down. Gordon and I waved once before the car rattled off down the driveway.

The sun had set. It was getting cold. As I walked toward the house I thought of Gordon Rogers' tribute to the woman I had been. Already in looking back she appeared a complete stranger. Perhaps she always had been. Perhaps this was why I'd been able to refer to her as "she," as "the woman." Now that I was I, the daughter of the Father, she seemed even more foreign. Did Paul, the would-be murderer, feel so? When Paul met God, did he look back upon this other self as Saul, the stranger?

Whoever this woman was, it seemed that she had served me well, had trudged through hell for me and for this I must be grateful. In time I might even come to love her along with God's other sinners.

What lay ahead, the development of the new me, would be a lengthy process and one not to be approached in haste or disquiet. The recognition of this wasn't in the least fearsome; on the contrary it was curiously exhilarating. To start a job worthy of more than I had was a challenge, for well I knew that there would be more; the Father would supply it!

Going back into the house I was glad to be alone. Glad even that Pete was in New York with Silas for a few days. Jim would be home in an hour or so—presumably would be home—and my batteries had to be recharged in readiness.

Jim. Was Jim one of my half-gods? Well, wasn't he? Wasn't this marriage a product of drunken choice, of egotism, of cruel irresponsibility toward Si and Alan and Pete?

There was no doubt of it. In admitting this I felt myself relax in an incredible fashion. If Jim was a half-god, then—then I *could let him* go. If he was merely a sop to boredom, why, then both of us were half-gods; I to him, he to me, and really *should* relinquish one another. That made our marriage expendable!

199

Into this moment of easy-out, of snarled values, came the picture of Gordon Rogers. "No," he was saying, "no marriage is expendable. Irrespective of motive, marriage is a holy state which you have entered into lightly."

No. The easy-out had been evil speaking; evil befuddling the basic issue of the fact of marriage itself; one marriage to be made decent and useful, one out of three.

Evil spoke again. "No, no!" it said. "Start fresh."

Another Voice intervened. "Start fresh where you are," it said.

"Without liquor? Without sleeping pills?" evil cried.

"With Me," the other voice said.

And my heart cried: "Yes, yes, with You!"

An upsurge of strength filled me. Strength and hope and joy filled every cranny of me until finally I laughed out loud and held out my hands.

"Oh, Alan, Jim—find This too! *Find This*," I cried.

And now what should I do with the lovely strength? How might the rest of the day be used for decency? Yes, today.

The sly voice insinuated itself: "You're hurrying. The minister told you not to hurry—"

"Oh, go away, go away!" I told it. "That wasn't what he meant and you *know* it."

What could I do? Well, I could get Jim's dinner.

The idea of this was so preposterous that I laughed rather wildly yet the idea stayed with me. It wasn't too late. The deep-freeze bulged with steaks and chops and everything imaginable. And there must be cookbooks somewhere.

And—and have pity on Jim! I prayed.

There was a stack of cookbooks. There was *The Joy of Cooking*—that's how you knew the name, wasn't it? And you were going to buy another—see, how extravagant you are?

There was a stack of cookbooks and a million ways to cook steaks:

"Steak with Kidney Pie"; revolting!

"Steak with Puff Pastry"; imagine!

"Steak, Broiled"; atta girl! (page 300)

"Steak: broil under an electric grill. Sear quickly—". Sear? What was sear? I looked in Webster: "Sear, to wither, dry up. To burn, scorch or brown, also to brand with hot iron." I howled with delight. All but the last would be simple, but the kitchen was short on "branding irons."

Okay, "brown."

Baked potato, peas, apple pie and coffee.

Thank goodness I made excellent coffee; all drunks make excellent coffee.

Ventilating fan roaring, tea kettle piping, sweat running off me, and every inch of the kitchen loaded with plates and pots and pans and bowls. It was almost two hours later when Jim opened the back door.

I waved a fork. "Cooking's no joke," I stated. "I'll eat everything I ever said. Look at those peas. They either burn or boil over—dinner's all set. I *think* it's all set."

He halted in his tracks. "You—*cooking?*"

"That's what the book calls it. Oh Jim, I hope it isn't too awful! Here goes the steak, everything but talcum powder on it. Get washed, will you?"

He went through into the pantry. Pushing back the swinging door, he said: "How about a cocktail?"

"There's hardly time. Anyway I've quit. If you want one, hurry."

The door swung to. Whatever his thoughts he kept them to himself. Nor did he comment on the meal. We chewed in silence and I will say it was chewable. After Jim had finished he lit a cigarette and went upstairs with the newspaper. I was alone with the plates and pots and pans and bowls. This was the end of Lesson No. One.

I looked over the mess and said: "Thanks, I made it."

CHAPTER FIFTEEN

The day of meeting and talking with Gordon Rogers had been perfect; the day that followed was a horror. Day of the ordeal: "Ask your husband's forgiveness, and ask for another chance."

I believed Gordon, I trusted him, but—but what about Jim? Hadn't he been—?

Skip that! That's Jim's business; you're the one about to be house-cleaned; you, Liz. Who was it bitched up this marriage? Who was the fall-down drunk? Who jumped in the pit? Who landed in All Angels Hospital?

But "another chance," a chance to what? That one's easy; you're starting to climb up, aren't you? Well then, Jim's the first step. How could you be silly enough to hope to take, say, the tenth step till you've taken the first!

There wasn't any question of having to wake up that morning because I'd been wide awake all night. Without dope I couldn't seem to get the knack of sleep and anyway I saw now that that oblivion hadn't really been sleep. It was passing out. At least my so-called brain was clearer, free of fuzz, of hangover. Yet how could I dare face Jim without the assurance of liquor? Where would the energy come from? The fine phrases?

The answer was: they wouldn't come unless from Him. I could look forward to a day propped up by nothing in God's world except the God Who made it. Liz, the shorn, the stripped, clutching the Father's hand, but the hand was there all right!

I wasn't such a goop as to try to get Jim's breakfast. He was a species of the Can't-Eat-Early variety and would have turned green had I fluttered in with underdone bacon and overdone eggs. Is there anyone more revolting than the horrid happy people who insist upon doing favors which aren't favors? I once had a roommate, a bird-on-the-bough character, who woke me from sound sleep to slip a pillow under my head so I could sleep better.

No, I was being given intelligence enough to stay upstairs. The ordeal between Jim and myself was scarcely in the bacon and egg class. To ask forgiveness presented little difficulty. I was a pro at saying I was sorry, but this was going to go beyond mere asking. This was the difference between remorse and repentance and if you don't think there's a difference, look 'em up. The first is getting plotzed, regretting it, and not having the remotest intention of quitting. The second is staring drunkenness straight in its bloated face and determining to spit on it for the rest of time.

Notwithstanding my stomach's spiral loops, it never occurred to me that I could sidestep this if I wanted to. The truth is, I could not have sidestepped it due to the alternative, the losing the Father. That was too dreadful to contemplate. Back to the black pit? No, thanks! Here at last I was hitched to something true, something wondrous, glorious, unlimited and I was stuck with it. I knew this, accepted it, *had* to.

Therefore, since God's specialist had advised this, I was stuck with this too. I would do precisely as Gordon said. Here was one of the ditches Pete talked about and after tonight, my bones might lie in it forever, unmourned, unattended, and so what? By and with God, I was going to brave the ditch or bust!

All that day through I prayed myself hoarse: "Help, please —help! You're the Boss now—*help*."

Becoming jumpier by the hour, I cleaned the house. This may sound a cinch to you but it was no cinch. Every blessed deed had to be done the hardest, the most awkward way. How handy is a vacuum cleaner if you never looked at one? How handy is a can opener if you work it backwards?

Hours before time I started dinner. My mounting respect for housewives was neck and neck with a mounting sense of urgency; hurry, hurry! My impatience was the same as had governed all previous actions only now it seemed to apply to me instead of others. Liz Hatch had to learn to do things right. Oh God, *change* her, fix her quick!

Toward sundown I was a basket case. Pete's second gear had been forgotten, the quackgrass, root by root, forgotten. Reaching to help me was the Power Which fashioned the universe—But I wanted a miracle-in-a-minute. It was absurd, I know, but, you see, I did perceive totally and absolutely What This was I had been given. When you're raised from the dead, you know it! The Glory in All Angels Hospital had left no doubt about Itself. Yet I did not know how to use what had been given me. I kept forgetting to flip on the switch to receive the current.

Exhausted I stopped at a window, to watch the sun slip down. "Day by day," Gordon had said, "or better, hour by hour." It had been twenty-four hours since he said that, twenty-four long, long hours. I sighed.

The snow had melted, leaving the ground as soggy as my heart felt. I stayed at the window, fighting for peace, for strength, for courage, for fine phrases to soften Jim. Usually I was so sure of what I would say, so articulate.

Suddenly the hopelessness of the task overwhelmed me. Not

just Jim but all of it. Alan; *how could I ever be at peace about Alan?* And who would believe that this Glory Which had come to me was anything but a newfangled fad? Who would even believe I'd really stopped drinking? And I; what was *I* going to do? What would I myself be like in this strange new work which lay ahead? What would I talk about, what would I do with my time, my nervous energy? Who would be my companions?

Suddenly it was too much. In utter panic I grabbed a coat and ran outdoors. There just might be news of Alan waiting out in the mailbox—oh God, if only I could know whether he were dead or not dead! If only I could be certain, *ever.* What a fool to go on hoping!

There were letters but none concerning Alan. I walked so seldom that the trip up the long driveway had tired me and I leaned against the mailbox, breathing hard. It would be nice to talk to Louise Patton but there wasn't time; that damn dinner! Turning back I halted; around a bend in the road came a figure on a bicycle. It was coming toward me and bicycles were rare on our dirt road so out of curiosity I waited.

It was a woman about my age. A fat, blowsy woman, with purple face and stringy hair and block legs stuffed into thick cotton stockings. She puffed by and as she passed, her small pig eyes stared, watering and vacant. I stared back. Stared at the enormous thighs pumping up and down, at the enormous rump overlapping the narrow seat.

My head moved to follow her. Loathing filled me; coarse monstrous creature! Why would anybody so obscene parade her awful bulk on public roads?

I hated that woman. *Hated* her!

Then all at once I saw myself hating her. Saw me, the pampered, standing by a mailbox, loathing someone whom I had never seen before. Someone I knew nothing whatever about; a woman who might be straddling a bicycle because she couldn't afford a Lincoln Continental. Who might be monstrously fat because her glands were sick, who had pig eyes because her parents had pig eyes.

I was bent with shame, a shame in proportion to my scorn.

How—did—I—dare! I who had been blessed with every gift the world could offer, and more, far, far more, with forgiveness! I who had felt the Presence of the Creator of the world!

I walked back down the driveway and shame walked with me. Somehow, in time, the shame became a cleansing, a sort of soul's cathartic. The last thing I cared to think of was the woman on the bicycle yet I made myself, knowing I must think of her and of every other human being in terms of children of the Father. Daughters and therefore sisters, my sisters! Sons and therefore brothers; my brothers!

Oh, what a time this was going to take. It would require beginning at the beginning; re-education of even the unconscious. Nevertheless it had to be; if I was the Father's child, this woman was His child. And Jim—Jim was His child. And so must be left to Him! It was not I who could hope to change Jim or what Jim wanted of me. All I could ever hope was to accept, and assist in, the changing of myself.

I, Elizabeth, was under law now, the law of *Truth*. As yet no pattern had appeared, only straws, but these straws were plain and unmistakable. That woman had been a straw; my shame, another.

When Jim returned, wonder of wonders, he said: "Hello." He ate dinner, a dinner slightly reminiscent of the night before; chops instead of steak, boiled potatoes instead of baked, spinach instead of peas, blueberry pie instead of apple. Lighting a cigarette, he left the table, but instead of going upstairs, he sat down in the living room with the evening paper. I took this for a good omen. At least I wouldn't have to tear after him and beat on his bedroom door.

Maybe dinner had been better. Not enough better to get lightheaded about, just better. The kitchen was the same shambles as the night before; it took more than an hour to clean up. I was acquiring a profound respect for housework; a cinch, my foot.

Finally it was done. I went through the back hall to the servants' bath—oh, lovely unappreciated days before the war! —and smoothed my hair and put on lipstick. But certainly with no intention of being alluring. Habit, I suppose. The mirror showed me a thin, strained face and I told it: "Don't start shaking. Take it easy."

But I was shaking. My hands shook so that I ran cold water on them, drying them mercilessly. Bracing my back against the glass shower stall, I shut my eyes.

"Father, I'm going through with this," I said, "but I'm not going to like it. I guess this is some of what it means to be a Christian, not all gravy, not all light and joy! I don't quite see why I've got to do it, so please be around. Please be there and don't let me muff it!"

For several minutes I struggled with myself. Yes, I would do this, I argued, because this mess was my mess, fifty per cent of it anyway. I did need to be forgiven many many things, by people as well as God, and I did need to make at least one marriage work if I could get the chance. Living by the Father meant *living!* If I was to live this thing, the first step was Jim, not that Jim was more important than anybody else but he was *here.* He was right here in the living room reading the paper and this made him my baby; what sense could there be in making amends to the world if I wasn't willing to try to make amends to Jim? It was the same as Pete's going back to Yale; the place you flubbed is the place to start over.

"Lord—just *be* there!" I prayed.

The living-room draperies hadn't been pulled and the windows were huge black mirrors. Jim and his newspaper and the gracious room were reflected in the black mirrors and reflected again in the mirrored wall around the fireplace. There were too many Jims and too many me's.

My hands sought each other and gripped hard. As I sank down in a chair opposite Jim I thought back; it had been many weeks, months really, since we had any more than briefly spoken. The fact of this and all that had gone before— all the scenes I had created—and all that lay ahead pushed at me, walling me in, hemming me from words which might reach him.

Please, please help.

"It's been a nice day," I offered.

My voice broke. I coughed and tried again.

"It's nice Pete will be home for Christmas—"

"Home?" The word was overemphasized.

"Yes, he doesn't go back to college till the January term."

Jim raised his eyes from the paper. "What home? This may be sold by then."

Sold?

My insides caved. "Oh?"

"I listed it the day you went to the hospital. If you'll stay on hand to show it, it will sell faster. See that it's kept clean, will you?"

"You mean—? Yes, I'll keep it clean," I said. "Only—"

"Only what?"

I looked past him at the glow of the lamps in the black windows. Beyond them was the terrace enclosed by a low hedge of juniper. A breeze had come up and the juniper was waving gently, seeming to beckon encouragingly.

"Jim, I—" I began, "I want to thank you for coming to the hospital. Pete tells me you were there and it was good of you. I appreciate now, in part at least, what a terrible thing it was to do to you, to Pete, to everyone. To myself as well. It—it was the climax to years of self-pity and—and I wouldn't blame you if you couldn't forgive me but—but I'd be grateful if you'd try. For that and for all those other awful mistakes I've made. And—and I'd be grateful if you'd give me another chance. I'm beginning to realize what kind of person I've been and—and— That's all."

He folded the newspaper lengthwise and placed it on his knee.

"Why the confession?" he asked.

"Well, it's—" Never had I been so inadequate.

"It's—Jim, it would require explanations and I know you're dead sick of explanations. And anyway I couldn't expect you to believe what's happened. Something happened in the hospital—an awakening, I guess it could be called. It happened and it's going to make a different person of me. Not all at once of course. I haven't any idea how long it'll take but it's begun and it'll go on. I don't expect you to believe the last part either but—it'd be wonderful if you were willing to take a chance," I ended lamely.

His expression told nothing. He waited to see if I had finished and then he got up.

"You're asking for another chance, eh? I'll think it over. I'll give you the answer in a few days. Goodnight. I have a meeting, Health Board."

I heard his car make the turn off the gravel driveway onto the dirt road. That was close to a mile off, the wind must be just right. Not knowing how I'd gotten there, I found myself kneeling beside my chair. This was the first time since Acapulco that Jim had bothered to tell where he was going. Perhaps this too was a straw.

Covering my face with my hands, I said: "Our Father Who is in everything, thank You."

It was late when I went upstairs. The wind had risen and outside the bedroom windows the bare trees swayed and tossed like giant, many-armed figures in some strange game. I watched and as I watched my heart swelled with a nameless joy. A mysterious bursting thing which made me want to sing and never stop singing.

High overhead two planes were passing, their lights competing with the stars. How very small they were. How very small man was and yet, how marvelous! How very marvelous when he alone, in all this vastness, could think and could express his thoughts.

But hadn't man muffed his greatness? Yes, for the most part, yet in my lifetime alone man had made men—*some* men —treat one another with partial decency. The sweatshops, the chain gangs, the treatment of the insane; why, the very STOP sign at the end of the road was man's admission of the rights of others.

Stick to Liz Hatch and the greatness she had muffed. Leave all the rest to Him.

That night I slept an hour or two, more perhaps, more than I suspected. I must have for I remember being astonished at how refreshed I was. Less Zombie than in ages.

After I'd eaten breakfast, I called the bookshop in the village. "This is Mrs. James Hatch. I want a Bible," I said.

"Yes, Mrs. Hatch. What kind of a Bible? A good one?" the clerk asked.

"A good one?" I repeated.

"I mean, expensive. We have regular ones and—"

"The regular," I said. "One to read, not to admire."

"Fine. Will you pick it up? You know we're closed tomorrow."

I'd forgotten tomorrow was Thanksgiving.

"I'll be down this afternoon," I said. "Thanks."

Thanksgiving. Oh no. Thanksgiving was the yearly shindig at the Webbs' on Long Island, the house where Jim and I were married. There'd be a thousand people and ten thousand *cocktails*. No, not yet! Maybe Jim wouldn't go—but yes, he'd go. He liked Sue and Tony better than he liked being closeted with me. And then, as the phone rang, I thought, Well, Pete will be here; he will go with us. Wise Pete.

It was wise Pete on the telephone. Calling from Si's house.

"Hi, Christian," he said, "how goes it?"

"Great, boy. Peter Addams, you're not talking where your father can hear you, are you? He'll think we're nuts."

"Get used to that," he laughed. "Christians have been considered nuts for centuries. Say, Mom, if it's okay, I'll stay with Dad till Monday. He's kind of lonely—you know."

I knew. I was the one who'd made him lonely, so as greatly as I wanted Pete home, I was ashamed to say so.

"Of course," I said. "And, Pete, tell Si—tell him he's one of the things I'm thankful for this Thanksgiving."

"Sure will, Mom. He'll drop dead but I'll tell him. See you."

"See you, Pete."

Thanksgiving day was what Thanksgiving days should be, cold, windswept and bright, like a glossy calendar of "over the hill to grandmother's house"—no that was Christmas! *Christmas when the house might be sold.* But I wasn't to think about that. That thought had to be wrapped up and slung on a top shelf with all the other horrors I mustn't dwell on.

One ditch at a time.

Today's ditch would turn out to be a chasm: "No thanks, no cocktails. I've quit drinking."

"Quit—? Hey, everyone, Liz turned down a *martini!* She's quit *drinking.* Here, Liz, hold it while I drop dead!"

This was what everyone was going to do, drop dead. Even Pete had said it about the message to Si and what was a kind message compared to a sober drunk?

Well, a pox on it!

From here in, I wasn't trying to make a hit with anybody but Him. Stopping liquor wasn't a decision I'd thought out and resolved to do, anything but. Stopping liquor was no more a resolution than running from a burning building was a resolution. Self-preservation, that was all; life or death. There would be tons of decisions I couldn't possibly carry out on my own but this I could and would. I was going to do this and if it meant sitting in a corner, going, brr-r, brr-r, well, it meant sitting in a corner, going, brr-r, brr-r.

I dressed myself to the teeth; the works. Jacques Fath mit mink mit diamonds. If poor wallflower was about to be revived, I'd be the swankiest wallflower, the best-dressed corner-sitter on Long Island.

Driving over beside Jim, I tried to remember what I used to talk about before liquor. Let's see now; what did Randy and I talk about?

You didn't.

No, before then. Back in the moonlight and honeysuckle days, what did I talk about?

About moonlight and honeysuckle. You'd be a dilly, wouldn't you, trying to revive that!

All right. Then *later*?

Later was Prohibition.

Ho hum. Prohibition.

I turned to Jim. "Jim?"

"Don't talk. Can't you see the traffic?"

Don't talk.

Okay, *don't* talk. Suppose you never uttered another word, your average'd be damn—darn high!

I was scared stiff and, being scared stiff, the thing to do was burn bridges, one right after the other, the instant I got there. No bridges, no retreat.

The first bridge: "Sue, my love, Tony darling. I've quit booze—isn't it *ghastly?*"

There were indeed a thousand people and indeed ten thousand cocktails. And a thousand times I stated: "No, thanks, I've quit—isn't it *awful?*"

Of course all I had to say was: "No," but once an exhibitionist always an exhibitionist. (Well, almost always.) There was preservation in this as well as show-off; the more repetitious the bigger the backlog of safety. I now had a face to save!

The afternoon wore away, and wore away is the phrase. I felt my mouth; it had frozen. The grin was painted on and was going to stay painted. The only person worse than a drunk is the ex-drunk who disapproves of drunks—the smug self-righteous biddy whom you remember *when*.

This I determined to avoid if I died of it and, children, I've come close. There's reams on the art of getting sober but who ever mentions the art of staying sober? Yet it's ten times tougher unless you live alone in a lighthouse, not because sobriety itself is hard but because we, the sober, make it hard.

Dry drunks forget so easy. Instead of nodding brightly, we attempt rational conversation. We split our sides at bum jokes, particularly jokes we ourselves have told the teller ten minutes back. We encourage bores so as not to be thought boring when actually, there's not one blessed thing anyone has to do except not hang crepe. And not—oh, *not be ashamed to be sober!*

And God love me, I didn't and wasn't.

I was marvelous. Maybe a little too marvelous.

"Johnny, you *couldn't* be funnier!"

"Angel, I *adore* your hat—it is a hat, isn't it?"

All of it unnecessary. All a total waste of steam.

I did a thing I'd never done; I ate my head off. And coffee, vats of coffee. Balancing a packed plate of goodies, I spied Jim —he was eating of course—and saw him watching me eat. I waved a celery stalk and miracle of miracles, he waved back. Then the crowd reshuffled and he was lost from sight.

A very nice fat man shoved my elbow. "Oh hi, Greg," I said. "How nice, how's Elsie? No, I haven't met Mrs. Rich—hello, Mrs. Rich, gorgeous party. Only I'm a drunk who's stopped drinking."

Mrs. Rich was fascinated. "Really?" she breathed. "Really

and truly? How wonderful; I do wish you'd talk to my husband."

"Not me," I backed away.

"No, honestly I do wish you would."

"Not me!" I said vehemently.

I might be drunk on not being drunk but I wasn't fool enough to pound the tambourine. Too familiar, too well remembered were the long-nosed pussyfoots, the: "I do hate to say this but really you do drink too much."

Where is the drunk who doesn't know he drinks too much? Show me one. He knows it better than anyone; he knows the drinks he's snuck that you don't dream of. Forget it, Mrs. Rich. When Mr. Rich wants help, he'll ask for it. Me, I'll stick to my own sobriety. An hour at a time.

I did get hooked however. Not by Mrs. Rich for Mr. Rich but by a man whose name I never heard. And I was prouder of the way I handled it than of anything in my life. Yes, proud!

About the time Jim and I were talking of leaving, hours earlier than usual, a very tall, very drunk, very dignified man shoved between Jim and me.

"How do you do?" he asked.

"Sober," I replied.

No response. This too will pass, I thought.

But it did not, thank God.

"You are a most attractive woman," the man enunciated carefully.

"Thanks, I—"

"Not young," he went on, "yet what has attractiveness to do with age?"

It was stupid not to recognize the question as rhetorical. Looking as attractive as I was able, I said: "There appears to be a difference of opinion. The Latin—"

"Kindly do not interrupt. There is a rumor about that you are sober; is that so? Answer, yes or no."

"Yes, indeed," I answered.

"Not, yes indeed, merely, yes," he corrected.

"Merely yes," I said.

"Ah, then the rumor may be considered correct. There is also the rumor that this is quite extraordinary."

"Quite is right," I nodded vigorously.

"Answer, yes or no."

"Yes," I said.

"Ah, then both rumors may be considered correct which is extremely rare. Be good enough to explain, madam."

"Explain how it happened?" With such protocol I mustn't jump the gun.

He bowed. "If you will be so good."

Help, Lord, *help. What shall I say?*

The truth, was the answer. The *truth?* Horrors! I looked around me. It seemed perfectly awful, inconceivable that I should attempt to speak of God. Here of all places, and I, the runny-nosed Christian, yesterday's drunk, tomorrow's—*what?* I, who loathed *good* people! And Do-Good people even more.

Then I heard Gordon Rogers' words: "It was you who found the Father. Not some *good* woman, but you, a *sinner.*"

Okay, the truth, so *help* me, God!

I lit a fresh cigarette.

"Well, it was this way; I—I tried to take my life, one week ago today this was. But it didn't work. When I came to, in the hospital, it was dark and I was alone. And then—then I wasn't alone. The Father was there with me."

"The father?" the man asked.

"Yes, the Father with a capital F, the Father Almighty. He was there with me and He's been with me ever since and, well, I—I wouldn't be able to hear Him if I were drunk."

"He *speaks?*"

I blinked up at the man. I hadn't thought of the Father as actually *speaking*—

"Yes, He speaks. He speaks just like you and me; that's funny, isn't it? You'd think it would be in Thee's and Thou's, but

215

it isn't. I guess that's so we can understand. Remember the trial of Joan of Arc? They asked her if God spoke to her in French and she said: 'I hear Him in French.' Well, it's the same thing. And that's the story of what happened to me. Does it make sense?"

"Yes, some," the man answered. "A little. Thank you."

I've thought and thought about that man and his answer. How could what I said have made sense? And yet he must have hated drinking to have asked at all. And if one is desperate enough, well, any seed may grow.

We drove home and I was extremely happy. Quiet inward happy, not fun-happy. At peace. I'd managed to stay sober and still hadn't been a wallflower!

And then I faced a fact: No dame is a wallflower among drunks! Not one; not the walleyed, the tongue-tied, the bow-legged. Each drunk turns a woman into the gal he'd most like to be drunk with, he invents her all by himself just as I'd been inventing men. Today was no test. The test would be to be sober among the sober.

That night before Jim closed his bedroom door he stuck his head out and said: "Good job, Liz. You can be proud of yourself."

Good job! My heart soared; hope, *hope*.

On my night table lay the new Bible. Inside the cover I'd pasted my bookplate, one with the sketch of me holding a cocktail in each hand. Though it looked terrible, looked profane, I'd put it there deliberately. To serve as a constant reminder.

Below the bookplate I wrote the date in ink: Thanksgiving 1946. I was childishly delighted with my Bible. Half the world had Bibles but not me. I'd never once opened one and now I was about to, to learn about the Father.

A splendid night to begin: Thanksgiving night.

CHAPTER SIXTEEN

Gordon Rogers was right; it wasn't much of a church. A skimpy weatherbeaten structure sandwiched between a gas station and a quick-and-dirty called Art's Place. When I'd edged the car between two Chevies which might or might not have held churchgoers I got out and stood gazing at the building, seeming to see it but actually no more seeing it than a girl sees the box her engagement ring comes in.

The name, St. Something, was in chipped gilt letters and above the entrance was a chipped gilt cross. Yesterday at this time the cross wouldn't have held any significance for me personally. It would have stood for somebody named Jesus who got crucified because of somebody named Judas; a symbol which in a fashion I couldn't explain had come to epitomize the whole of Christianity.

Today it was beginning to be more than this. Today it stood for somebody named Jesus who just possibly had gotten crucified for somebody named Liz. Last night I'd read Matthew. At midnight I finished the last chapter and the only chapter in which I didn't find Liz Hatch was the first, the "begats." She was Herod, she was identified with a bunch called Pharisees and Sadducees and she certainly was identified with that voice on the mountain top, insistently in favor of making bread out of stones.

Most especially was she Peter, the side of Peter that wanted no truck with public humiliation. Peter had turned out to be a tremendous comfort. The Sermon on the Mount had been appalling, Jesus' parables obscure and often meaningless; but Peter I understood. He was right down my alley, one of the pasture-over-the-fence boys. If there was hope for Peter and obviously there was, there was hope for Liz.

I suppose this is blasphemous?

Why is it? Who says so? Does the Bible say so?

It most assuredly does not. It is in the Bible that Peter's faults are listed or where else have we learned that he reneged when the going got tough? That blasphemy business is nonsense. Peter isn't *Saint* Peter in the Bible, not by a long shot; he's entirely human which is why he is such a comfort. It just goes to show what the Father can do!

Had Gordon's church been named for Peter I might have been more at ease, but it was not. It was St. Edmund's and I hadn't run into Edmund, still haven't. As a matter of fact I'm not up on saints; my job is Liz who is in no imminent danger of sainthood.

I hesitated before the closed door, feeling shy and intimidated. I'd picked the early service simply because it was early and now without breakfast, my stomach was being heard from. With a hand which was moist inside its glove, I pushed open the padded door.

The church was empty. There was no sound at all. At one glance I saw that it was empty and yet at once I knew that it was not. The narrow aisle, the pews, the altar were alive with a Presence Which awaited awareness. As my own awareness grew I recognized overwhelmingly that the Father was here as surely as in this past week He had been everywhere.

My heart was throbbing wildly in my throat and wrists and

up and down my arms. I waited and at last peace came. On the altar the candle lights were tear-shaped and I moved steadily toward them. At the front pew I halted, my eyes riveted on a large window high above the altar. It showed, in profile, a bearded man kneeling in a garden. The early sun, in shafts of ruby and emerald and sapphire, was emblazoning the figure which presumably was Jesus; a Jew named Jesus who went about saying he was the Son of the Father.

Last night after reading Matthew I had switched off the light and lain in darkness reappraising all Jews. I'd always scorned the Jew and Matthew was filled with them, many of whom justified my opinion of them, but not all. No, not all. Knowing Jesus was a Jew, it yet had stunned me to find Him one and therefore, gradually, I had started to realize what later I was to realize to the fullest, that it was the Jewish people who alone had found and kept alive the One and Only Father. That without them it was extremely doubtful whether there ever could have been the One Father.

For anyone familiar with Greek and Roman history and their collection of carved fathers, the Jews' relationship to God, the Father, simply could not be laughed off. Either the Jewish God was my God or the Bible was untrue and I was in no state to buck the Bible. It would have been like a lone swimmer disdaining the only life raft in the middle of an ocean. If the Gospels were gospel and it looked as if they had to be, my personal debt to the Jews was incalculable. Never, never again would it be possible to be anything but indebted to a people to whom I owed not only my sanity but my very life. That stained-glass man in the garden, who indefinably was commencing to superimpose himself upon the Father, was a Jew and so forever I, Liz Hatch, was linked to the Jew.

I continued to gaze at the window and then I sat down in the front pew and bowed my head, not praying, merely tasting the peace and for the first time, thinking of Jesus in capital letters. The Son. I rested and after a while I raised my head to find Gordon Rogers standing at the altar, his back to me. I stared at his white robe which somehow made him anonymous and then bowed my head again.

Out of the stillness came his voice:

> " 'Almighty God, unto whom all hearts
> are open, all desires known, and
> from whom no secrets are hid—' "

The ageless words rolled down from the altar and poured over me, their beauty the beauty of the centuries, time-tested. Some call them soporific and for some they are, but for me they were and have remained electrifyingly vivid, these simple words of common prayer.

In no way did they seem impersonal, rather the opposite since surely it was I whose heart was opening and surely the One Who had opened it knew all my desires and from Him could no secrets be hid. These were words exactly describing what had happened to me and was happening and my heart recognized and welcomed them.

The voice continued:

> " 'Ye who do truly and earnestly
> repent of your sins—' "

It was to me, Liz Hatch, they spoke; was it not I who was repenting? Not Jane Doakes; *I.* It was I who had sinned; others too had sinned, the world sinned, but this was no longer a concern of mine. Sins other than mine were now the Father's affair.

> " '—and intend to lead a new life—' "

Oh, yes, that! *I did indeed intend to lead a new life!* Where it would take me I could not hope to guess but it certainly would be without the jug and without self-pity forever and forever. Amen.

This much I knew because here at last was a Leader to be looked up to; I who'd been without direction had found direction. I believe it is like this: we humans find that which we are in greatest need of and believe that which we are ready to believe.

Finally I heard the Lord's Prayer and my voice joined in timidly, becoming stronger at the end:

> " 'For thine is the kingdom, and
> the power, and the glory—' "

A moment of silence followed. Looking up I saw that the figure in the white robe had knelt below the figure in the garden. With no conscious will I found that I had risen from the pew and was going up the short steps to kneel behind the two of them.

The voice spoke again:

> " 'We who are not worthy so much
> as to gather up the crumbs—' "

Worthy? I?

Oh, no, no! There could be no question of worthiness. This was not a person I was coming before. This was the Lord God. What would I be doing here if I considered myself worthy? Even then I knew there was no question of worthiness and I thank God I did for it was the beginning of humility; that humility which bears no resemblance to self-abasement. Humility is not remembering one's weaknesses: it is giving God credit for one's strength.

Now the minister had risen and was standing facing me. In his hand was a small silver plate and on it were tiny pieces of bread. He was offering a piece, saying:

> " 'The Body of our Lord Jesus Christ
> Which was given for thee—' "

I saw the Man I'd met in Matthew. The *body*, the body of that One Who called Himself the Son! Who slowly and subtly was now beginning to impose Himself upon the Father and thus link all who believe in the Father. Gratitude welled in me, gratitude, that sister of humility.

Why the Son had felt it necessary to give His Body for the world, I did not know and do not know and yet He did so and now it appeared that I was included. I, Liz Hatch. Tears of gratitude to this lonely man ran down my cheeks.

Humility. And Gratitude. Both new. New gifts waiting to be unwrapped and used. The piece of bread stuck to the roof of my mouth and I let it stay while I attempted to wipe away the tears. Now the minister was back, holding a silver goblet, saying:

> " 'The Blood of our Lord Jesus Christ,
> which was shed for Thee—' "

I saw the Man I'd met in Matthew. Spit ran off His face. I saw the cross. On it was the Man and people wagged their heads. "Save thyself," they said, "come down." And He did come down to all who would receive Him.

It is not clear to me why the Lonely Man felt He had to die like this or die at all. Was this the only way to show Liz Hatch and show the Jews and show Alan and Pete and Jim and Si and Randy and the woman on the bicycle that He and we are the Father's and the Father is *worth* dying for? I do not know. But I do know that He did come down and that He comes more and more each day, this part of God called Christ.

Lifting my face I drank of the cup. The wine loosened the bread and they were swallowed together. And it was many months before I learned that a priest does not give the bread and the wine to a person who has never been confirmed. To say nothing of a person who was never baptized.

What a tender gracious thing! If only ministers would minister, would be content to fertilize the first tiny seeds of faith. Gordon is so humble he would not be able to imagine what he did that morning more than ten years ago. He would not be able to believe it was he who gave one woman a picture of what the Church should be.

After the service I drove home. Thanking Gordon, I got into the car, scarcely hearing his wistful remarks about the empty church. It was beautiful, I told him, and shook hands and drove away. I recall the joy that was within me. The sense of freedom, a sureness unlike anything I'd ever known. I remember wishing there was someone to share this with, wishing Pete were home, wishing I might tell Jim. Oh, what Jim could be if he too found This.

A strange car was parked by our flagstone walk. I drove into the garage wondering who was here so early; a patient probably or someone from the county medical board. But there was no one in the living room, no one downstairs. Then from above I heard voices, heard Jim saying: "There are six bathrooms. Two downstairs."

And I knew instantly. Knew that strangers were inspecting our home, knew that if they bought it, this marriage of Jim and Liz Hatch would most likely never be turned into anything workable. I stood stock-still and then, as though their not hearing footsteps would keep the house from selling, I tiptoed to the back hall and into the servants' bath. Dropping my fur coat, I removed the brown velvet beanie and, for lack of anything else I smoothed my hair with shaking fingers.

This was the day I had hoped Jim would give me his answer and perhaps he was giving it, the one answer Gordon Rogers had asked if I could take. My mind switched to the Man on the Cross. I thought, is this my cross? This and Alan would make two—

"But You—You never deserved Your Cross!" I said aloud. "I have."

Then I said: "*Help* me. Help me not to bellyache, to take whatever I'm intended to take!"

The door to the bedroom was opening.

"Here are the servants' rooms—oh, hello," Jim said.

I grinned crookedly.

"Hello," I said.

He introduced a Mr. and Mrs. Somebody; they'd been sent by a real estate firm and it seemed they liked the house.

"Is it easy to take care of?" Mrs. Somebody was asking.

Oh, you betcha, I wanted to answer. Four servants'll do it easy—but you can't get 'em, see? It's miles from nowhere and servants don't like being miles from nowhere. Instead I said: "Oh—yes." Because it really would be easy if a woman had been brought up a woman in place of a Brain.

"That's what I thought," she told me. "Now, would you want to sell the rugs and the draperies? The draperies especially. All those windows."

I looked at Jim.

"Why, I—I guess so," I said. "We haven't talked about it but I suppose if the house goes, the rest might as well go."

The woman smiled sympathetically. "I know how you must feel. It's a lovely place. You must hate to give it up."

I said: "Yes, but—but sometimes we don't learn to value things except by letting them go."

Jim cleared his throat. "And here's the bath. And you'll want to see the basement. The equipment is entirely electrical."

The three filed out. At the door Jim turned.

"I've got to go out in a few minutes. Liz. Oh, by the way, the answer is, no."

The basement door clicked; the-answer-is-no.

I stared at the door; the-answer-is-no.

Oh, by the way, you are not forgiven.

Oh, by the way, you are not to have another chance.

I stumbled upstairs. Shutting the door to my room, I sat down. A car drove away and another car and I started to get up and sat down again. It was best to sit down, to be as quiet as possible because this was going to be a long day. A long day stretched ahead and not merely this day but all the rest of the days of my life.

Nights, too.

Days without liquor. Nights without sedatives.

And what if this couple decided not to buy the house, what then? Was I supposed to keep on showing it to others, hoping and praying and never being sure?

Self-pity, a Voice said.

Yes, it is. That's right, I thought.

"All right, You take over," I said aloud. "Take *all* of it. It's too much for me!"

The couple did not buy the house. No one came close to buying it for almost a year, a year difficult to describe as there was so little action in it. In looking back that period seems to have been spent getting the hang of living with myself, living without fear and without encouragement. Any growth was a hidden one which few observed and which I myself often doubted.

Should you be wondering why I was dope enough to stick to such a slow, unrewarding path, that's because you've not been drunk enough, long enough. It's also because you haven't met up with the Lord God Who somehow is clever enough to compensate for the loss of a self like this. Any change in Liz Hatch was a change for the better. I was flying by the seat of my pants but away from that lifelong island of Self.

The flight was into a new dimension. The discoveries made weren't new discoveries, only new to me, just as America wasn't new, only new to Colombo. One day I tested dimensions. Getting on all fours, I shambled around to see what could be seen from that position and nothing could be seen but what your cat sees. When I stood up though, ah, there were the lovely furnishings, the gay paintings, the bright windows, and beyond, the treetops and the blue, blue sky! Like America, they'd been there all the time. Nothing had altered but my point of view.

So bit by bit I was creaking my life upright. I had sobriety and I had health. Even the doctors admitted that. As my mind healed, my tattered nerves healed. And it wasn't a miracle unless the mind's control of the body be a miracle; on this basis, there were daily miracles. For instance one dilly of a miracle was that never again did I ask Jim for another chance nor was I a martyr nor did I shed one tear that was not a tear of wonder and gratitude. I had shot my wad, *quelle* wad, and no cee-gar!

I guess I must have been ashamed to ask again. What it amounted to was that I too was unconsciously learning that a sacrifice which no one wants you to make is not only darn tiresome, it can, if pushed, become a vicious type of pride. Also, no matter how I regretted the sad botch of marriages one, two and three, the deeper I went into Christ's words and into the books of His specialists, the greater became my belief that none of these marriages had been marriage in its true sense. Marriage, like liquor and pink pills, had been an escape from the job I was now engaged in. The three, Randy and Si and Jim, were steppingstones, not husbands. So while I continued to pray about Jim and Liz Hatch, in my heart I was as weary of us as I was of martinis.

What I was finding out was that if I was a mess, whatever I did would be a mess. My first and main job was to get acquainted with the Father and gradually I did. God is a habit. The habit of Him is acquired precisely as other habits are acquired, by plugging at it, by desiring it sufficiently to stick with it.

226

Since I had all that back junk to unlearn, I was having to go back and start at the beginning. "To begin again is to be born again," someone said, and this is true and this is painful. What birth isn't? Birth is no cinch. But then, life is no cinch either.

My friends, ninety-nine and nine-tenths of them, were embarrassed with me. It was great, simply great that I was still sober; great stuff, showed great character! But—but the God part, hadn't I gone off the deep? Religion was great, simply great, but, for God's sake—"Excuse me, Liz!"—for goodness' sake, you wouldn't be going to a convent, would you? Or the Salvation Army, oh, Liz, you couldn't, could you!

I'd have liked to. At certain times, four white walls and one blue uniform would have been heaven. Plenty of nice clean rules and regulations. No choices. No, is-this-right-and-that-wrong? No screwed-up nonsense about swearing or not swearing. What drove me nuts was someone apologizing for doing the identical things I'd always done. It put me in the christer class and I abhor christers.

And yet more and more I was troubled, as I myself must have so consistently troubled others, at the bandying around of the Father's name and the Son's name. This living, one foot on the pagan side and one foot on God's side, is a straddle; two points of view, your values changing but still not jelled. Occasionally, as I'd get bogged down in what were sins and what were not sins, my sense of humor would vanish completely.

Sins are like Kleenex. You pull one and another comes, and another, and another. Except that sins come in a variety of sizes: papa-sins and mama-sins and teenie weenie baby-sins. The papa-sins, the Ten Commandments, are duck soup, but the subtle ones, the psychological ones—brother! Ones such as: Am I being proud of not being proud? Am I getting drunk on not getting drunk? Is my love of God just one more affair, *some horrible perverted exhibitionism?*

As I found myself out of step with those around me, I shouldered the blame; I would say the habit of guilt is as old as the habit of God. There was one innovation however in that I no longer resented the guilt nor had the urge to hoist it off on someone else. My road had branched off, that was all, and while this road was lonely and sort of freakish, I could accept it because the other had been so much worse.

My load of guilt bothered Gordon Rogers. He said: "Guilt over past sins is a sin in itself, Liz."

"What isn't?" I grinned.

"Not funny," he said. "When God forgives us, who are we not to forgive ourselves? The memory of sins can be wallowed in, too."

"Good old haircloth," I mused.

"Yes, the old haircloth. Despair becomes an indulgence. Religious orders have died of it."

"I know," I agreed. "But what about hangover sins? Repeated ones; quackgrass? How can you be forgiven sins you continue to commit? If you quit, you're forgiven—sure! And that promise is with you always, but leftover sins? My criticism, my impatience, my intolerance; they're still going great guns. How can *they* be forgiven?"

He smiled. "What do you think it is to be a Christian? Do you think a Christian automatically becomes a saint?"

"I never gave it a tumble. If I had, I'd have said that to be a Christian meant to stop doing what you knew was wrong."

"And what do you say now?"

"Now—well, now I guess I'm Paul's girl, doing what I wish I wouldn't, not doing what I wish I would! Though I would think that if we had real faith and honesty, knew right from wrong, we'd *do* right."

"Effortlessly? With no labor?"

"No, I'll take that back. I guess the Christian is the guy who falls flat and gets up, falls flat and gets up, falls flat and gets up. It's that getting-up that makes him a Christian."

Gordon laughed his wonderfully rich laugh.

Nodding, he said: "As you would say, I'll buy that."

The day came when I discovered that the God I was falling flat and getting up for, was also in control of my checkbook.

This was a painful discovery and came about in this fashion: I'd been praying for the poor of the world. Truly and earnestly, with all my heart and soul and knees, I was praying that the poor be fed and clothed when suddenly, before my eyes neon lights flashed: How about the bill on your desk for $235 for one hat and one suit? You feed and clothe them!

It knocked the wind out of me. From Gordon and Pete and fifty books I'd heard and read about the Father speaking. I myself had heard Him but quietly, more like one's other better self, never in neon lights. Suggestions, rather than commands. This was a command and no mistake. What He was saying was: "Don't pray for miracles. Don't ask Me to do what you can do yourself!"

It was right of course. It was the truth and like all truth it was adamant, and changed my life by redirecting my expenditures. When God is your Banker, you're hooked. Gordon well nigh fainted when I called to ask if he could use $235.

"I've just found out I owe this," I said.

"That exact amount?" he asked.

"That exact amount. For today. Undoubtedly there'll be more later," I told him. And there was. And how.

Sometime that spring a singular change took place between Jim and me. He was home more and more and both of us were more relaxed, able to laugh over little things or over nothing. All trace of the caustic Lady Killer had vanished nor was I any longer Liz, the Glamor Puss. In some ways it was disconcerting, like narcissi turning out to be turnips.

Our conversations over the sale of the house were curious conversations; to hear us you'd have thought it was a house we liked but didn't live in. Each evening I would report on the people who'd trooped in and out at all hours and while Jim didn't appear as avid as before, his questions did assume a set pattern. Who was here today? What were they like? Were they people of taste?

I'd sort them out: "Mm-m, yes, I guess so."

"They better be!" Jim would bluster. "Couldn't have this place cluttered up with lousy furniture."

One evening I told of an attractive youngish woman who'd been there.

"Chic," I said. "Plenty of dough."

"What name?" Jim asked.

"Didn't get it," I said. "All I know is she was blond and smart and well-heeled."

"Oh—and did she like the place?"

"Yes, a lot. Only she wanted a smaller one. Just for weekends. She lives in town."

"Yes," Jim said.

It never for an instant occurred to me to analyze that "yes."

This was the spring that I first began to truly see growing things. It was scarcely believable that all other springs had held such breath-taking loveliness. I'd read of carpets of wild flowers and here right under our own trees was such a carpet, gloriously patterned and so continuous that a single step would crush a dozen blooms.

And birds. Hundreds and hundreds of birds which surely must have nested in these trees for generations. And rabbits, squirrels, chipmunks; I spent hours feeding baby squirrels and baby chips, the foolish creatures which knew no better than to trust a human. I would sit on the terrace, grinning like crazy—oh, this had getting drunk strapped to the mast! Then I'd stop grinning to peer over a shoulder, hoping no one had caught me. The façade of Liz had crumbled but no one must know, no one must think her a sanctimonious old so-and-so.

One Sunday after church Jim called from the driveway.

"How'd you like to take a short ride, Liz?"

It had been a long time since he'd invited me to do anything and my spirits rose. "I'd love it," I called back.

The ride was very short, about ten miles.

"What are we seeing?" I asked. "Something special?"

"A new house," he answered. "Isn't even finished. I went by it the other day and thought you might like it."

My heart sang. Was he, could he be thinking of a new house for us? A house free of bitter memories, in which we might begin again? Oh, if it is so, *thank* You. There are other jobs I'd rather do but I believe You want this marriage righted, so—thank You!

It was a darling house at the tip of a wooded lane. In many respects, except for being all on one floor, it was a miniature of our own house. Huge windows and a huge fireplace.

"Oh, Jim, it's sweet!" I said.

He grinned. "Really think so? How should it be decorated? What colors would you use?"

I ran from room to room. There were only four. Two bedrooms, a roomy kitchen and a large living room. Even I could learn to keep this snug!

"Oh, I'd do every bit of it in different shades of yellow," I told him. "From deepest chrome to palest jonquil—"

"Yellow, eh?"

"Yes, like spring. And the draperies everywhere—throughout —a deep evergreen, like our spruce; rough silk perhaps. Yes, rough silk. And no carpeting. Just throw rugs of brown, earth-brown. And upholstery in browns and greens with hardly any pattern; soft plaids and heather mixtures. Oh, it would be sweet, completely sweet!"

On the drive home we were so almost gay that I dared to tell about baby squirrels and baby chips.

"Call me St. Liz if you like," I said.

No further reference was made to the little house and I understood. If I were patient this would come later. What Jim did say was even more wonderful. He said: "Nobody can ever tell me there isn't a God. Not after the change in you, Liz."

CHAPTER SEVENTEEN

The next anyone heard of the dear little house on the wooded lane, it had been decorated to accord with my most minute suggestion and was being occupied by Jim and his new wife. This is one woman I did want very much to see and never have seen unless she happens to be youngish and blond and chic and have plenty of dough. Some years ago it required the Lord God Himself to prevent me from searching her out and mopping up Westchester with her. Now I merely wish the lady well and trust she likes yellow.

The handwriting on the wall must have been titanic, I imagine, for anyone whose perspective had not been addled by past successes. What's more, the alcoholic, dry or drunk, is a congenital ostrich, so there was Liz, praying her head off, notwithstanding refusals to give her another chance, notwithstanding her home being up for sale. What if it did sell, need this mean that the marriage was washed up? There were other houses, weren't there? The cute little one with the four rooms, for instance.

And God was in on this. And God could do anything, couldn't He?

He could and did. He does indeed work in mysterious ways.

His course of action turned out to be diametrically opposite to mine; not that my plan wasn't good, it was. It was the timing that was off. There's a point beyond which nothing can be salvaged.

When Sue and Tony Webb decided to move to California, I never for one moment dreamt how soon I would be following. In June my son Pete completed the term at Yale and rushed home. He had covered himself with B pluses, head man in his class; a prime example of a person functioning at top potential once God moves in to direct the show. The result was fantastic to others but Pete and I knew the answer.

He was tired, however, and restless; the offshoots of the soldier's wanderlust. A classmate had asked him to Denver for a month and that would be great, wouldn't it? Si would stake him if it was all right with me and then maybe later—

"Of course, lamb," I said. "Go ahead. You don't have to sell me."

Gosh, Mom, that was wonderful. I was a good kid. And he honestly did have a scheme for later on. Later perhaps he and I could—but never mind, he'd write. Here was the Denver address. And stick to the rock pile, Mom. You're doing swell!

Louise Patton from up the road drove along to the airport with us. On the way she asked Pete if he didn't think the change in me was remarkable.

"Well, no. Can't say I do," he answered. "You see, it wouldn't seem so remarkable to me because I've always known what she was like inside."

I have had three compliments in my life which I value above all others. This was one of them. The other two were almost identical in implication although the people who paid them were about as far apart socially as people can get. One was from a fisherman at Nantucket, a salty whippersnapper of a man. "I guess you're 'bout the commonest woman I ever seed," he said. The third came from a long-time admirer, a most sophisticated gent, a polo player named McKnight Follansbee. On my left shoulder I carry a jagged scar, the aftermath of being tossed from a horse. Mac's contribution to my favorite sayings was paid at a dinner party where I had on a strapless dress and where the dame next to him remarked: "What a shame Liz has such a *conspicuous* scar." Mac's answer was: "Knowing Liz, I'll bet she regrets she doesn't have one on her right shoulder to match it."

Nice. But naturally Pete's was the nicest.

The rest of June and most of July passed in reading, in prayer and in foolish hope. Outwardly life looked the same; parties, summer theater, polo games. We, the Hatches, gave a fancy whingding at the country club for the dear departing Webbs, and the cost pained my conscience as greatly as the smile of sobriety pained my face.

Outside of God and Gordon Rogers I found only one group which truly approved of me: bartenders. Though a bartender be a drunk himself he will dote on the dry alcoholic, respecting him, guarding him from the fervor of the sopping wet. My bartender pals would bust my nose before they'd permit me the tiniest sniff of beer.

My scintillating new bar routine went like this: "Hi, Nick, how goes it? A Horse's Neck, please—without."

And always Nick and Co. beamed. "Still on it, eh? Thatta girl. Say, Mrs. Hatch, you oughta talk to Mrs. So-and-so. She's hittin' it kinda hard; couldn't you give her the word?"

God forbid, was this to be my life work? A sort of swanky Carrie Nation? Surely God had better plans for me than that! Not that it wasn't worth while and not that I, Liz, was worth better but, suffering cow, must I be a mere Follower-Upper *all* my days?

Singularly rewarding however were Mrs. So-and-so's frequent cornering of me in the Women's Locker and Mr. So-and-so's whispered questions on the dance floor. These sessions were elaborately secretive, proving, to my surprise, how vital is the anonymous in Alcoholics Anonymous. My own approach had been so opposite, so completely positive that everyone knew I was a drunk even better than I knew it. Secretive as it was, however, I was able to drop a word here, a word there, concerning the Power which had made me stop, the Christ risen in me attempting to get through to the Christ arising in them. More often though we'd bogged down in this: "God, you've got guts, Liz—wish I had your character!"

For some reason they appeared to have to hand me the credit rather than God to Whom it belonged. That was, and is, a stumbling block. People prefer whatever guts you show to be your guts, not God's, your strength, not God's. It's less trouble, I suppose, to picture a Liz Hatch altering her own way of life than to go to the bother of investigating the Almighty. To admire a fellow human requires mere sportsmanship whereas to admire God requires humility.

Pete's project for the remainder of vacation arrived airmail toward the end of July. He still had a yen to go places and while this was only a proposal, mind you, why couldn't the two of us join up in Texas and make a tour of Mexico?

"—and think of the help you'd be in Mexico, Mom, after having been there so often. I can fly to Laredo and you drive down; we'd really need a car."

Dropping the letter on my lap, I wondered if I could take going back to Mexico where Jim and I—where a part of us, perhaps an imaginary part, had drawn its last breath. And then I thought of how, in marrying Jim, I had failed my son Alan, and must not fail my son Pete. The everlasting problem of divorce; the offspring of a former marriage versus the husband of the present marriage. Choosing between responsibilities was foreign to me. Wouldn't it be AWOL to ditch the situation with Jim or was this flattering myself? Above all, what would God want?

I decided to put it up to Gordon Rogers.

"Of course it would be wonderful to go off alone with Pete," I told him, "but, Gordon, wouldn't it be unfair to Jim?"

He fairly bristled. In retrospect it occurs to me to wonder if Gordon in his sheltered corner had heard rumors that were not to hit me for several months.

"Indeed it would not be unfair," he stated flatly. "Jim Hatch isn't the only person on earth. You owe a debt to others too. What about all those years Pete was overseas?"

(And Alan. What about all those years that were owed Alan, and might not ever be repaid?)

I sighed. "Yes, but, Gordon, isn't Jim the job God wants me to stick to now? The first time we talked, you said—"

"I remember," he broke in, "and that's exactly what you've been doing. For heaven's sake, Liz, no one's obligation to God is confined solely to a single individual! You're ready for expansion. Go try your wings."

I hooted. "What wings, your Reverence?"

He laughed his lovely laugh. "The ones you keep bound down with haircloth. Go, Liz. It'll enlarge your viewpoint."

Jim had no objections. Not only did he not mind being left alone, this would give him the opportunity to run out to Kansas to see his mother.

In speaking of Mexico I know that both of us were forcing our minds to keep off Acapulco, to keep out any memory of the man and woman who had seemed to find love there.

"Well, try and miss me," I cracked. "We'll be back early in September."

"Sure," he said.

I love motoring alone. Quite modestly I am the most magnificent of drivers and the roads south of the Deep South are great for going. Get shed of Arkansas, and the highways are broad bands stretching before you, all straight, all yours.

I'd traveled it several times but never by myself and always with the curious notion that this world was my world. Now that it was the Father's, yea, even Texas, it was wondrously new. Little by little I found myself released from Jim, found myself handing the sorrow of my son Alan over into the keeping of the One Whose son he really was.

Gordon's words: "Go try your wings," fitted themselves to the tune of the motor. Go try, go try, go try your wings. Go try—reach for the treetops, you fumbling Christian! Did not Christ say: "Freely you have received, freely give?" He sure did. So hand me a victim and I too would freely give—

And lo, about a hundred miles below San Antonio there arose a victim, as fine a specimen as you'd hope to see.

Route 81 to the border is essentially townless, going on and on, bisecting vast wastes of nothing. The convertible top down, the self-made wind howling, I was by myself in God's world when suddenly, far ahead, I saw a tiny speck. Too tiny to be a car, it could be an animal or it just might be a human. If so, what a perfect opportunity!

It was a human. A plodding Mexican, old and bent double under a canvas-wrapped load as weighty as himself. The tiny guy must have been to market in San Antonio which meant days of trudging in the blistering sun with still no town in sight! Ah, what a chance for Christian brotherhood.

Singing *Sweet Adeline* at the top of my lungs, I over-calculated the distance and roared past the man. Backing up, I overcalculated and roared past him. Finally I jerked abreast, yanked the brake and beamed like an angel.

"Hi!" I cried.

No response. Under a brief gray and red serape, the figure stood stock-still, an alerted stillness like that of a wild animal cornered. The wizened face below the straw sombrero was the face of an ancient monkey, woeful, suspicious, prewarned.

I tried again, this time in my best Spanish: "*Buenos dias, señor.*"

238

Scraggly chin whiskers vibrated slightly and this was all.

Furious at not knowing words for Come on, pal, get in, I'll take you where you're going, I substituted frenzied enthusiasm. Jumping out, I tore around to open the car door. I pointed to the wide seat, crying: "For you, please—*por usted, favor!*"

Black-button eyes flicked mine and never since the world began was anyone less eager to receive what someone had determined to freely give. Who are you, you indecent woman in man's pants? the eyes asked.

Unaware that my attitude was typical of the old-time meddling missionary, I decided he didn't know what was best for him and went into action. I laid hold of the pack, slid it over his head, thereby dislodging the straw sombrero. Having dumped the burden onto the back seat, I picked up the hat, shook out the sand and cried again: "*Por favor, señor.*"

He turned to eye the pack. It represented only the Good Lord knew how many hours of toil and barter, and where it went, he went. There could be no hope of competing with this grinning, shoving, babbling creature. He gave up and let himself be pushed inside.

I had him now; there are no door handles on a Continental. I shifted gears and the car leapt through first to overdrive. Sand flew, wind screamed and my Christian Obligation settled down to anguish, the wiry prehensile hands clutching at the leather seat. From mile to mile I would turn to beam on him but in time, some of his anguish infected me. The good deed was backfiring. One more of those favors that are not favors.

I slowed down. How about a round of entertainment? The radio, the buttons which run the windows up and down, the cigarette lighter. I went through my repertoire and drew a blank. He accepted a lighted cigarette; the rest was wasted talent.

A fantastic thought hit me; suppose I'd long passed his destination? Suppose a faint, unnoticed trail, ten miles back, had led across the desert to a wisp of smoke that marked his home?

Home; what was the word for home? *Casa* was house; try *casa!* Flinging wide a long brown arm, I swept the desert.

"*Casa?*" I yelled.

His sole response was to duck the arm in abject terror.

Okey, *casa* was out; try town; the word for town was *poblado*. Roads below the border carry signs, POBLADO PROXIMO, which means you are coming to a town.

"*Señor—señor! Poblado proximo?*" I yelled.

Nary a twitch of the chin whiskers.

Panic clutched me. The budding Christian was fouled up. The situation had run the gamut from intended kindness to pathos to the ridiculous and now it had become nightmarish. In my desire to share was I intended to share forever and forever? There were no towns in sight, no cars to hail. Nothing but sand and sky and sun and him and me.

Squinting into space I prayed for help.

Rounding a bend I found a parked car.

I know it sounds as if I believe God parked that car for my especial benefit. And indeed He could have but as it turned out I guess He didn't. Of instant comfort was the sight of the Texas license plate; everybody in Texas spoke Spanish. The three men who were changing the tire would be able to clear up the predicament between me and my silent partner.

I called to them: "Am I glad to see you! My pal here thinks he's kidnapped. You speak Spanish, don't you?"

The men were delighted with us. They admired the car, examined us and said: "No. Can he speak French?"

French, bless Pat!

"No, of course not," I said. "Can you?"

"No," they chorused.

So it was a nightmare.

I thanked the linguists, waved goodbye and started off.

I now got down to business and prayed in earnest. Had this been a whim, it would have been a simple matter to dump the sorry figure, to assure myself that I was Liz, the bountiful, and if the object of such bounty was not bowed down with gratitude, he should be. This was not a whim however. Cock-eyed, yes, but not a whim. Except for the encounter being a chance one, my act had stemmed from a sincere, though un-considered, wish to share the love wherewith I was being loved. It had been meant as a mustard seed of kindness and surely mankind was choked for lack of kindness.

Praying silently I began by informing God, the Father, of a fact He already knew:

"Father, I am a sap. Instead of helping You, I'm harming You! Now—I don't ask You to break any laws, but if it's right, will you get me out of this? Thank You. Amen."

I felt better. I offered the little man another cigarette. A claw reached up to take it.

"*Poblado proximo?*" I persisted feebly.

And there on our right, halfway up a rise, was a road sign in English with below in Spanish, POBLADO PROXIMO.

Boy, what service!

The *poblado* was scarcely a *poblado*: a combination gas station and general store, a few rakish shacks. And not an American to be seen. Clusters of Mexicans squatted or stood about, laughing, gesticulating, talking. The arrival of a car was a big deal; they accorded it impressive consideration.

A teen-age boy ran out. "Gas, lady?" he said.

Then he spied my passenger and stopped dead. His eyes popped and his mouth was a big O. The others were seeing him too and as word spread, they edged forward step by step, shyly yet doggedly. In less than a minute the car was semi-circled by rows of dark faces, three deep, gazing from me to my friend and back again.

"Gas, yes!" I hurried to say. "But, boy—oh, *please* don't let him out!"

The little man had one leg over the door and was scrambling for his pack. Throwing out an arm I pinned him back and could feel the body shiver in outrage.

I cried to the boy: "Oh, please—I, I want you to—to *tell* him something—"

It was now or never. There was barely a moment in which to hope to quiet the hate I had felt surge up in him. And then —all at once the answer came. An answer so distinct and true that my arm dropped and I could relax.

"Tell him," I said, "tell him I picked him up because I love Christ."

You could have heard a baby sigh. Here and there black eyes rounded in partial enlightenment. Finally from man to man, from woman to woman, there sped a murmur. The word *Cristo, El Cristo*, was breathed wonderingly to be passed on with lingering tenderness.

The boy blinked. He drew closer and, gradually, very gradually, his astonished mind believed me. He ran around to the other side to speak to the little man, and the bystanders listened and gradually they too believed.

Because it was the truth, it was believed. I saw this and waited, deeply grateful. I could also see that now it had become important to the others that the old man should believe. We watched him, all of us, watched the meaning penetrate, the whiskers quiver, the jaw drop.

"*El Cristo*," he murmured. "*Por—por El—Cristo*."

Si, that was right, we nodded; for the Christ!

I reached to push the right door button. The door flew wide; the way was free. Motioning to the pack, I asked the boy to take it; the man did live here, didn't he?

Yes, lady. The old one lived here, in the brush a mile or so.

Still the old one had not looked at me. He stood dazed, attempting to fit the words to the memory of that wretched ride. It appeared that he would take his pack and go away and all I would ever know was that while I had not made things better, happily I had not made them worse.

But, no, the head was turning toward me. The monkey eyes were bright with tears.

Softly, most softly, he said: "*Gracias. Mil gracias, amiga mia.*"

He had thanked me. He had called me—*friend.*

My heart trembled. Here again the Lonely Man had come down to rescue a poor blundering fool. Once more I had fallen flat and gotten up.

Seeing Mexico with Pete, from Pete's point of view, was a wholly new experience. The change in me, however, in what interested me, accounted for most of the difference. What price night clubs when you're sober? When you can see the entertainers' dirty necks and count the cost of rotgut and remember all the years of weary, wasted nights? It is a feeling having no resemblance to disapproval. It's boredom, pure excruciating boredom.

Churches had taken the place of bars. From great cathedrals with golden altars and marble saints to moldy village churches with dilapidated plaster altars, their huge doll-saints stuffed with sawdust and costumed by J. C. Penney. Either too grand or too garish, yet none to be spurned because of the near to tangible reverence of the worshippers. God is fearsome and at the same time, Friend.

The tremendous difference between the Latin God and the Anglo-Saxon God seems to me to be epitomized by the Latin farewell and the Anglo-Saxon farewell. "Go with God," they say. "Take care of yourself," we say.

Pete and I were doing mostly three-night stands. Like his grandpa, Sam, Pete was relentless about going everywhere, seeing everything. After a month I rebelled.

"Can't we take a week off?" I begged. "I'm pooped. They say Orizaba is gorgeous. I've never been there."

Old Pete scanned the guidebooks on Orizaba.

"Maybe," he said.

"No, *please*. It has the highest mountains rising from the deepest jungle; snowcaps to orchids. And, oh yes, a swimming pool with gardenias floating on top. Fresh ones every morn. They tell me one man doesn't do a thing all day but rake out the bruised gardenias. That's what I choose for my next incarnation; I want to be a bruised-gardenia-raker."

My son's reply showed more interest in reincarnation than in Orizaba. "Say, Mom, what about this coming-back business? Do you believe it?"

What a big question to ask so new a Christian! But I swallowed and said: "You know, Pete, I'm beginning to think of this life as a sort of whistle stop in the immense circle of eternity. We climb off and we climb on and the choices we make here, for better or for worse, are what decide the next round, for better or for worse. Cause and result. Action and reaction. This isn't new and it isn't profound, but how else can you account for my great opportunities and Jane Doakes' lack of them? It sure isn't luck. God doesn't operate on luck; is it called luck when one tree bears fruit and another doesn't —the heck it is! It's work and care, *cultivation*. While I'd be the first to agree that it's impossible to imagine my earning anything but a good sock in the jaw, still, who knows? Maybe I was a respectable, hard-working Jane the last time around!"

"You've had a sock or two," Pete suggested.

"Yeah. And *given* more. Both you and Gordon tell me I blame myself too hard, well, I don't think so. Blame should be based on whether you knew better or didn't know better, and boy, I knew better! Oh, Pete, think if I had died before I woke. Think if I'd arrived at the next chapter, drugged— Not that I won't get it anyhow; 'to him who has not,' *not used fully what he has*, 'will be taken away even that which he has'!"

A broad grin stretched his mouth.

"I can't get used to you, quoting Scripture," he said.

I snorted. "You better grin when you say that! I don't like being classed with Scripture Quoters."

"But you are one—"

"No, no. What I'm doing or trying to, is find out what all those words mean to me. Just to me. Then learn to apply them, just to me. Not to you, to anybody, just me."

"Well, aren't all Scripture quoters—?"

"No, sir. Not from where I sit. The Scripture Quoter, by and large, is the Spiritual Quiz Kid. The Professional Christian, showing off. He's jelled in Thee's and Thou's. He believes God spoke to Gutenberg in fourteen hundred and something and hasn't been heard from since. Does he give a hoot what God says today? He does not. All he gives a hoot for is pinning somebody to a wall and mumbling: 'First Thessalonians 5:17.' For cat's sake, memorizing the Bible isn't being a Christian! Repeating what Paul said, *even what Jesus said*, doesn't amount to a hill of beans unless the repeater truly applies these words to living here and now, *today*. How about the kids who tear around predicting the end of the world in quotes—well, they're all wet because Jesus Himself said: 'No—man—knows.' "

He started to speak and I raced on: "It is—it's got to be hypocrisy to believe you're one of the few who know all about God! I find I only like seekers, those who are forever seeking. The rest, the ones who've found and settled, and the ones who don't look at all, I do not like. I can see I'll have to learn to love them but I'll never like them."

"God's angry woman," was Pete's comment.

"Yes, and I better stop that too. What I won't stop is, detesting hypocrisy!"

"All right," he agreed. "But watch it that while you're detesting hypocrisy, you're not detesting the hypocrites along with it."

"It's going to be rough," I said.

CHAPTER EIGHTEEN

Orizaba, beside the gardenia-laden pool, was where I first heard what Pete had determined to do with his life. My life was teetering on a tightrope but not that of my son. One handsome afternoon about the middle of our stay we stood talking to a native boy who was holding a baby jaguar he'd found in a nearby jungle. The creature was all head with flecked green eyes and soft scraggly fur. I'd asked if I might take it and was rubbing a velvet ear when, behind us, an expensive Oxford accent commented: "If he were any older, that would not be safe."

It seemed an obvious comment; notwithstanding we turned and smiled politely. A few feet away, on a chaise longue, sat a large man in the late seventies, a most impressive figure in a handmade suit of black broadcloth. His shirt was hand-loomed linen and on his left hand I saw the ring of a Prince of Rome. It was the head however which was the most distinguished feature, a great leonine head with masses of snow-white hair.

Responding to our smiles he took a gold-headed cane and tapped a foot in its fine glove leather. "See how swollen this is?" he said. "It was caused by a leopard bite on a safari many years ago."

I made my eyebrows climb. "Not really!" I exclaimed.

This was all he needed. He moistened his lips in anticipation of fresh audience and proceeded to recount the experience in that amused, belittling fashion used by sophisticates the world over. Leopard bites? Ah, one expected such trifles, don't you know? As he talked I examined him, realizing that the elegant old gent was very lonely. Eager for company, he like the rest of us was willing to pay by being interesting. The costly aura added pathos; so often the best upholstered are the loneliest.

On an impulse I handed the jaguar back to the boy, took Pete's arm and strolled over to the man. I introduced us; I was Elizabeth Hatch and this was my son, Peter Addams.

At this moment there appeared from nowhere a manservant in black silk alpaca. Bowing decorously he addressed the personage as "Your Royal Highness," anointing the phrase in oil. What else was said could not be overheard but this one phrase ably accounted for both the aura and the loneliness. How doleful to be an H.R.H. in an era when nobody gives a damn.

The servant vanished and H.R.H. returned to us commoners. He asked our indulgence for not rising; the foot, don't you know? But would we not be seated? And the names, would I be good enough to repeat our names?

I was good enough. I repeated them and clearly saw the name Hatch bounce on the tiled terrace. The name Addams did better.

"Addams," he mused. "Ah, yes, the name of my investment banker. Silas Addams of New York."

Ah, yes, Silas Addams, the all-wool boy turned senior partner of one of the largest and finest brokerage houses. Si, the fog; the one husband I could have loved had I known then what I knew now, had I forgotten myself sufficiently to care to penetrate the fog. Si, the father of the dedicated Peter. Was son like father? Yes, he was like both of us, the best of both of us; the cream. In Pete, Si's dedication to business and mine to self, identical compulsions, had been rechanneled to help mankind.

Smiling somewhat smugly, I said: "Then it may interest you to learn that this young man is the son of Silas Addams."

It did indeed interest him. The worldly eyes creased with childish pleasure. Like me, the Royal So-and-so enjoyed coincidences.

"So. So you are the son of Silas Addams, well, well. And are you in the university, Peter?"

"Yale, sir," Pete told him.

"Ah, Yale. And later, will you enter your father's firm?"

I was sure this was far from Pete's plan so I waited with intense interest.

"No, sir," he replied.

"No? What will you do?"

Pete did not even glance in my direction as he said: "I will go into the ministry, sir."

The ministry! A son of mine a minister.

I hung on to keep from falling off the chair.

Then, as the thought deepened and caught fire, as it linked itself to the everlasting chain of man's service to God, my heart leapt. My son, marching behind, and with, and before those other fishermen, my son leaving his richly prepared nets to go in search of men!

Oh, Father, Father, my heart cried, now I see what it means to have a cup run over.

A weary sigh escaped His Tired Old Highness. The great head had fallen back upon a cushion. The bored eyes closed while the Oxford accent drawled: "Lad, if you had lived in all the countries I have lived in and known all the people I have known, I doubt whether you would feel humanity was worth this sacrifice."

A year ago it might be I'd have agreed, but now I wanted

to strike out at the handsome cynical features. What answer would Pete make? How could a boy brought up to mind his manners rebuke a man fifty years his senior?

Father, *show* him, I prayed.

Already Pete was answering. "Well, sir, Jesus Christ didn't feel that way," he said.

Spoken in complete courtesy, it was the squelch supreme. Not even His Royal Highness cared to go on record as contradicting the Son of God.

Our drive home, interrupted by Pete's insatiable curiosity, took longer than we'd planned. Our arrival in Westchester left barely four days till college opened; a frantic rush. Laundry, dry cleaning, buttons off: "Gee, Mom, it looks funny to see you sew—hey, where's my tennis racket?"

My baseball mitt? My Bible? My new gray flannels?

"Hey, Mom, did you swipe my *Screwtape Letters?*" (It was the other way around; Pete had relieved me of most of my C. S. Lewis and several other religious finds.)

Jim seemed as usual. I cannot put a finger on one single flaw in his behavior which might have tipped me off except possibly an excessive friendliness. He actually seemed pleased to have me back and I guess he was, though not for the reason I supposed. In a manner close to gaiety, he would kid Pete in English with Spanish endings. He asked all the proper questions about Orizaba, about Mexico's summer climate, particularly about Nacho; how was *el Nacho? El Nacho*, I regretted to report, had been away. Off somewhere in South America piloting a plane for someone who had something to do with gold mines.

"He'll steal 'em," Jim laughed.

This wasn't Jim, the husband, the hoped-for friend. This was James Culpepper Hatch, surgeon, in the process of softening the victim. The scalpel was about to fall. Numb the victim with sedatives, it deadens his awareness and thereby makes him easier to handle. The technique was one he used daily in the hospital. Catch the victim napping, off guard.

And she is, too! No woman was ever more off guard than I the night Jim brought home the papers to be signed.

This was the evening of the day Pete left for New Haven. Jim had said he wouldn't be home till after dinner so I ate alone and went out onto the terrace. The air had a touch of fall in it; a lovely evening, so peaceful after Mexico. The very birds were quieter than Mexican birds. By the time Jim's car came up the driveway, it was dark. I remember calling to him as he switched on the living-room lamps.

"I'm out here," I called. "It's heavenly."

I could see him standing in the light of the tall pewter lamps on the refectory table. As I sat there, smiling, my one thought was, What a relief it must be to find a wife sober rather than in her former condition. The thought was in no way self-righteous. It wasn't anything but grateful. If I'd grown up some, it had been a gift and there wasn't any doubt as to the Giver.

I had expected Jim to join me, instead he said: "Come in, will you? I want your signature."

His raised voice carried a brusque tone. Recognizing this, I yawned, got up and went inside. The light made my eyes squint and as I rubbed them, I saw him staring at me oddly as though he hadn't seen me in a long time.

"God, you look wonderful," he said, "brown as mahogany."

I smiled within myself. God was right! His sun tan outside; His peace inside. A deep peace filled me and almost immediately there was need of it for Jim was holding out a sheaf of papers and an uncapped pen.

"Here, sign these," he said.

I yawned. "Sure. What are they?"

"The deed to the property. In triplicate."

It will be hard to believe that his manner did not register

but it did not. That Jim was referring to the room in which we stood, to the tall trees, to the sweep of meadowland, did not cross my mind. I took the papers and the pen and went over to the desk. I pushed a lamp button and sat down.

"What property?" I asked.

Before anyone could have said: "Oh, my broken life!" I learned in no uncertain terms what property he was referring to.

"For the love of Christ, *this* property! *This*. It's been for sale, hasn't it? Well, by God, *it's finally sold*. Sign where the red checks are. Don't bother to read the crap. Just sign."

When you don't want to believe something, you don't believe it. At least not until it's been rammed down your throat. So even now I didn't understand. I understood the actual words but their meaning didn't seem reasonable. How could a sheaf of papers take a home from those who'd built it and transfer it, in the scribble of a pen, to some stranger?

Possibly it was not entirely conceit and wishful thinking which were numbing me. Possibly God's mercy had a hand in this for I recall laughing. An airy social laugh.

"Why, James, you astonish me," I said. "I didn't know you ever felt that anything that involved money could be crap."

Here was a hangover of the habit of phony lightheartedness. A stall too. A futile instinctive stall; the mechanism of escape taking over, doing what had been asked of it so many years. In every life there comes some one circumstance which the mind refuses to admit. And I believe that always this concerns a death, a death of sorts; death of a body, a nation, a relationship, a soul, a habit. What was occurring here was the mortal blow to the pride of one Liz Hatch.

My pride was and continues to be clever, tortuous, devious. A pride compounded by a terribly ingrained need to prove, especially to myself, that I am a person of greater worth than

I truly know myself to be. It was always far more essential for me to win out than for those other blessed ones, like Silas, who are able to accept themselves for what they are, big or small. The junkman may well respect his self and the king despise his self, depending upon individual acceptance.

Up till this very moment, I do not believe I had honestly thought that Jim Hatch would deny me the chance to revamp our marriage. No one ever had denied me. In addition there was now my certain belief that this was God's will for us, for all broken marriages. Close to a year had been spent praying for insight and strength, daily, often hourly prayers, so was it credible that I should be denied? This was the one, the only course, I'd been able to visualize as being acceptable to the Father.

I remained at the desk. Knowing I had lost, I sat there, stunned, refusing to admit it, sidestepping the inevitable. A hammock, swinging jerkily between two ways of life, the way of self and the way of self-surrender. The way of self was admittedly for the dump heap and yet if the way of self-surrender did not include life with Jim, a new, decent, useful life, then whatever it was to be was inconceivable.

A young, young Christian this; unused to God's slow plans.

Unconsciously my fingers were turning the pages, in triplicate, of the death warrant to my pride. The fingers shook and the pages rattled and the red checks danced. Except for the rattle of the paper the room was still, as still as though I were by myself. Into this stillness there popped the memory of an item I'd read lately. It seemed that the ancient Greeks didn't have street flares; each man supplied his own light by affixing tiny lamps to the toes of his shoes. These tiny lamps shed light three feet ahead so when he'd walked three feet, there was light for three more feet. And so on. Three feet, then three more feet.

I waited, allowing the shaking hands to rest on the desk.

I waited for light for the next three feet and while the waiting was revolutionary in anyone so self-willed, I did not have any special sense of the Presence of the Father. He must have been there because, slowly, very slowly, I did realize that I was being *willed*; not *what* to do, what *not* to do. I was being willed not to undo what the past ten months had done. The fact of my continuing to sit there, dry-eyed and under control, was itself proof of what the past ten months had accomplished and this must not be tossed overboard.

At last my left hand took Jim's pen and forced my right thumb and right forefinger to grip it, to grip it so tight that the nails turned blue-white. Now the pen would write, now it could be made to write where the red checks were. And it did write. Line after line was signed, Elizabeth Burns Hatch, the signatures clear and decisive, pressed down for good measure. In signing there was some faint ray of comfort at having finally given up one of the many, many things I'd had and never earned. I hadn't earned this house because Jim had not been earned; Jim had been grabbed, and at great harm to others. This house was built on sand and the winds had come and blown it down.

There were no words to be said and for once I didn't say them. I put down the pen carefully and stood up, making my eyes ignore the room which had just been sold. Someone else was going to live here, someone whose name I hadn't even noticed.

I left the papers and went upstairs and closed my door. The room was dark but the terrace below and the trees that surrounded it were aglow from the living-room lights. I leaned against one of the four-posters and my mind left my body and traveled from room to room, visualizing their furnishings, superimposing their colors on the darkness. While my body stayed behind, my mind's eye conducted a tour.

Here was the room prepared for Alan. Very masculine, as

you could see; pine and green-brown plaids and moss-green carpeting. Of course Alan had never seen his room; Alan's scorn of the marriage embraced the house that had gone with the marriage.

And here was the lime-and-olive guest room. And here the lemon-yellow guest room, the one the Webbs liked so much, darling Sue and Tony who'd gone into tailspins at moving but who now were writing wildly joyful letters concerning one Sierra Madre, California.

And this was Pete's room. Here, ladies-and-gentlemen-of-the-tour, is the messy bedroom of that great Divine, the Right Reverend Peter Addams. (Oh blessed, blessed Pete—pray for me!)

Come now, we'll go below. Observe, please, the spiral staircase. Handwrought railings, fancy, eh? The hall, the library, the living room, see how beautifully they open up for cocktail parties. And come see what is jokingly called the servants' quarters. And the kitchen, formerly used for snitching drinks.

This, naturally, is the pantry, also excellent for snitching quickies. Into this pantry and out, has gone a variety of servants, long, short, black, white, yellow. There's one or two whose spirit is still here. Here, beside that sink, still stands a fine Negro butler named Jackson, up to here in silver, silver goblets, platters, service plates. He is objecting: "Too much polish. I wouldn't like to work for you-all if you get four-time married."

What memories crowd a house, especially when the winds come to blow it down! An awful solitude enveloped me. A relatively simple matter to repeople those other rooms, to check them off and back away and make my first farewell, but now I stood in the bedroom and here—Lord God, what memories! How deeply I hoped that the two who'd bought this house, if there were two, would come together here, would truly live in it. It was a room too large for one, too empty and too crowded.

A swift impulse made me whirl to confront the bed I leaned against. Shaking its posts, I defied its past inane importance.

"I'll get *rid* of you!" I cried out loud. "You, and the rest of the make-believe!"

This bed, this pair of beds, their slender fluted posts topped by canopies, had been designed for the virgin-bride and her first bridegroom. Then, being too elegant to discard, they had inherited each successive bridegroom; one woman and three men. The same woman but not, no, no, not the same man! All at once, this had become obscene.

What a mad assortment of passion these beds had witnessed; violence to frigid timidity to veiled indifference. Drunkenness, tears, suicide; what had they not witnessed!

Suicide. Now, why was it I had tried to take my life?

Let's see. What was—what could it have been that was so much more intolerable than the position I was now in? Oh, yes. It was—it was that the man downstairs had desired me in Mexico but not in Westchester. *Love of God, imagine it!*

See—see then, the change which God has wrought?

See? Any fool could see!

Now that the man downstairs did not and clearly never would desire me, I was amply capable of telling these three-marriage beds that they were obsolete, that the trappings of love are trappings, nothing else! Yes, a fool could see the change and the comforting knowledge of this made me begin at last to face, perhaps to accept a little, the blank wall I was up against.

I faced it out loud. I said. "You, you, Liz Hatch, who have never been rejected have been rejected. You."

"You have been—you have lost."

The words were reiterated. Stressed, dinned in, over and over: "You—have—lost."

"Yes—but wait, *wait!* You have lost, but you yourself are *not* lost. *Think.* Think again of what you were and what you are, not much, certainly, yet by comparison, a Mover of Mountains.

"Indeed you have lost! And have been found."

The pain of the castoff is bitter agonizing pain. Despite my continued and intense tutoring of self with words I knew to be true, great waves of pain swept me. My newly awakened soul, pummeled by the old and the new, was as yet a feeble thing to brace itself between the pull of self and the pull of God.

At last, dully, there seeped into me a faint but exquisite ecstasy. Slowly the ecstasy mounted, mounted and encircled and eventually cradled the pain. As I let go somewhat, I saw plainly that rejection such as this would, ten months ago, have been more terrible, far more terrible than death. While now it was extremely painful, the pain was wrapped in ecstasy.

Back and forth, the pain. Pain chopping down, amputating pride. I, Elizabeth, born Burns, was being cleansed; brought down, emptied, scrubbed raw, in order that one day I could be of service. These blasts of pain were wild winds which either one stands up to, exultant, or which knock one back into the dirt. In an immense way it was comparable to something known to me. As a pilot I knew that when you wish to rise, high, *high*, you slam straight into the fiercest wind. A force that was pride was beating at the craft that was Liz and ecstasy was the rudder.

A Voice said: "This is a cross."

"Yes," I said.

The Voice said: "It is yours. Pick it up."

"Yes," I said.

Each loss is a cross. The loss of Alan and now this, the loss of hope for what I'd believed God's plan for Jim and me, were crosses. Possibly arms of the same cross. And self-hewn, in part, at least. In my spare time, I had been a manufacturer of sorrow, for myself and others, and the result was a cross.

Life is a junkyard of crosses. There is no way to avoid crosses yet a thousand ways to avoid picking them up; to reach out and falter and fall and never rise; to lift up and grow weary and hand on to others; to sidestep, smiling brightly, insisting that life has no crosses, that no such woe exists, and if no such woe exists, why then, of course, the cross itself does not exist.

My cross existed. It was not imaginary; Jim Hatch had seen to that. It was real and lay before me. My only choice was whether to pick it up or not pick it up. My choice to accept or to reject. In choosing to accept it, I chose God. God in place of liquor. God in place of lies. God in place of fear. God in place of shame. God in place of waste. God in place of death. Truth, hope, peace, usefulness, life. I was going with the Father, the One Whom I knew now I had always sought. I was going along with Him. I, like the salmon, had labored tortuously upstream in a blind instinct for return to the Source.

There was no way of imagining where this might lead. Nor was there the slightest conception that I had gone a little nuts. As I look back on that loop-the-loop I see that my state was one of shock, and why not? There was the psychic shock of the suicide attempt, the overwhelming shock of a first-class sinner meeting up with her Maker, and the shock of Jim yanking my hopes out from under me. Instead of being dead, I was alive, instead of a drunken, selfish bitch, I was pretty darn well behaved, instead of having a husband and a home, I was out on my ear. Shock, you bet!

The truth is that, although I was indeed going with God, I was scared out of my wits. Three feet of light, yes, and beyond it, *darkness*; no markers at all. Jim was by way of being a stinker and not only this, he was totally fed up with me, the brand-new saint. Yet the brand-new saint appeared to prefer the stinker to wandering off into the Unknown.

Me, I was a marrying gal; I loved men, all men, and the

idiotic fact is that I was certain that from here in, I would be giving them up forever and ever, amen. How could I have dreamt that in giving them up, my life was to be jam-packed with them, that almost never was I to be without men and more men? Precisely as in giving up liquor I was to become intimately acquainted with Skid Row.

The Lord God invented humor, and keeps His best jokes to Himself.

CHAPTER NINETEEN

Surely God's sense of humor embraced those last weeks in the glass-walled house. It was as if the final scene of a grim tragedy has been mislaid or scrapped or perchance the playwright has slit his throat and Noel Coward is flown in to whip up a frothy substitute. The leads are the same, the set the same, but where are the black clouds, the rolling thunder? The beating of bosom? The piteous wails met by sullen silence?

They ain't. The day following the signing-of-the-papers, the curtain rises on light comedy where a male sophisticate and a female sophisticate arrange to part, at the same time managing to suggest a future get-together. The happy sequel or your money back. On some top shelf two ragged masks are located, dusted off and slid in place and presto, here are the crude but eager greenhorn from Kansas and the poised Society Dame. Two halves of a tired apple with only the core missing.

In attempting to evaluate the farce, I would guess that the male's reversion has stemmed from embarrassed relief; he'd expected a ruckus and there is none. Whereas the female's, well, this was a matter of holds barred. The female is involved with her Creator and her Creator's code, coupled with ignorance as to what her Creator really wants, forces her to accept what the male wants. Three weeks of double talk ensue. A ridiculous performance in which two supposed adults ignore the pay-off by the simple expedient of postponing it.

To give the female, Liz, a break, a thing I seldom do, I'll state that these antics are no plan of hers; she's fresh out of plans. Her old ones are no longer admissable and a new batch has not been stocked. The habit of God was a one-way telephone, to be used for listening only, and if opposing voices, opposing directions, cluttered the air waves, can you wonder? For the first time she too was in the role of novice. As God's greenhorn, she was unable to trust herself and so was trusting that Jim's talk of separation, "being alone for a year to think this out," might be according to some higher plan. It could be a parole, to end by saving her from striking out on her own.

Part of the joke was on Jim. He need not have been so cute, so wily, but then he knew what I did not know, that the separation was for keeps. How could he be certain that if I did know, I wouldn't take to the jug? Perhaps stage another suicide? Outwardly my behavior was good, but women are women. The angle which his clinical mind couldn't possibly have guessed is that the wrath of the woman scorned, though devastating, is mere spit on the bounding main compared to the downright thrill of a new-fledged self-respect.

It will come as a surprise to Jim that, with or without God, I'd have let him off the hook sooner had he had the sense to tell me about the "other woman." Pride is a gruesome guy yet like Achilles, he has his weak spot. The wife who won't admit that the husband in love with somebody else is a goner is a prime jackass. I've been a heap of nasty things in my day, a snit, a bitch, a drunk, a weeping-willow; but rarely, very rarely have I been an out-and-out jackass. Not where men are concerned.

Understand—if you can—the cross-rough I was caught in.

On the one hand was a banged-up marriage; on the other were my fear at having to stand on my own and my recent and very deep realization of marriage as a sacrament. My string of broken vows had been revalued and my fledgling soul was rocked. I who'd been so careful to make these vows before a minister—no J.P.'s for me!—saw now that "for better, for worse," meant for better and for worse.

Marrying someone was quite a bit more than escaping wall-flowerism. Quite a bit more than a chance to dump a bossy papa; quite a bit more than a Roman Holiday, a floor show, a green pasture. Marriage was a union sanctified by God and reaffirmed by His Son. So see what I did? I took fear and wrapped it up in Scripture as Christians have been doing, lo, these many centuries.

And Jim Hatch could have stopped it. All he needed to say was: "Look, Liz—" Instead he left the door open for me to stick my foot in, praying befuddled prayers, hoping befuddled hopes. Hope is long and hope is merciful; it can also end in a kick in the tail.

The kick came later, airmail. In the meanwhile, the finis was mugged to the hilt by two comedy characters and what a waste! What tension for Jim and his blond lady, what need-less hurt for me, dragged out through months of absurd dilly-dallying. It would have been a darn sight kinder to chop it off, kinder on us and on our public. For of course we had a public. Every man, woman and child we ever knew stood about open-mouthed and a few may have suspected the pay-off and again maybe nobody did. I wouldn't know nor does it matter. My own unsuspicion was a matter of past conceit plus fright divided by present faith plus an overestimation of Jim's hon-esty. I still confused rudeness with honesty. Jim was rude and ruthless therefore if there was another woman, he'd have said so. If he really wanted a divorce, why would he go to such lengths to concoct a separation?

261

In order to anticipate all questions as to where I was going to spend the "year's leave of absence," Jim reminded me how dearly I loved California; I dearly loved mountains, didn't I? I dearly loved the sea, dearly loved the climate and dearly loved the Webbs and as the Webbs were in California, ergo, California! He really wished he could be there himself.

"Then maybe you'll come after me?" I suggest.

He smiles. Why not? Stranger things have happened. In a year most anything can happen.

Now that the heroine's destination is set, the tempo of the comedy greatly accelerates. It's like a motion picture with the operator gone nuts. The heroine already feels that she is in two places at the same time; she's with the hero in West-chester but also she's in California about to be brought back to the place she never left. The heroine is agog at the prospect of being called for and escorted back to the place she never left. "Oh, Jim," she cries, "that will be heavenly! Darling, you won't forget me, will you?"

Forget her? The hero is shocked. Has anybody ever forgotten her?

She interrupts, wide-eyed: "I didn't mean me so much as the past year; you won't forget how nice it's been, how peaceful and—well, sober? Remember this, won't you, and not the ugly years?"

Why, certainly! Wasn't it human nature to remember the best? Especially when the best was the last?

"The last, Jim?"

The most recent.

Hook, line and sinker: "Why, of course, darling. Jim—where will you be while I'm in California?"

Why, that's right, by God, he hadn't told her, had he? And when he needed her advice so— He'd rented a place in town, a hole in the wall on West Eleventh and would she look it over? Perhaps fix up the dump?

"Jim, I'd just adore to," she cries, "but why a dump?" Well, for a year. She knew how men were. (She does indeed.)

"When the year's up," she hesitates, "Jim, when the year's up, where will we—?"

Now, they weren't going into that. That would come later —when would she like to inspect the hole in the wall?

Hook, line and sinker: "Oh, *any* time. The sooner, the better."

The answers to the public are now set.

"That's right, the house is sold. The sale clause said three weeks—gosh!" Three weeks in which to sort the trappings of three marriages. Three weeks in which to keep down hook, line and sinker, and keep on praying, believing, that sometime, somehow, three feet of light will come to mean light for Jim and Liz Hatch. Three weeks to make ready and then—go.

"That's right, Jim's rented a place on West Eleventh. Small, exactly right for one. Be sure you ask him for weekends, he'll miss the country terribly."

"That's right, I'm running out to California." *Running* made it sound soon over. And *running*, while not quite credible to the Christian Liz, had been part and parcel of the pagan, the B.C. Liz.

And Jim would probably fly out, then naturally they'd come home together—

"Home, Liz? Where are you going to live?"

This is one question the witness is not briefed on.

My mind flashes back to the picture of a child standing before me. His name is Peter and he is looking up at me, a raincoat in one hand, a ski boot in the other. "Sure, Mom," he says, "but where'll I *live?*" I hear myself say: "Why, you'll have two homes! *Two* instead of one." A black lie. No one, *no* one can have two *homes!* Houses by the dozen, yes, but only one home. Two homes mean no home!

(Alan, you had three "homes"; have you finally found one?

263

Oh, Alan, heavy, heavy you hang over my heart—take him, Father, *take Your son off my heart!*)

I turn to face my truly interested friend. "You know, at this point, I honestly don't know where I'll live." Or if, I might have added.

"But, Liz, your furniture! Your lovely things—"

Ah, here the ground is steadier. Here is one decision having to do with new values, a new way of life. This can be handled deftly.

"All to be sold," I announce. "Or given away. The works, outside of odds and ends, a painting or so, the Chia Ching bowls, the flat silver, this and that. You know."

Lining the wall stand carton after carton, barrel after barrel. Silver coffee urns, teapots, trays, vases, boxes, bowls; thirteen enormous cartons of silver to sell or give away. Barrels of porcelain; dozens and dozens of service plates, breakfast sets, luncheon sets, dinner sets. Barrels of crystal; goblets, wineglasses, cocktail glasses, cordial glasses, highball glasses. Cartons of blankets and blanket covers, satin puffs, monogrammed linen, bath towels the size of tents. Maids' uniforms, housemen's uniforms, butlers' livery. Custom-made lamps. Dozens upon dozens upon dozens of trappings, of paraphernalia to clutter the lives of the upholstered. And upstairs were the closets, row after row, hung with clothing, enough to dress an army of D.P.'s.

(Oh Father, Father, *I am ashamed.*)

"But, Liz, you aren't selling—?"

"I sure am. Or giving to the church to sell. My next house'll be so compact I can do the work myself—"

"For the rest of your *life?* Good God, oh, forgive me, good heavens! We thought this was a phase. Liz, you're crazy, communistic or something but—if you're really going through with it, how much for the refectory table?"

Oh. Oh, not the old refectory table! It's so—its Jacobean rungs grooved by the scuffing of countless monks.

And, oh, *not* the Queen Anne secretary. Nor the rosewood game table! Nor the carved breakfront nor the Sheraton desk with its history glued to a secret drawer. And not the walnut highboy nor the chubby maple lowboy nor the—dear God, hold me tight! This is another kind of death, *the death of material things.*

As soon as possible I drove into town to Jim's apartment and that first visit seemed almost illicit. We had arranged to meet between five and five-thirty at the converted brownstone, second floor back. He'd given me the keys, one for the street door, one for the apartment. When I let myself into the vestibule I caught myself peering over my shoulder, then treading lightly past closed doors, just like the old days. Jim and I were still together yet so apart that it had some of the feel of a *rendezvous* in a New York hideaway.

It was a hole in the wall all right. What was sad then is silly now; going to such lengths to prove celibacy when from past performance it had never entered my head to doubt Jim's celibacy. At any rate, the dark little rooms aroused my sympathies as I suppose they were supposed to do; oh dear—poor Jim. Here he'd be slaving in the city, while I had the whole state of California to enjoy!

An insult, this, to my intelligence? What intelligence? I swallowed it whole. I tracked down painters, hung draperies, scrubbed woodwork, robbed Gordon Rogers of furniture I'd promised the church thrift shop. I stocked the tiny kitchen, the tiny bath, the tiny linen closet. Gullible cluck, I even went so far as to make up the ostentatiously single bed.

Jim appeared to be quite unable to get his fill of my esteemed advice. The most fantastic sequence of those three weeks came toward the very end. To look back on it, it could not have happened but it most assuredly did. At the time it was funny as well as pathetic whereas now it's hilarious.

Late one night, the second from our last at the house, Jim

is down in the basement, I in my bedroom. Jim calls. I jump a foot.

I am in bed, reading. Holding a finger in John, the Beloved, I drop my battered Bible, its pages question-marked, written into, underlined. Often, after completing Jude and starting over—I skip Revelation; it scares me pink—I'm amazed to find certain question marks: What didn't I understand about this section? It's perfectly clear now. Others remain, something I still don't get.

Till lately, hours of every day have been spent reading, studying, translating words and incidences into today's living; Jesus said so and so about such and such; how can that be applied to my life? Always it is His love and sacrifice which overwhelm me, going on and on, giving, never taking! And those few, so few, who listened to Him—if He came today would I be one of the ones to stop and listen? Probably not.

These last weeks I have been staying close to John. His Jesus is the kindest, the gentlest, the easiest to know. I cannot let my heart be too troubled nor too afraid. All those books I've bought, stacked there against the wall, are great for new angles on old sayings but not many are good for bandaging the heart. John's Jesus says: "I will not leave you comfortless—"

Jim calls: "Liz, where are you?"

I hold tight as I have been doing. "In my room, Jim. Want me?"

Jim's clothing fills thirty feet of closet. It is as yet unpacked; suits and hundreds of ties hang on racks. I've wondered at this because the built-in bureaus are emptied of shirts and underwear. The shoes have gone to town but the hats are still here; Homburg, derby, porkpie, snap-brim, top hat, last summer's panama. Why? Why the demarcation? I find out!

Keeping a firm finger on John, I do what I am learning to do; I wait. Sit and wait. Should Jim want my advice, this is good, isn't it? Isn't any need for me a step toward whatever future the Father has in mind for us?

What Jim has in mind turns out to be a Fashion Show. It lasts two hours.

My door is ajar and in walks Jim, the country-club-Jim in tweeds, the porkpie at a jaunty angle. Back and forth he strides, the bare floor echoing hideously. He swaggers, he hesitates. His eyes are not cold, not arrogant now, they are young and questioning.

"Say, Liz, are these tweeds right? Do they fit? How about the hat?"

"Well, Jim, I'm really not too crazy for porkpies—"

The porkpie zooms across the room, discarded.

He exits. He enters.

"Say, Liz, how about this pin-stripe?"

This Oxford gray? This gabardine? This cashmere? This hound's tooth? This check? This plaid? This herringbone?

"God's sake, check the ties, will you, Liz? Throw out the ones there's any doubt about."

And morning coat and tails and Chesterfield and polo coats? And topcoats and overcoats and sport coats, trench coats, raincoats? And piles of sweaters? And slacks upon slacks upon slacks?

Special strides appear to go with special outfits. The successful surgeon of distinction steps out briskly, head slightly to one side. The sportsman swaggers. The opera escort, or escort to El Morocco, saunters nonchalantly. Man about town, about country, about where-have-you; the custom-made kid from Kansas.

Inside me spirals of laughter rise to be choked back. Humor often gets the truth before the brain grasps it, grasps the picture of a male running from a female, being certain to run in the costume she assures him is correct for running. Oh, yes, she does!

Long ere now I have entered in completely. For instance, the striped tie with the checked suit—*better catch that:*

"Jim, don't you think a plain tie with checks?"

"Sure. Goddammit, I *know* that. I keep forgetting; knit for winter, silk for summer."

Perhaps I ought to have made a chart— "Well, more or less. And, sweetie, Tattersalls are a touch busy with figured materials. Save 'em for grays and dark blues, single-breasted."

"Say, that's right. Thanks."

All decisions are final. No matter what else can be said of the lady-about-to-be-bounced, her taste is unquestioned.

Gordon Rogers' poor are falling heir to heaps of finery. Here a dinner coat of too vivid a blue yet fine for a woman's suit; here an ulster too belligerently British yet fine to keep grandpa warm; here a chalk-stripe with too broad a stripe yet fine for some teen-age hotshot.

Here and here; thumbs up, thumbs down.

Jim is jubilant. Safe for one year at least. "God, Liz, thanks a million!" Wonder of wonders, Liz gets kissed, somewhere between the cheekbone and the collar of her bed jacket. And not only that, she's about to be further rewarded by a celebration, a last-minute send-off.

"Tell you what. The last night, Liz, we'll paint the town; 21, a show, night club, how 'bout it?"

Paint New York on coffee? Drape apprehensive nerves in smiles and snappy comebacks, those comebacks so forced nowadays but which Jim still admires? Drive back to the country alone in the wee small hours to get up bright and early for the Communion service Gordon is giving you for the very last time before you start for California?

"Wonderful, Jim. Shall we take off from your apartment? I could have cocktails ready for you. See you around five-thirty."

After the door is shut I sit concentrating on the long list

of items to be taken care of tomorrow, and tomorrow. This alone is real, this and the mass of luggage grouped about the room; case after case of pigskin in brown moiré covers. Wardrobes, hatboxes, shoe boxes, book bags, brown moiré dress bags, all with pigskin monograms. E.B.H., E.B.H. plastered everywhere with here and there an old piece marked E.B.A., A for Addams. Even one marked E.B.T., T for Trowbridge. Former dynasties. Former identities.

Why was I so mad for monograms? The chameleon, off with the past, on with the present; E.B.T., E.B.A. are dead, long live E.B.H.! Had initials been my sole identity? A preoccupation with symbols to be unstitched and thrown out as I'd attempted to throw out responsibilities?

I get out of bed and go into the bathroom. While I brush my teeth I examine the reflection in the mirror; here is a woman who always seems to be going somewhere, who less than a year ago stood in this exact position, gulping a handful of pink pills. A pink ticket, destination unknown. Here again the destination is unknown, not only that, it is journeying *into* the Unknown. This time however she is being accompanied and knows it and this alone gives her courage.

God knows I did not want to go. A year was a long time and California was 3,000 miles away and distance makes the heart grow fonder for someone near at hand. Jim was a man peculiarly attractive to women and I had to keep this in mind so that whatever came would be easier to accept. The fact that no one can lose what she doesn't have didn't occur to me and yet I do remember that for one fleeting instant I did get an inkling that Jim and I would never be together again. Because what actual need did Jim have of me? Of anyone for that matter.

And I, wasn't I a taker too? Was I capable of love? Take garden-variety sex love, what an advantage women had! Woman's role demanded merely being "on location," being a

269

terminus, a haven. What if it were reversed? What if my personal need of someone required me to supply a bridge by which we two became one, would I feel intensely enough to make this possible? Of course not!

Take maternal love, that wise, simple, strong, undemanding love rather than the fiercely possessive, indulgently protective flutter-mutter which makes the child unfit to meet his job, his world, his God. One, a preparation; the other, a crippling handicap. Take love of friend; could anyone who'd indulged in the selfishness of drunkenness dare to call herself "friend"?

And how absurdly limited were man-woman love, maternal love, friendship love compared to the love Jesus talked about! These even at their best were isolated flutterings compared to the love which loves *without* desire, *without* pride, *without* return, which learns to love where it cannot hope to *like*. Which loves in spite of, more often than because of. Which keeps the heart open and the mouth shut. Which labors and labors to see another's point of view. Which fears to tread and so does not intrude. Which, dissociating self, hopes on and waits on and understands, praying quietly.

So what, Jim Hatch did not love me! This was the Father's business! My business was to practice love where I was not loved!

To love someone who was kicking you out sounded extraordinarily ridiculous but it was not ridiculous; it was Christ's idea. He repeated it again and again, and if there was ever anyone *not* ridiculous it was the Christ. So, while as yet I was unable to subscribe wholly to His idea, I had to subscribe to Him, and not because He commanded it, not because the Bible said it, but because it *worked*. My way of life had led to the Valley of the Shadow and already His way was the way of unimagined peace.

When I stayed with the Father and His Son, I lived. When I did not, I died.

I died a little now. I cried: "No! I will love You but I cannot love Jim."

Yes, a Voice said. For by loving all men all men know that you love Me.

"Yes," I sighed.

So grandiose and far-fetched was my notion of Christ's kind of love that I never imagined it might be expressing itself in the act of rummaging through packed suitcases to find a particular gray silk suit Jim liked on me. It was a heck of a nuisance, but how could it be love? Love raised the dead, stopped armies, caused a mad dog to lick your hand, inclined Mrs. McNasty to lunch with the colored charwoman.

It didn't enter my head that it might be a young soul's groping toward conquest of self that made me sandwich in that trip to Jim's apartment, that made me mix martinis, content not to taste one, that made me applaud a play I'd seen and told him about and he'd forgotten, that made me sit hour on hour in Harlem dugouts, listening with burst eardrums to Jim's pet be-bop, that at long last, steered the Lincoln back to the country to the Pattons' house, past our own driveway, past our own dark and empty house.

It was though, love is precisely what it was. To sacrifice, with no hope of credit, one's feelings, one's time, one's energy, one's interest, to another is a form of love. It had to be, for unselfishness *is* love. It has to be love to work to ease another's embarrassment at the dirty deal he's handing you. And in his fashion I'm sure Jim suspected what I was doing and was grateful, grateful for no scenes, no maudlin tag ends, no poking into ashes to find a hidden spark.

No, the love of Christ begins wherever you are with whatever you have on hand. It was His love in me which kept me from making a jackass of myself when the moment came to say goodbye. Here, if ever, was the moment to fall apart.

Instead I said: "Thanks, Jim. Bless you. I'll write when I get work."

No wit, but no sobs either. Two tired people parting for the night.

Louise Patton, brusque angel that she is, was waiting up for me. Angel that she is, she went straight to bed, saying: "Good girl, you made it. See you at seven. If there's anything you want, don't mention it. Goodnight, kid."

I packed the gray suit, wiped off the lipstick, brushed my teeth.

I knelt by the bed. "Thanks that I made it," I said. "Stick close tomorrow. Tomorow's a tough day."

I got in bed and my eyes closed and it was tomorrow, a tough day.

CHAPTER TWENTY

There are as many beginnings to this world as there are awakenings of individual souls in this world. Man's genesis is at the very instant in which he's forced to recognize that he stands alone with his Maker. That he has been cut loose from all externals which hitherto sustained him. Such an instant comes once only in a lifetime and this morning was the morning of the first day for Liz, the shorn.

Irrespective of how good the morning of the first day looked to God it didn't look good to me. A dull drip of a day, suited to my state of mind. The October countryside reflected me. In place of fulfilling its bright autumn destiny, the fields were nipped and soggy, the trees limp with faded yellow leaves. Those leaves and I were both out of a job.

I am allergic to goodbyes. Sam, my father, used to say there were seven points of departure and all of them were, git up and git. I agree and so had left the Pattons as quickly as possible and would leave Gordon in the same fashion. It was good of him to serve me solitary Communion. In receiving it I would ask the Father to tide me over for, crystal-clear as my trust in Him was, my trust in myself had hit a new low.

The little church was drab as always but I no longer thought of it as drab for now I knew what was inside; inside was God's Grace made personal by the gracious heart of Gordon Rogers. This was the Father's House and as I pushed open the padded door the Father's peace reached out to enfold me. A near to tangible thing, this compound of faith and prayer.

The altar candles had been lighted and high above them was the bearded man kneeling in the stained-glass garden. The Jew, Jesus, a good friend of mine. Between the candles gleamed the altar cross and above the cross, the man; below the cross was the service in readiness for the remembrance of the man-made-God. "Do this in remembrance of me," He said.

As I write, I look back on six years of other churches, other ministers, and marvel at the love within this church, this minister. I have heard ministers announce that under no circumstances was anyone permitted to take the bread and wine unless he were confirmed, and have marveled that Gordon never failed to remember that the Lord's Supper was the Lord's, not Gordon's.

I've seen a minister refuse the cup to a sad-eyed woman because she was wearing lipstick. I've heard a minister ask a woman to leave his church, *his*, not Christ's, because she wore no hat. How do they dare? Lipstick may be a badge of courage to conceal quivering lips, and as for hats, it was Paul, not Christ, who was concerned with millinery. If a priest does not know the difference between Paul and Christ, what in the name of Christ is he doing in a pulpit!

The most terrifying menace to the world is not inherent in the word *atom*. The most terrifying menace lies in religionists who masquerade as Christians, whether in pulpit or in pew. The most terrifying menace is the church's insistence upon its laws rather than the Laws of Christ, thereby breeding pride, hypocrisy and strife, both in pulpit and in pew. Man wrangling over piffling dogma and calling it Christian and wondering why the ones who stand outside the Church turn from the Church in hopeless scorn.

Christ had no dogma, no rules, no regulations and gave none. Christ said to love; "Love one another." *Love!*

Does love split hairs? Does love belittle? Complicate? Does it confuse method with essence? Bog down in *How* and so lose track of *What?* Does love inform the searching heart that it must memorize the rules before it may receive the Christ? No, it does not, for Christ is *not* a game; Christ is the perfect merger of the Creator and the created. The Christ is He Who was, and is, proof positive, that that which was evolved is expected to go on evolving until at last it has become divine.

Eons pass and infinitely slowly the slime that has been in the dark evolves toward the light. The light warms it and it comes to seek the light. Finally it cannot live without the light. Eons pass and the living thing evolves into the animal, and eons more, and the animal into man and now, imperceptibly, the pattern alters; something new has been added. Now the growth is not by mere instinct alone; the animal-into-man begins to think. Eons and eons pass and by the power of thinking man grows to find life's greatest gift, the power of choice.

When man uses his power of choice to reject the light he reverts to animal. When however he accepts the light, reaching higher, ever higher, he gradually, through countless ages, comes to recognize the light as love and finally the love as God. Then and then only is man ready to begin the final stage in evolution, the evolving into that which is divine, that for which he was first created. The Choice stage is painful beyond all other stages and so the most rewarding yet. And man is getting closer, slowly in infinite pain, he is getting closer. The more man wars the more futile man sees war to be, whether the war be between nation and nation or between you and me. The Spirit is snowballing; man will make the grade. In spite of the religionists, man will make it!

Gordon Rogers is one of the rare ones who snowballs the

Spirit. He is one who has long perceived the light as love and the love as God. And he holds up that light to *all*, not daring to do otherwise. It gives me duck-bumps to think how easily, in those early days, I might have met the minister who does not minister. Had Gordon's concern been with custom instead of soul, what would have happened to me?

You can see how natural it was that later when I came to join a church it would be the Episcopal Church. From the start, through Gordon, I'd found it at its very best, its profoundly beautiful words interpreted by love, its insight epitomized by the insight of its priest. My very first Communion and now my last from Gordon were deeply reverently personal; two gathered together and Christ coming to join us as He had promised.

In these years of stumbling and falling flat and brushing myself off to stumble again, the only tears I ever shed are at the wonder of the holy mysteries of the bread and the wine. I cannot explain why yet I always weep at the wonder of the One Who made us continuing to remake us through the nourishment of the remembrance of His Son's Sacrifice.

Nor can I explain even remotely why the remembrance does remake. I know the bread is bread and not Christ's Body. I know the wine is wine and not Christ's Blood. Still worship, worshipful appreciation does exalt these symbols into living actualities. This is accomplished, I believe, by reminding us and making real the lengths to which one Man went to show that the Father is worth dying for. The triumph of faith. One of the wonders which cannot be, and is.

That last morning, after Gordon had left the altar, I stayed on. Thinking of Alan, praying that he had found his home, wherever it might be, still secretly believing that someday he would return. Thinking of Jim, praying he would find peace. Giving thanks for Pete, for Gordon, for the Pattons, for what lay ahead of me, whatever it might be.

"Father, give me a real job," I prayed. "I have to be of use. And I expect You to help me. Thank You that I do expect it. Amen."

Gordon had removed the vestments and was waiting in the dark vestibule. He is seldom articulate and when he spoke it was haltingly.

"Liz, I—I've put such store by the person you've become. Liz, what are your plans?"

I looked back into the church. "I have none. I've no idea what I'm going to do. All I do know is, whatever it is, it must in some way contribute to the coming of the Father's Kingdom here on earth. I'm so late, Gordon. I've used life, now I must be of use."

Pointing to the altar, I said, "That's what I prayed for, up there. To be of use."

At this precise moment a thing occurred which demonstrates how much more inventive God is than His children; a thing which a year ago I'd have dismissed as coincidence. From outside the door we heard voices and then one voice crying: "No, no, George, I said the Lincoln. Put them in the Lincoln."

My car doors were locked and there were other Lincolns, nevertheless I stiffened. What the—put *what* in the Lincoln?

I shoved back the padded door, practically sprawling a snappy figure in heather tweeds. The figure righted itself, tweaked a felt hat in place, and made a grab at me. It was a young woman I shall call Sally and Sally was drunk, crocked to the mascara at 8 A.M.

"Oh, thank God," she gasped. "Liz—Liz darling, I'm going too."

"You are indeed," I said testily. "What are you talking about?"

"I'm going with you. To California. You can't go all that way alone—that's terrible." The words ran together and the flavor was clove.

Terrible, my foot. It was going to be heaven. I had work to do on myself. Three thousand miles of Sally? For cat's sake, I barely knew the woman! Members of the same clubs, an occasional bridge partner, occasional elbow-bending partner in the days of elbow-bending. No, thanks. This was too much.

"No," I said. "No."

Squaring my jaw, I watched the flushed face crumple, watched the eyes fill and overflow.

"Sal, you're nuts," I said. "You're hysterical. You're—"

"Drunk. Say it, say it! Liz, take me, please," she begged. "I've got to stop—you did. You can show me—oh please, please, it's my only chance!"

Her only chance. My glance flicked the Rolls town car, the liveried chauffeur, George, the row of luggage encased in gray corduroy, adorned with silver monograms. The rich. The poor, damned rich—

"Take it easy, Sal. Who knows about this? How did you find me? What about Logan?"

I could see her picking a path through the questions, the tears coming faster than ever.

"I—I phoned the Pattons. Logan—oh, Liz, Logan has left me! Last week—I can't find him. For God's sake—help me!"

In my mind's eye I saw dear Logan. The ramrod, the never-do-anything-wrong, the perfect—perfect poop! But where were the three small girls with the tight brown braids?

"Sal, the kids. Where are they?"

"At Mother's. With mademoiselle. Liz, if you won't take me, I—I think I'll have to kill myself! I think—"

"What with?" I asked. "Stop that drivel. Here, take the keys. Tell George to work your junk in somehow."

She caught her cloved breath. "Thanks, Liz, thanks! I'll be so good, I won't drink, won't talk, won't—"

"Shut up," I said wearily. "If you won't talk, start now."

Laughing and crying, she ran to George.

I turned to Gordon. His eyes were bright with amusement and with something more.

"You'd better not laugh," I told him. "This is terrible. A catastrophe! Oh—I was planning on being *alone*."

"You were?" he asked. "That's odd when you were praying to be of use. It would appear that the Lord God has taken you at your word; and are you going to dictate the terms? No, Liz, you've been alone long enough. It's time for action. For sharing. If you can help Sally, you most certainly will have contributed to the Father's Kingdom. 'By their fruits'—by results—'ye shall know them.' Being inconvenienced, Liz, is a small fraction of what it means to be a Christian."

"Sal, come here," I called. "Gordon, would you say that thing you say on Sundays, the one about His Face shining on us? Sally might just as well start right; there'll be churches all along the route."

Sally had the hiccups.

I bestowed a filthy look; a fine obbligato to prayer! Suddenly rebellion returned; what was this all about? This silly expensive dame asking help from another silly expensive dame who herself was barely hanging on the ropes? Sally should be told to go home and mind her business and permit me to mind mine.

She was not told, however. Instead I took her hand and said: "Now listen, you. Bow your head."

The door swung to and it was very quiet in the vestibule. I thought, now there are three gathered together, two who seek and one who has found. The one who had found raised his hand and indicating the outline of the cross, said:

> " 'Unto God's gracious mercy and
> protection we commit thee.' "

No, that wasn't it. That wasn't what he said on Sundays. About to speak, I looked up but Gordon's eyes admonished me. To the accompaniment of hiccups, he continued:

> " 'The Lord bless thee and keep thee.
> The Lord make his face to shine upon
> thee, and be gracious unto thee. The
> Lord lift up his countenance upon thee
> and give thee peace, both now and
> forevermore. Amen.' "

"Amen," I echoed forlornly.

Amen. So be it. Hooked.

And not so much by Sal as at my own request. I was discovering what I now know to be true; it's dangerous business to pray for a thing you're not positive you want. Prayers are apt to be powerful according to the intensity of the desire behind them. Jesus said that where the treasure is, there will the heart be concentrated, so watch it. Should the old ticker be concentrated on a Cadillac, the chances are you'll get a Cadillac. Then, children, as He also said, you'll have had your reward! All right, I'd wanted a job, I'd asked for a job. I'd found it. People are my treasure, I guess; are where my heart is. This is true of most alcoholics, I believe, wet or dry.

Now my trip had been ruined. A thousand years might be as a day in God's sight, but in mine, a day was a day and I was trying not to waste one, let alone ten. Sal would sneak the bottle, would chatter, weep, giggle, groan, and futhermore she would snicker at battered Bibles.

She did nothing of the sort. She was wonderful. As a matter of sad fact, Sally spoiled me rotten, stopping where I wanted to stop, leaving when I wanted to leave, eating when I was hungry, sleeping when I turned off the light. Quiet as a mouse, sober as Carrie Nation, accommodating as an angel.

At first I was embarrassed at anyone seeing me kneel to pray at bedtime. I did what I always do when self-conscious, I laughed it off by saying: "Maybe you don't see it, Sal, but nowadays there's an iron band around every bed I get into. I seem to have to thank the Father before He'll let me aboard."

"I think it's nice," she said.

As the miles rolled up I appreciated fully that my obligation to Sally went a lot deeper than ten days of forced sobriety. The fact of her not making a problem of herself didn't mean she had no problem. A drunk doesn't quit being a drunk by staying sober ten days or ten years. The remedy isn't one of time or denial or repression. The remedy is substitution. The substitution of some goal, a challenge so great, so liquor-proof that whatever causes the drinking, known or unknown, is a flimsy obstacle by comparison. With Sal, and all drunks, it has to be new wine fit for a new bottle. Christ had a parable for this.

It bewildered me that Sally should have jug-trouble. As I got to know her, it was evident she had a large supply of God; a thousand times kinder than I, more patient, more thoughtful, more humble. To me she appeared to have so much more of a self to respect than I ever had that I couldn't see what she was running from.

Was it the old story of undervaluation of self? Could it be a case of the square peg trying to whittle itself into the round hole when all the time the trouble is with the hole? Here was Sal, the salt of the earth and yet—was she? Salt is more than to bring out flavor, more than a preservative; salt is also an irritant, an abrasive. She might be a walking sermon on the mount but could you picture her kicking the hypocrites out of the temple? Or say, standing up to her dear husband when it counted?

Jesus Christ was no panty-waist. His record and the record of His followers, crucifixions, lions' dens, shipwrecks, are not exactly panty-waist records. The glib ones who scoff at the spiritual way as a pleasant pill have quite obviously never swallowed that pill. Behind the pretty talk, or better, no talk at all, stretches the steep narrow trail, nor does the trail get

281

wider; it just occasionally appears to as you yourself get smaller.

Was Sally willing to give up as much for God as any drunk gives up for liquor? She thought prayer was nice; how nice? Nice for every whistler in the dark, or just nice for me? She said she wanted to stop drinking, but how? By osmosis? Her pinning her faith on me was dangerous because God was going to be around and I wasn't. Five days had gone already.

Five days devoted to a silent review of my own top-heavy past. This was what I'd planned to do and thanks to Sally I was doing it. As a crusader I was a flub. According to Gordon, however, crusading was a must of being a Christian so, California being a big state, if I was going to take on its problems I better clean up some of my own. Sam had ceased to be the Big Alibi, he wasn't and never had been wholly responsible for the B.C. House of the Late Liz. There was a long line of crusty Scots who had conditioned Sam and through Sam, me. How about my pa's pa? And my pa's pa's pa? How about his domineering ma after whom I was named? And her ma? And her—nuts, how about Adam and Eve!

What about my mother? While Sam was the main squeeze, what about her? One so beautiful that when I turned out to be not so beautiful it was necessary for me to corral the malest male in sight to prove how unessential mere beauty is. And had been proving it ever since, at first unconsciously and later, very very consciously.

Holy cow, what did it matter what your parents, what anybody did to you, Freud to the contrary notwithstanding? All that mattered was what you did to yourself when your day came. Like it or not, the day came when you bent over, swept up the pieces, glued them together, and took it from there. You yourself were a matter of what you did with your pieces.

If this was true of me it was true of my sons as well. If it tore the heart out, the weight of Alan had to be lifted. The sorrow of him and of the harm I'd done him were blocks on the road to usefulness. Lift him up and let him go, *let him go!* Even if he were still alive, I still had to let him go. Alan's outcome was Alan's business. Grief could no longer block me from forgiving myself in order that I might learn to forgive all. So, son, you are released! My love pries you loose. My love hands you over to Him Who is the Source of comfort.

I ached with the loss of my grief. The roots of it only Alan's return could pull up and yet, in time, even the roots might blossom. The flowers of pain are understanding and generosity and compassion.

Well, let's have the husbands next.

Randy, could you and I have made a go of it?

I honestly don't know. I'll cut it short by saying that you weren't any more to blame than I. It was youth, Randy, and fear and glands and ignorance and Queen Victoria. It was the whole parade of selfish Adams and selfish Eves making their selfish choices since man supposedly became man. Nobody's fault and everybody's fault, the fault of us all in a floundering, God-blind world. "All have sinned and all are guilty."

Learning to love is the world's first task. The first task of every human, commencing with me.

And now Silas.

Si, could you and I have made a go of it?

Yes! Yes, we could have. I've been over it and over it, *ad nauseum*, and while it's possible that without the jug I might never have married you, it's certain that once married —oh sure, *sure.* Why, if together, we had known half of what I now know, we might even have made a *holy* marriage!

However, since might-have-beens are out, Si is out.

And Jim? Could you and I—can we?

No, not yet! I hurt too much. *Wait*, Father!

How the Father must have grinned; a Liz so bent on scraping barnacles off others, so loath to let herself be scraped. So loath to let her dead die.

I whimpered a little. Well, Father, this isn't easy. After all—!

There came a blast of color. There came a mighty roar: *Easy? Who ever said it was easy? Simple, yes, as one, two, three. But easy? NEVER!*

The Voice was stilled. The color stayed.

Blinking, I rubbed my eyes. The New Mexico sun had set. Its passing had dyed the heavens in a magnificence of overlapping purples and crimsons and pure gold. I was understanding more and more why people in the Bible were forever traipsing off to the desert to rest awhile. The desert did not disturb the way the sea disturbed. The desert left you be, its immensity above personalities, above haste, above recrimination. A today-place. A yesterday-has-gone-and-tomorrow-has-not-come-place.

Why wouldn't the desert, a desert, be good for me? Suppose there were a house on that far hill? A pink house, the pink the color of the sands at sunset?

I turned to smile at Sally. "Sally, you've been an angel. Look, New York is a world away."

She removed the dark glasses. Her lips quivered as she said: "I—I wish it were."

All right, the time had come, I thought. She was flying home the day we hit Los Angeles and if the Father in me was to be of any service, it'd have to be quick. It would be ghastly to flunk my first assignment.

My hand touched hers. "By the way, Sal, did I remember to tell you that I've never liked women much but I believe I'm going to love you?"

Her eyes crinkled at the corners.

"I'm glad," she said. "I need it."

"Of course. Who doesn't?" I agreed. "You not only need it but you merit it."

"No-o," her voice broke, "no, I haven't earned anything, and—and Liz, I think it's too late."

I prayed: Father, hang onto us. This is going to be a whing-ding! Out loud I said: "That's the bunk. Look at the guy on the cross next to Jesus—look at me."

After the usual dinner of unchewable steak and limp French fries, Sally made her nightly call to the three small girls with the brown braids. All was well, all was fine, and Daddy was fine too; Daddy was at the Harvard Club. Why was Daddy at the Harvard Club, Mommie? Sally reassured them, put down the receiver and turned away, covering her face with her hands. A while later she was able to tell her story.

It didn't take long. It was merely another example, perhaps an extreme one, of mixing sportsmanship with sex. The man, unmarried then, was crazy for Sally while Sally was crazy for Logan. (Why, I wouldn't know.) The man begged her to divorce Logan, begged her to, well, you know what he begged her to. Sally stood firm. The man wasn't at all bad, in fact, he was pretty darn snazzy and there were some fairly ripe love scenes but nothing more. Sal wasn't even tempted.

"I just don't feel that way about you," she told him. "And if I did, I couldn't possibly do that to Logan." Then she made her big mistake. She said it wasn't fair of him to ask her when she was married and he wasn't—

He took her up fast. "And if I ever do marry, then will you?" he asked.

She'd thought this a good out. It seemed safe. The man was fundamentally a nice man, or she thought so, and if he married he would be as loyal to his wife as she wanted to be to Logan. So she promised. They shook hands on it.

285

The love-making had gone on—off and on—for about two years. Then—

"Don't tell me!" I broke in. "The guy married and, married or not, he wanted Sally and Sally, like a perfect damn fool, crashed through. A deal was a deal!"

"Yes. The very day he got back from his wedding trip. Oh, Liz, it was awful! *Simply awful.*"

"Nice boy," I said.

I could picture Sally, a cockeyed lamb off to slaughter, blue ribbons flying. How mixed could you get? A deal with a jerk taking precedence over a deal with Almighty God.

"Okay, get this," I said. "It was adultery and adultery is a sure-as-hell sin, but, Sal, sins are forgiven! The price is the knowledge that you have sinned and true repentance—"

"But Logan—Logan will *not* forgive!" she sobbed.

What the—?

"What was that? You *told* Logan?"

"Why, of course I told him! How could I go on living in the same house, and not tell him?"

Here for sure was repentance. As for hell's fire punishment—

"How long ago was this?" I asked.

"Four years."

"Four *years?*"

Hold it; the smallest brown braid couldn't be over two. Oh, so that was it! Dear Logan could crawl in bed with an adulteress but somehow he just couldn't bring himself to forgive her!

I breathed deep, praying that what I was about to try was right.

"Sal, you can now toss out the jug forever and forever, amen," I stated. "This dear Logan whom you love so just doesn't happen to be God, irrespective of his opinion. Love him if you must but never, never again permit him to set himself up as judge. There is only one Judge, the Lord God Almighty, Maker of heaven and earth and Logan. God is your Judge and since Jesus Christ, His Representative, forgave adultery, who the hell is Logan? Now, my girl, this is what you do; you get yourself a Bible and you study it. You fly straight home, go straight to Gordon Rogers and tell him what you've told me. He'll positively pull the stuffing out of Logan because if there's one thing the Father hates more than drunkenness, more even than adultery, it's the *hypocrite!* You're free, young woman, free. And God is the One Who did it and you and I are going to thank Him. We're about to pray, believe it or not!"

The notion of praying out loud embarrassed me more than I had ever been embarrassed in my life, yet I would do it if it killed me. Mustering a quavering voice, I said: "Father—our Father Who's right here in this motel, Sally and I thank You for forgiving drunks, for forgiving adultery. We—we also ask that You forgive Logan the sin of being better than other people and—and please prove to Sally that she doesn't ever have to run again. Except toward You. Amen."

I was appalled at myself. Not daring to look at Sal, I dove into a closet and took down two coats.

"Here, c'mon, we'll take a walk," I mumbled. "I can't endure the menace of those ghastly cactus lamps another second!"

The desert night was a sight to behold. Sal and I were wrapped in a sky of navy blue from which every diamond in the universe sparkled green and blue and red and orange. We didn't walk. We stood spellbound.

"He made this," I said.

Sally's face was grave and lovely in the starlight.

"Yes, I think He did," she said. "And I think He changed you. And if He can change anybody else, He can change me."

And He did.

CHAPTER TWENTY-ONE

Never was I more alone and less lonely than at the Webbs' new home in Sierra Madre, California. I arrived there to find the place locked and notes thumbtacked on every door. Sue's father had had a stroke, he was dying, and she and Tony had flown east and had no idea how long they'd be. There'd been no one for me to report to along the way so they hadn't been able to contact me. The notes must have been written in installments for each contained some additional item of information and each was sorrier than the last. They were desolate at not being on hand to welcome me. The keys were next door; the deepfreeze was loaded, the cleaning woman came three days a week; oh, *damn*, the last note said.

After rereading them I plunked myself down in the walled patio beside a spendid sea-green swimming pool, the shape of an artist's palette. (Ah, California!) This was the moment to determine whether to go on a binge of self-pity. It was a temptation. In place of friends to be brave in front of, in place of jokingly relating how Jim had given me the bounce and at the same time proving myself the strong right arm of God, I was anticlimaxed. I faced an empty house hung on a cliff. The fact that the house was charming was meager comfort. It ought to be charming, it had been difficult enough to locate. To reach here the car had wedged up canyons, straddled boulders, climbed cow paths; the charm was merited.

Just as I'd about made up my mind to shed a quiet tear for poor Liz, something diverted me. Above me sprawled a big old avocado tree and from it swooped a hummingbird the size of a lapel brooch. Gyrating back and forth, up and down, it considered me for a landing field and almost came to rest on the tip of my boot. There it hovered, the tiny, the most exquisite jeweled object. I dared not breathe.

Slowly I raised my eyes and everywhere was the beauty of God's creations, waiting to be enjoyed. Garlands of deep red velvet roses festooned the high brick wall, bees hummed in and out the roses and in the avocado, birds chatted with one another. To the north, tiered the golden-brown Sierra Madres, folding in upon themselves, fuzzy and rumpled as if a giant had spread across them a mammoth rug of beaver.

Ecstasy poured into me, an ecstasy which grew and grew, a joyous bubbling-over. I who once had thought to find happiness in the conquest of men and more men was close to overwhelmed at the trust of one small bird. It was a feeling identical to prayer; the swift awareness of man's glorious and everlasting indebtedness. An awareness and an acknowledgment and the humility that these two bring. I laughed a laugh of pure gladness and frightened the hummingbird yet long after it had gone it stayed in my heart. I had been made welcome after all.

In the days which followed, I seemed to be healing, waiting to grow strong to venture forward. In that garden, surrounded by growth and movement, thoughts of Alan were constantly with me and it came forcibly that I'd been wrong to think of Alan as gone. Alan was not gone. He was "missing" as I had been missing. One day, like me, he would be found, would let himself be found, and then we two could become acquainted, not by forgiving one another but by being forgiven. Of all the gifts the Father's love might bring, this was the most desired, the most dear.

Those days in the gray and yellow clapboard house and in the walled garden were perfect healing ones, devoted to reading, studying, thinking. Prayer ran through them, hinging one day to the next by a golden hinge. My prayers were and are undistinguished prayers but they are real. They are in my words and as I speak and think in the vernacular, my association with the Father and the Son is in the vernacular. A very simple relationship. And now I was learning how to listen; I would lie in the garden, listening, listening. Speaking to God and listening for Him to speak to me in the same vernacular that I myself used. Why would He speak in any other way and expect me to understand? Since I myself once spoke four languages, was it unreasonable that my Maker should speak mine?

I was hungry for Truth, and the Father and the Son are Truth. The Father is the Creator of Truth and hourly recreates it, and the Son is the Father's Explainer Who lived and died and lives forever for us who cannot live alone. As those quiet hours passed, the knowledge that prayers are answered became a vibrant certainty. Both of my prayers at the altar of that little church at home had been answered; to be alone to rest and to be of use. It was merely the order which had been reversed. I saw more and more that the Father and the Son have no limitations beyond the limitations my faith puts on Them. If I expect all from Them, I will get all; Their kind of all and in Their own good time, not mine.

My first Sierra Madre Sunday rolled around. Sunday, God's peculiarly special day. The day to enter His peculiarly special House and meet others who desire to know Him, or think they do. Here, I guess, is as good a place as any to take a crack at disentangling a portion of the fuzz about churchgoing. In doing so it should not be necessary to explain that I know nothing whatsoever of theology and care less. I know nothing of creeds and dogma *and* care less but there is one thing I do know; I know that the Stop sign on the corner exists because the Church exists.

Maybe I'm silly for Stop signs. I've used them as an example before and my reason is that, like God, they are so simple. If you think the Stop sign is unimportant, you're mistaken, chum. Whatsoever things are considerate, whatsoever things concern the rights of others, are charitable, are decent, have come about not because of statesmen, or politicians or individual Christians, these are due to the weight of the pressure of the Church Universal, wherever, whatever, however.

I used to think that the Church was as good or as bad as the people in it. I was wrong. The Church is good, period, and man cannot make it bad no matter how he tries. One can take the purest silk and use it for a dust rag but it remains pure silk. The Church is God's and therefore good and being good, it has survived the use it has been put to, has survived its own clergy, its own members, its ageless persecution. I can damn God but God is not damned. I can belittle His House but His House is not belittled.

There are those who argue that the Father can best be worshipped in private. I'll buy this and yet Christ told us to do it both ways, in private and together. He talked about going into closets and He also talked about not hiding under bushel baskets. He Himself belonged to a group, He Himself went to the Synagogue and was reviled there as we today revile Him, but He kept right on. He still said: go and tell!

There are those who argue that the Father can best be worshipped in nature, in music, in painting, in writing, sure, why not? He is the creator of nature and of creativity and if He's truly worshipped, He's worshipped everywhere, in everything, alone and in crowds. The hooker is, as someone said, He can be, but *is* He. So, if we're so doggone worshipful, what's the matter with cleaning up His House? God knows it needs it!

It quite positively is *your* business whether you go to church or not. Yours and the Father's. But it is my business when I'm asked to swallow a phony reason for *not* going. And in my opinion any reason that applies to you and not to the good of the whole is a phony reason. Think; think of a world in which every last person did what the non-churchgoer advises; can you imagine a world without one single church? Can you imagine America without one single church? Your home town without a single church?

You can't, can you? So till the day arrives that every last person *is* worshipping the Lord God Almighty, until His Kingdom *does* work here on earth, we'd best support the one institution that even pretends to serve Him! Sam, my father, used to say that college couldn't hurt a wise person and might help a damn fool. This goes for the Church too.

I and ten trillion others have said that it wasn't the Church, it was the people in it—how right, how right! But is the answer to rid ourselves of the Church or to rid the Church of hypocrites? Or to help hypocrites learn to be genuine? Compare the Church as an institution to Democracy as an institution. All of us are well aware that hypocrisy, greed, corruption, gnaw like termites into the fabric of our government but do we tell ourselves that Democracy is not worth fighting for? Some do, of course. Some move to other countries, especially countries where the exchange is favorable, and there they squat, deserters, self-expatriates, shrill irresponsibles, chewing the hand that feeds them. Thank God, these are few in proportion.

Therefore, it seems to me, the answer to the tarnish in the Church is the same as to the tarnish in government. The answer is to expose the pretenders, the apathetic, the turn-coats; crowd out the greedy; challenge the pinheads. Help them to become real Christians. Even Jesus picked one stinker, one out of twelve, but did he desert the eleven? All churches have their stinkers, in pews, in pulpit, but, who knows, if I attend I just might help a stinker. I once was one myself.

The point is this: the Church is the Father's House and it is holy. I cannot see how I can call myself Christian if I hug my God to myself and ignore my responsibility to His House. I must fight for Truth. I must help delete hogwash. I must convert if possible the sanctimonious mealy-mouths. The Church Universal, Jewish, Roman, Protestant, misused though it be, is all that stands between man's individual liberty and man's mass slavery.

If you think it's the big bad bomb, you're nuts. Russia has the big bad bomb, what it doesn't have is God! What are Communists taught to hate most? The Church. Junk the Church and the Reds will grab the earth.

To join God's army at army headquarters, or not join it, appears to me to be the difference between tackling evil with one's own private popgun or tackling it with the massed artillery of massed faith. It isn't remotely a case of private worship versus public worship; it's both, both are required. When I walk up those steps I broadcast Whose team I'm on.

For me at least, Church is far more than an obligation. It isn't an institution which requires me so much as I require it. It isn't a place where I find God so much as a place where I take Him. Where I take what I have been able to gather of Him. I bring Him and therefore I receive Him in this, His Recharging Station. And you can bet your bottom buck that there's more power in any church, stinkers notwithstanding, than any individual can ever absorb!

That Sunday morning in Sierra Madre I slid off the cliff

293

and went church-shopping. Not recognizing one denomination from another and caring less, it was chance that landed me again at an Episcopal church. Or maybe it wasn't chance. Maybe the Lord God felt I should meet John Hunt.

St. James Church is in a town a few miles west of Sierra Madre. A plush town and a plush church. The building is a white pile with fancy gray-gloved ushers and a fancy marble altar with a fancy carved Christ. Its fanciness angered me. Before I'd even seen the minister I was furious at him, furious at any minister who had more to work with than Gordon Rogers.

A scarlet-robed choir filed up the aisle. The music was excellent and this too angered me when I recalled Gordon's sour organist and worse than sour soloist. At the end of the procession walked two rectors, *two*, bless Pat. One in his late sixties, and one about my age. Humph, I thought, mankind starving and churches throwing money away on truck like this—

I didn't approve of such goings-on and so, sermon unheard, I wasn't going to approve of the minister. The Son of God was poor and lowly and this layout was not poor and lowly. Jesus was born in a stable and I'd bet this minister was born in a top maternity hospital. Jesus rode an ass if he was lucky, and I'd bet this man rode a big fat Cadillac. Ministers didn't have to be Christ, I didn't hope for that, but when they deliberately set themselves up as His representatives, some of Him should rub off on them somewhere.

In this splendid Christian judge-not frame of mind, I sat and churned. Gradually however the familiar words got to me and I felt myself untighten. By the time the younger of the two men had entered the pulpit, I deigned to examine the program. His name was John Hunt, D.D., and a string of other initials. The subject of the sermon was: *Are You Using All You Have?*

That sermon was written for me. It was addressed to me. Now that I know John Hunt, I know that every single person in every crowded church in which he speaks, and that is plenty, always feels exactly as I felt. Unless you happen to be dead you have to feel this and maybe even if you are dead. Because John's words are plainly and simply and terribly the truth. When he speaks, he speaks to you. When he asks if you are using all you have, he is asking you. It is wholly personal. It is precisely as though a long finger were pointing from the pulpit to a spot a half inch above your conscience.

Strangely the text for the sermon was not the one about the talents. It was the story of the loaves and fishes, of how one young boy's generosity persuaded 5,000 others to share what each had been hoarding for himself. If there was a miracle in the story it wasn't a miracle of conjuring up mere edibles. The miracle lay in the fact that unselfishness does breed unselfishness. While the bread and fish were undoubtedly bread and fish, they were also symbolic; symbols of each person's power to strengthen those about him through the sharing of what he possesses, however small.

It relieved man of responsibility, Dr. Hunt said, to call any unusual occurrence a miracle. A miracle was supernatural, beyond man's powers, whereas the consummation of an ideal demanded the full use of man's powers. Miracles could be left to God; ideals could not. The example set by the boy with the five loaves and two fish had only been supernatural in the sense that it was and is so rare as to seem miraculous.

Did not the people in this congregation sidestep the ideal by considering it beyond them? he asked. For instance did the woman in the beige suit in the second right-hand pew set the example this boy had set? Did she proffer every loaf and every fish, be it one or a carload? The amount did not matter nor did the quality. God was not concerned with quantity or quality, providing it was the most and the best one had. God

295

was concerned with *totality*, the totality of sincere and continuous effort. If the most and the best the woman in the beige suit had was half a loaf and half a fish, half a loaf and half a fish were eminently acceptable.

Dr. Hunt had a great deal to say on the subject of money. If the woman in the beige suit did not think of stocks and bonds as loaves and fishes, she was morally mistaken. And if, by chance, it should offend her to have money mentioned from the pulpit, she was indeed impractical. Who did she think paid Christ's bills? Christ had been in the red since the day His work began. How then was the woman able to convince herself that Christians gave all they could *without* being asked? That would be the millennium and the millennium would surely come but it had not come and in the meantime *who paid Christ's bills?* Who paid His plumber? His electrician? His utilities? If it wasn't the woman in the beige suit, who was it?

The woman realized at once who paid them; *she* did! She might not care to pay for carved Christs or red-robed choirs but there wasn't any way to avoid the necessities of the Church and its obligations. The words addressed to her had been so direct that she saw she owed, not what she'd felt to be a fair compromise, but *all*, all she had been given. Her now healthy body, her now clear brain, her education, her personality, her contacts, her numerous advantages, her position and prestige, her bank account. These did not and never had belonged to her; they were gifts loaned by God, the Father. And not for her pleasure nor even her well-being except as her well-being was directed toward the Father's well-being.

These gifts had been loaned to be used to free the earth of misery and herself of guilt. Never once had Jesus promised ease; never once had He promised pleasure or popularity, or praise or credit or self-satisfaction. All He ever promised was the certain joy of no defeat. Defeat lay in holding back, in holding out. In kidding one's self that Christ, the Explainer, meant this but could not have meant that, in striving for His peace yet refusing to pay the price He paid. There was no middle path. It was total surrender or it was total defeat.

"Sell all that you have," He said.

"God is concerned with totality," the minister had said.

The words went on, beating at me. They slapped my face, chipped my heart, slashed at my pretension of being a follower of Jesus, the Christ.

The minister had finished his sermon. He was turning toward the altar. He had finished except that one knew he would never finish.

I did not stand for the closing hymn. I dropped to my knees and remained there. The choir sang past; the congregation knelt briefly for the benediction, followed by a moment's silence, and then the organ pealed. People greeted one another and after a long while the aisles emptied and it was silent.

I do not know how long I stayed there. A creaking noise aroused me. An old man was creaking a cart up and down, the cart heaped with red hymnals and black prayer books. I watched him and as he came near, I said: "Where would he be now?"

The old man cocked his head. "And where would *who* be?" he asked.

I smiled. "Dr. Hunt."

The crinkled face smiled back, crinkled like an old prune.

"Ah-h—who knows?" he sighed. "That man! Try his office, lady. Through the cloister will be quickest—with him, we've got to be quick."

I was very quick. Yet, when I stood outside his office, when I saw him writing at his desk, the head with the thick salt-and-pepper curls bent forward, I was tongue-tied.

It had been many many years since any man could make me ill at ease. It was Christ's Spirit in the man, the Holy Ghost, the Holy Spirit, the part of Himself which Jesus promised to send all men and *does* send to all. John Hunt had no more of Christ than anyone, than I! It was that he *used* what he was given and I had not.

I waited outside the open door and finally I coughed, then wished I hadn't. The head jerked up and startlingly blue eyes examined me.

"Hello," I gulped.

He dropped a pencil and stood up.

"Hello. Who are you?" he said.

"I—I'm not too sure," I quavered. "I—I want to talk to you. To the *Christ* in you."

The blue eyes widened. Thick black eyebrows rose to furrow a broad brow and the almost too wide lips curled in astonishment.

"You are a convert," he stated.

I nodded. "Not quite a year old."

John Hunt is a broad and solid man, his build the type one associates with football players rather than priests. His face is deeply tanned and running from nostril to lower lip are deep parentheses. Even when he stands perfectly quiet, which is seldom, one feels a sense of motion. His voice is low and rich, not chocolate-rich; the richness of great vitality.

"Come," he was saying, "come, sit down. There, is that comfortable? May I give you coffee? They keep the thermos filled."

I could feel his excitement. In another man it would have been the excitement I was used to but this was as far from that as neon from sunshine. This had to do with the new inner me and so served to quiet me.

Smiling, I said: "I was frightened but you make me feel an honored guest. I—"

"Why not?" he boomed. "Our Lord's first public act was to assure the success of a social function. Had coffee been required it could have been coffee as well as wine."

"In my case, *better*," I said. "I'm an alcoholic, a dry one. The Father took care of that, *fast*."

"Do you tell people this?" he asked.

"Why, of course—"

His eyes smiled. "Why do you?"

"Why, I'd think that would be obvious. It's a form of that ghastly word, *witnessing*. Whenever anyone offers me a drink, I always say, 'No, thanks, I'm an ex-drunk,' in the hope that someone who wants to quit will hear me and come and ask, how come?"

"And do they?"

"Sometimes. I didn't think it was too hot to begin with, but it's turned out to be—God sure knows His business."

His laugh filled the room. "He does indeed. Tell me about yourself. Tell me about all of it. Go back to where God found you—"

"God didn't find me," I interrupted. "He knew where I was all the time. *I* found Him."

"Tell it your way," he told me. "Start at the beginning."

I told the story better than I had ever told it, perhaps better than I ever shall again. A power was given me. It was as though this man and I sat at opposite ends of the base of an immense triangle, a direct line running from him to me and from each of us upward to a single point. The line from him to the point would be shorter than my line, a right-angled triangle, but both lines were direct and the converging point was God.

There is one continuingly curious element in the relating of what happened to me at All Angels Hospital; people *believe* it. I don't mean they necessarily believe it could come to them but they do believe it came to me, and this amazes me. I

299

think, now, *this* time they won't believe it; someone will snicker, or at least be bored. Or someone will ask a question I can't answer and my ignorance will invalidate all that happened. Questions such as, what do I think of the Virgin Birth? This one has come up several times and of course I can't answer it.

The only answer that makes sense to me is the only answer I ever give: "How could I know?" I say: "All I know is that a God Who could make the Universe could certainly decide how He wanted His baby boy born."

I believe that if the Virgin Birth *was* so, it was *easily* so. If it was not so, what difference can it make? For me, the Truth of Christ doesn't stand or fall on whether Mary was a Virgin; it stands on the change Christ made and does make in my life and in the lives of all who seek Him. The virgin birth was claimed for Zoroaster and several others but why should this alter my values one iota? It isn't Christ-born-of-Mary that makes Christ true for me; it's Christ-born-in-Liz. Nor is this blasphemous. Mary, most blessed of women, was the chalice for Our Lord, yet I too am blessed, one of countless smaller chalices, 2,000 years afterwards.

It is quite likely I do not understand the meaning of the word Theology. It seems to have innumerable meanings, mostly concerned with doctrines of assorted religious sects. I can see how dangerous it is to go too far off on your own but on the other hand it is supremely dangerous to settle for yesterday's Christ and not find today's. Why is the quickening of the Holy Spirit in Mary vital proof of Christ's Godship while the quickening of the Holy Spirit in you and me is merely an individual albeit comforting matter? I don't think so. I think it's the other way around. I can believe anything of Him, any perfect thing, because I know so very well that He does live and grow in me. He could easily have been born supernaturally due to the fact that 2,000 years later He was born again in me.

If you're interested in miracles, it was a miracle that John Hunt and I, two complete strangers, should sit in a room and know that Jesus, the Christ, sat with us as He promised He would and so knew we could not be strangers.

The room we sat in was as unlike the rest of the layout as could be imagined; a whitewashed cubicle with one window, one old desk, two old armchairs. No rug, no draperies, no pictures. A simple direct room in which to tell a simple direct story. When I'd told my story I didn't stop. Before John Hunt had a chance to comment, I said: "So we're up to now, to this morning—you really shocked me this morning. No, wait, I've dumped a great share of my possessions but still have come nowhere near giving up all I have. Now I see I've got to. I've been bargaining with God, maybe even blackmailing Him—if I give up drinking, would he please let me make a success of just this one marriage? So I toss out the jug and think, what a good girl am I; I give to the poor but only the amount I've been throwing away on a duplication of luxuries; luxuries for Liz, necessities for others. How mixed-up can one woman be? But how about this church? This is a pretty fabulous setup. I thought it was you but I guess not because this room, your room, is a cell. But if it isn't you, how do you stomach the rest? How can you justify carved marble and fancy robes when God's poor starve for bread and fish?"

In place of being defensive or holier-than-thou or going theological on me, John Hunt said: "Bread and fish can be food for the soul as well as food for the body; this is a truth you particularly are going to have to learn. A truth demanding the utmost in personal honesty and clear thinking. The group this church reaches and the group you can best reach would be repelled by sackcloth and ashes. Paul said to be all things to all people, to meet them on whatever level they are. Your preparedness does not lie with the uneducated or the under-privileged; your conversion would have little effect in the slums for their problems would be foreign to you. It is in your own class that God will use you. Your training will be invaluable in reaching the hardest class there is to reach, those like yourself whose privileges more often handicap them than inspire them. Your backgrounds are the same, the language is the same. You know the obstacles, the indifference, the rationalizations—"

I made a face. "You mean it takes a thief to catch a thief?"

"Well, doesn't it? Doesn't that account, in great measure, for Paul being the most dynamic of the early Christians? He hated Christians, had employed every talent to defeat them and therefore when he himself became one, who could know better how to refute the doubts and break through the sophistries? You must do the same. You must work against those frailties and temptations which you have experienced and understand so thoroughly. Such a dedication will not mean renouncing what you have, but—*rechanneling* it. If your usefulness to God is greater in pleasant surroundings than in a shack by the railroad, your surroundings will not be an indulgence; they will be part of your spiritual equipment."

I shook my head. "No, that's too difficult. It would mean constant soul-searching. I would be forever doubting myself, forever wondering if I was fooling myself into believing all the nice things were to make others feel at home when actually they were to make life easy for me. I'm sick of guilt. In denying myself I'll know I'm sacrificing—everybody will— there won't be any doubt. If I have nothing left to give I won't have to suffer making choices—"

"How true," he said. "You could enter a convent and scrub floors and show the world how lowly you were. You could take great pride in your piety and sore knees, feeling superior to the material-minded whom you might have helped. This certainly would be a great deal easier. It's always easier to resist temptation by eliminating it in yourself and withdrawing from it in others. Eliminating choice demands no further sacrifice, no scrupulous self-honesty, no pangs of growth, whereas it's work of the hardest type to employ your peculiar gifts in serving those whom God so seldom reaches and whom you yourself have now outgrown. It will be painful in the extreme to try to sell the straight and narrow to people who are impressed with you for the wrong reasons, for the material possessions you now find worthless."

"So I'm to have snob value? To spin a fine web and sit in the center, luring suckers? Well, I won't buy that!" I cried.

He laughed. "I'll say you won't. What you are going to do is labor at the work the Lord God has trained you for and with the tools He has handed you. You will stay away from convents and slums and waterfronts and stick to the group you know and therefore can help. God knows He needs workers in convents and slums and waterfronts but you're not one of them. Your fitness lies with those in the reserved seats in the arena. I can count a dozen Unreachables you'll shock straight out of their stupor, Elizabeth Hatch. Where do you plan to live? Here, I hope?"

"I don't know," I said. "My plans aren't settled yet. I'd like—I think I'd like to try a desert."

John Hunt smiled. "Elizabeth's period in Arabia," he said.

CHAPTER TWENTY-TWO

John Hunt was largely responsible for postponing my desert. He had me talking at A.A. meetings, talking with individuals, leaping onto platforms, knees buckling. He got me far out beyond my depth, in on conferences with spiritual Big Shots; ministers, Christian leaders, writers on spiritual subjects, what-have-you. Appalled, I did all I could to stay off soapboxes and don't think the gent in the long red underwear wasn't in there pitching! "Hey, p-isst," the devil would say, "tell 'em you're not ready."

The two days and nights before my first public appearance were just plain hell. I couldn't sleep, couldn't eat, couldn't breathe. Me making noises like an evangelist, what was this! Hah, here's the stuff the devil dotes on; personal pride mixed into duty is down his alley.

"Hey," he'd whisper, "tell 'em it isn't fair to God. Tell 'em you'd be letting Him down by speaking before you know how to do it properly. You want to get smooth—you want to do God justice, don't you? Well, then tell 'em."

I did. I told John Hunt I'd be doing God's Kingdom more harm than good, standing up there, mumbling, rattling to pieces.

John's expression was something I'm not apt to forget.

"You know He needs your help, don't you, Liz?" he asked.

"Yes," I gulped. "I'll be there."

And I was, rubber legs and all.

It was pride, of course, nothing but. It always is. When I'm scared stiff, and I still am, it's because I'm trying to go over big, because I want Mrs. Jones to say to Mr. Smith: "My, isn't she wonderful?" more than I want Mrs. Jones to say to Mr. Smith: "My, isn't God wonderful?"

People, individuals, weren't frightening. There was nothing unusual about people telling me their darkest secrets, often on sight. What a rare gift, this, and one I'd always taken for granted. Now I was seeing that it was not to be taken for granted; it was plain gravy, a gift, a "talent." A nifty circuit from me to somebody else, from that somebody back to God, that only got out of hand when Switchboard Liz started accepting more calls than she had plugs for.

Oddly enough, one of the calls came from John Hunt's daughter. Yet not too odd since the offspring of the most God-centered families are sometimes the most confused. Too much is supposed. God is papa's God and mama's God and that's just great but does it follow that because papa and mama are plugged in, daughter is plugged in? It does not. Knowledge is not acquired by propinquity.

Patsy Hunt and I had met several times. She was cuter than a cricket. She was sixteen, brown, long-legged and apparently adjusted so picture my astonishment when one fine afternoon she burst into the Webbs' garden. Very serious, very tense, she leaned against the brick wall and looked at me.

"Well, hi," I called. "What's on your mind? Want a swim?"

She shook her head vigorously and raced around the pool, skidding to a stop in front of me. Panting a little, she announced: "Liz Hatch, I want you to convince me there's a God! *Daddy says you can.*"

I could have shot daddy.

"Just like that?" I asked.

"Just like that," she nodded.

My gaze went from the intent brown eyes to the rumpled brown hills. The smog had blurred them and was blurring the setting sun. The red velvet roses were unblurred however and the avocado tree and the bright oranges and lemons hanging like varicolored ornaments on a Christmas tree.

Christmas wasn't too far off; *Christ*-mass.

I kept my lips from moving. "Dear Christ," I prayed, "I'll need a lot of help."

After a moment I said: "How much time have I got, Patsy?"

"I have to be back in an hour and a half," was the answer.

An hour and a half. Ninety minutes in which to prove Something sixteen years in the Hunt household hadn't been able to prove; it wasn't enough! She'd heard my story, the God part, at dinner in her own home and obviously this too had missed the mark, yet wait! It couldn't have missed completely because she was here; she trusted me or she'd never have come, daddy or no daddy.

Confidence flooded me. I'd been stumped but now I wasn't. Now suddenly I knew what approach to take. Pointing to a chair, I smiled.

"Sit down, Patsy, there. Now—now suppose you convince me there *isn't* a God. It shouldn't be hard because, as you know, I myself only met Him a year ago. Suppose you go back to the polliwogs and account for everything some other way. Begin with the sun and the moon and the stars and that rosebud and those oranges and the hummingbird. Tell me where *order* came from, and the very first seed of life. Tell about Abstracts; the need to protect the weak, to grow in knowledge, to stand up for what is right and the shame that comes from doing wrong. The human race, not all of it but those farthest from the polliwog, possesses these traits and if they don't come from a Higher Power, where do they come from? And then tell me, if there is no God, what was it that changed me and my habits? I'm not exactly a pushover, Patsy. And then finally, if there is no God, tell me why you and I bother to talk about Him? Nobody's ever seen Him and His Son died two thousand years ago so what *is* all this? Who ever got such a silly notion and why does it hang on?"

Ninety minutes was too long a time. Before an hour was up a flushed wide-eyed Patsy had proven that there simply *had* to be Something bigger than ourselves! Unless there was a God, the entire setup was luck, luck or else we ourselves were gods and both were crazy. Luck could not be counted on and Universal Laws *could* be counted on. And we, well, we weren't gods! So—so He *had* to be—surely I could see it, couldn't I?

Sure. I could see it.

Through all this period there'd been no word from Jim. None at all. But this couldn't mean that it was too late. Nothing good was ever too late; look at the thief on the cross on Calvary! What I wasn't looking at however was that the thief's reward for faith did not include his going back to right old sins. His reward was to be forgiven that he might go forward.

The thief was told that he would be with Christ in paradise. All right, but as usual we're up against semantics; what *is* paradise? Don't tell me that Christ, the Lord, was implying that paradise was a do-nothing place. That the thief was never going to have to do a lick of work to all eternity; is this likely? Not to me. The thief like us fell too far short of perfection and no state short of perfection could be God's ultimate for the thief or us.

No, I bet that paradise, here and hereafter, is a matter of workroom after workroom; "In my Father's House are many mansions." I bet paradise is a slow development of man's Spirit and each mansion, each workroom, each gradation, is attained via the corridors of labor, of denial, of wisdom, and finally of love, arriving sometime, somehow, at the Penthouse of Ultimate Perfection: the blinding Truth. The Very God of Very God, the Beginning Which had no beginning, the End Which has no end. I wonder sometimes if the part of us that survives isn't perhaps just that part that is the absolute good in us, the core. Should this be so, I shall enter my Father's Kingdom astride a gnat but I will enter It and so will you because there *is* no beginning and no end.

Okay. And now the cause of further postponement of my desert. This was the Stumble-Bum who taught me more about God than I could teach him for the simple reason he knew Him better than I did. The Stumble-Bum was a drunk. Why not? All dry drunks are up to here in wet drunks; if, as John Hunt said, it takes a spoiled brat to catch spoiled brats, it also takes an understanding heart to understand. A.A. has proven this, proven it magnificently.

I met the Stumble-Bum's wife before I met him—a woman who gave me an especially understanding heart, so understanding that had he been a murderer instead of a drunk, I'd have understood. She was a hairdresser, a good one. In fact she was a good everything: a good woman, good wife, good church member, good citizen; good, and the first to tell you. Never, never, had she done, been, felt, thought or said a single thing that wasn't perfect so why, she wanted to know, should she be saddled with a stumble-bum?

I saw why, saw and would have liked to tell her. What I didn't see was how to help the poor man because by that time I was going to help him if it meant chopping the good-woman into small bits and fitting her into a suitcase. Of all infuriating qualities, being "good" is the most! I happily serve sinners but what can you do for "perfect" people? When

Jesus said that the well had no need of help, He referred to the well-with-God, not the well-with-self. They stymie me.

I phoned John Hunt to ask advice. "Ah-ha, *that* type," he groaned. "About a year ago I fell into the clutches of a woman like that. For one hour she sat in my office telling me how dreadful her husband was and what a saint she was. He was this, he was that, he was a drunkard, and so on. Finally I stood up. 'Madam,' I said, 'were I so unfortunate as to be married to you, I'd be a drunkard too.' "

"Great," I gloated. "Thanks."

Naturally there wasn't an ounce of sense in saying this to the wife without the husband. If it wasn't said in front of him she would dismiss it as just one more injustice and probably would clip me bald-headed to boot. What a horrid woman! She must have robbed him of his last drop of self-respect or he'd have walked out long ago.

It took time and a bit of conniving to find a fairly foolproof reason for dropping in on them at home. Getting the address was easy and a couple of tickets for the Pasadena Playhouse would do the rest. I'd tell them I couldn't use the tickets and didn't want to waste them.

In looking back I see that this was a pretty dirty trick though at the time I felt I was the big Christian rushing to rescue the put-upon. Well, the Father had His own ideas. My condemnation boomeranged as most condemnation does.

The Stumble-Bum was home. Alone. And stumbling. A thin splotched man, the color of buttermilk. The instant he opened the door he decided I must be someone he knew and started explaining how he happened to be gowed. It was his head, he stated. Smog gave him headaches and a little wine now and then—

A little wine now and then. Poor wistful dope.

Interrupting what I well knew would be a dissertation on the superiority of wine over aspirin, I said: "Hold it, boy, I know. I used to be a wino. I drank wine because nobody ever gets *drunk* on wine."

The statement was so ludicrous that it stopped him. A dim smile picked at the loose lips and spread and spread till finally we laughed out loud together.

"That's rich," he mused. "Rich; *nobody gets drunk on wine.*"

Heady with progress, I bulled on: "And it isn't smog that gives you headaches, it's your wife. Why *do* you stay with her?"

The smile did not leave his face. It switched from amusement to forbearance.

He said: "I stay because I promised to. Marriage is a promise. I have no faith in myself but in God I have all faith—who are you, please?"

The question was a bucket of ice water. Right. *Who was I?*

I was the type I detested above all else. The type that plays God, that in other days burned people at the stake. Self-appointed judge-and-jury barging in on personal intimacies, without invitation, without knowledge or understanding or compassion. A damn Fix-It! This persecuted man wasn't improving anything by softening his persecution with alcohol and yet he *had* accepted the persecution and this in a fashion unbeknown to one Liz Hatch. His reasoning might be faulty, his heart was not.

Abashed at stomping in where angels were already in control, I backed toward the door. Here was a man who had made his choice long ago. How he stuck to it was his affair and God's.

My hand felt for the doorknob. Trying to answer his question, I spluttered: "Who am I? Oh, a—I know your wife. Never mind—I'll come again. Goodbye. God bless you."

"Oh, He does," he said. "He does."

Here was a sound lesson in the lesser evils. During the past year I'd been thinking of good as good and evil, evil. So it is but here I got a glimpse of a person who was doing the best of which he was capable; does Almighty God ask more? There's no question that it would have been better had the Stumble-Bum stuck to his shrew without stumbling, but what if he could not? There are operations so painful as to be unendurable without anesthesia.

No one is justifying drunkenness. It can't be justified. There are worse things, however. Broken vows for instance. Bumptious Christian Know-it-alls, for instance. He, drunk, was ahead of me, sober. Sometime later I ran into a man, at A.A., I think, who told me that the Stumble-Bum who wasn't a bum, had died dead-drunk; the heart gave out. So, for quite a while now, this forbearing soul has been learning how to serve God sober. I suspect there wouldn't be too much else he'd have to learn.

Jesus said: "Your faith has made you whole." According to this, neither the Stumble-Bum nor Liz were *whole* for neither one of us had gotten to the point of having faith in ourselves. What is being whole? Is being whole a state that requires no tending to *remain* whole? Is it treading water as Liz Hatch was treading water for Jim Hatch? Jesus never said that your faith would *keep* you whole. He didn't say: "Now that you see where your strength comes from, there's no need to use this knowledge to strive for greater strength." He didn't say this, not by a long shot.

The phrase seems to me to mean: faith in God brings faith in everything; in self, in others, in the *whole*, and so makes whole. Is faith something that believes Jesus walked on the water but not something that believes we ourselves can walk on water? No, this can't be faith. This limits Him because it limits us. Faith without results, "without works," is at best a soporific, a passive slap-happy reliance on a fairy godfather, part Santa Claus, part St. Valentine.

I, Liz Hatch, desire a faith that makes me greater than Liz

311

Hatch. A faith that humbles and at the same time exalts, that asserts that all Christians can come to be small christs, first in embryo, later, in *action*. The faith that makes whole is an awful willingness to take a chance on trying to be this small christ, to quit paddling in safe harbors and dare to try untried depths, trusting Him and therefore ourselves.

I, Liz Hatch, was only half a Christian, that first year, since I trusted Him but not myself. I did realize the God was not limited except as I limited Him; this was for sure. Were I receiving-set, I would receive. Did I knock, believing doors would open, doors would open. Seeking, I would find, but—but was I made of the stuff seekers are made of?

Up to now I'd had the notion that to believe in the Father and honestly desire to serve Him was the works. Now John Hunt was giving me a peek at what the Father might have in store for me. Harder and harder choices, more and more complicated decisions in the hope of lighting the lives of others via an increase in my own voltage. *What* a job! What terrible patience! The problem was not to die for God. The problem was going to be to *live* for Him.

It was Tony Webb who found me a place to start living, and none too soon either. Leaving Sue in the east to help settle her father's estate, he arrived back to find me exhausted, weary of well-doing. Tony is a lamb and it was marvelous to see him though sometimes I could have hit him. Sometimes I'd catch him overhearing my do-gooding, catch him staring at me as if I'd stepped off a space ship.

He'd shake his head. "I'll be damned if I can believe it, Liz—"

I could guess how he felt and said so.

"It's tough on all you who knew me when, but get this, Tony; I'm as far from being canonized as anyone ever gets. Think of the naturally good ones; take Sue, take Silas. They were better to begin with than I'll be twenty incarnations from now—not tireder though. Nobody's tireder.

"Tony," I went on, "I love you and I love your house but I want to find me a place, on the desert I think. Know any deserts? Nice big ones where everyone's deaf and dumb?"

"I know a peach of a one," he said. "Matter of fact Sue and I own acreage there; you can have some. There's a good inn too. Go try out the desert—it needs trying out."

A week later, a fugitive from John Hunt's soapboxes, I drove to Tony's inn on the edge of the Mojave. If the inhabitants weren't deaf and dumb, they at least allowed me to be. I read and prayed and slept and ate and it was well I did for it was here that I finally heard from Jim.

I heard from Jim all right. The ax fell on the desert. An ax in the shape of a bulky letter addressed in longhand. My fingers felt of it and sent a warning to my brain; it was too fat, they warned. Good news could have come by telegraph.

And why longhand? Jim Hatch wouldn't write a stay of his own execution in longhand. Or had he? Was that what this was?

Sitting in my room at the inn I slit open the horrid thing and counted the pages; eight of them. Eight thick white pages covered from top to bottom with Jim's tight cramped scrawl. While my eyes raced, the blood in my veins congealed.

The entire letter could have been condensed into one short phrase. *Don't come back ever* would have done nicely. Instead it was expressed in as many ways as there could be found to express it.

I won't enumerate the ways. The sum total was this: Dr. J. C. Hatch, the custom kid, wasn't having his wife back. Not under any circumstances. Not any. Not now or a hundred years from now. And who could blame him?

"This is it," he wrote, "and has been for some time. If you hadn't gone overboard on religion, you'd have seen it long ago. You don't happen to relish a third divorce which is all very commendable, but *I* do, so, for Christ's sake, will you get one?" he wrote.

I read on and on. I didn't really need to because all the time I think I must have known, deep down, that this was going to happen. This didn't make it any easier; it made it harder because it proved how I'd been dictating to God. I'd been so certain that I was appointed under God to right my marriage, just as though it were my marriage alone, as though I were the only party to it!

What arrogance! Actually, underneath, it had been the old pattern of ducking for cover, of playing it safe, of insisting upon an environment familiar to me, the assignment a rough one but still one I knew about. To sum up, I'd come close to persuading myself that the Creator of heaven and earth was going to let me pick my job, my subject, my locale, my goal, and then, of course, not even Jim Hatch would be able to resist the great Christian!

Well, he'd resisted me. With the greatest of ease. Both as a pagan and as a Christian. He just wasn't having any. Station J-I-M was off the air, the last station linking me to my pagan world, to materialism, to a preconceived assumption of prestige, to everything I'd always taken for granted. Jim had been a symbol of what I no longer could be or stand for. Even the hope of introducing Jim to God, of "converting" him, had been a phony prideful hope.

Almighty God had arranged what had appeared to be several miracles for my special benefit but He wasn't going to have a hand in this. And as for me, I could grab the jug and go haywire or I could accept it, one or the other. Before too long now I was going to have to make up my mind which of the two thieves on Calvary I was going to be. I could rail at God or I could admit I was getting my just due and ask Him to remember me. Two choices. One or the other.

I was at my main crossroad; the test of the realness of my faith. Of this I was completely certain, and certain that I would live or die according to the choice I made. I might whimper about how I'd labored for a last chance at a decent marriage, and this would be true. I might whimper as to what was the use in laboring when it got you nowhere; what was the use of faith and hope and prayer if you got your teeth kicked down your throat?

Sure, I could and did toy with catechizing God but I didn't get around to doing it because the mere toying showed how childish it was. Any god accountable to me, to my standards, my desires, would not have been worth worshipping. Nor would he have gotten worship. My God, the One I met in All Angels Hospital, hadn't introduced Himself in order that my personal prayers should hit the jackpot. He'd done so in order that His Will, not mine, be done; in order that I work for Him, *His* way, punching *His* timeclock. To work for Him meant being on call, a pipeline, a conduit, unclogged by the silt of self, ready to go into operation.

Now, once and forever, I knew that I was not the pipeline for one Jim Hatch, and what difference did it make whose fault it was; mine or his or the world's or all three? So what?

The crux was, it was too late.

Yet none of the labor of the past months had been wasted. None of it. None of the study, the prayer, the harnessing of desires, had been wasted in the slightest. These very battles were precisely what was going to give me the strength to accept defeat. Acceptance wasn't going to spring up full-grown in a minute or a month. It would take years, even the rest of my days, for there were going to be plenty of defeats, un-doubtedly as earned as this.

One clean means of cauterizing the wound of defeat was to take stock, to go back and inventory the junk that had been tossed out in the past fifteen months. A sniveling drunk, a pill addict, a would-be suicide, a quitter goofed to the gills on homemade misery, a lousy wife and a lousier mother. Liz, the spoiler, the waster, the silk-sheet bum. And worse; not only had I accepted the silk sheets as my right, I'd the gall to expect others to accept Liz, the bum—okay, *now didn't that prove what the Father could do?*

No wings yet, not a pin feather showing, but by the Eternal God, it *did* prove what the Father could do when you let Him!

The room in which I sat had a large window facing a small town surrounded by mountains. As far as could be seen were mountain ranges, black, brown and tan. I looked at them for a long time and finally got up, stepped across the scattered pages of Jim's letter and went outside to feel closer to the mountains.

These weren't like most high mountains, these were protective rather than forbidding. In raising my eyes to them and then to the burning sky above them I knew that I had made my choice; the test had been met. I was committed. The lump of battered pride inside me might be part of me forever but the past was about to be signed, sealed and delivered to the Father. And the Father would not file it against me. The past would be over and done with.

While I wasn't in the least conscious of God's Presence, He was there. He quite simply had to be there because of the choice I made. Were I on my own, I'd have chosen the jug, the pills, the eternal shroud of self-pity. This was what I always had done and without Him I'd have done it again. And again.

But—*You were there!*

What a great bloated fool I'd have been, greater than ever before, had I not chosen You! As You and I well know You were All I had in the wide world; All anyone ever really has, and more, *more than enough.*

Jim Hatch had been an episode and the episode was finished. And all that went with it, and had preceded it. All I had counted on so long; power, position, possessions—bye, bye, babies!

And money, ah, yes, money. Once John Hunt had pointed out today's counterpart to loaves and fishes, it was a cinch the bank account would dwindle fast.

Going with You seemed a lonely choice to make yet in no way was it so lonely as the other would have been. I knew all about the other and was beginning to know this and this way I wasn't going to be alone. It's the being alone that is the horror.

Returning to the inn, I picked up the letter, folded the pages and put them in the envelope. My heart began to beat faster and I waited for it to quiet and then went and washed my hands and face and used the brightest lipstick I could find. Down the long hill to the north, at the town's one drug-store, was a pay phone. I was going to drive to town and in that phone booth I was going to burn the Bridge of Human Dependism which had started building fifty years ago.

Like all phone booths, this one stank of tired cigar butts. The back plaster wall was filthy with time and doodlings; numbers, suggestions, comments, hearts with arrows; Ed loves Hazel; Tim loves Hazel. Hazel must be quite a gal. Waiting for Western Union I contributed yet one more deathless classic: J. NO LOVE L. A rusty stab at humor.

The weeks ahead, it was safe to say, would be what you might call short on humor. How well I knew the anguish, the disesteem of divorce. Who better? Also, this time, for a change, the odium would have to be taken in place of given. Also there would be no substitute pasture, no other man, to deaden and rationalize the anguish. The knife of publicly acknowledged failure would turn in the wound again and again.

With my whole heart I wish it took as long and required the voluminous red tape to marry people that it does to divorce people. How many could stand the gaff? In this case, maybe the Holy State would have the opportunity to be truly holy!

317

My bridge-burning telegram consisted of three words.

"All right, Jim," it said.

As the quarters and dimes clinked down their slots I breathed deep of the rank air. The bridge had begun to burn. The House of Hatch was falling down, falling down.

The house had been built on sand and when the winds blew and the rains came, the house had collapsed and great was the fall thereof.

CHAPTER TWENTY-THREE

Well, I would just have to get another house. Here on the desert maybe, but built on rock this time.

Deserts are in the category of things you're crazy for or distinctly not crazy for. Should the magic hit you, you go buy a pink house without ever really looking at it because it's what the house looks at that gets you: weird Joshua trees, surrealistic cacti, flame-topped ocotillo, on vast green-dotted dunes merging into vast rolling mountains. It's the vastness that does it. An on-and-on immensity which, unlike the sea, seems to require nothing of you. "I am here, take me or leave me," the desert murmurs.

The pink house, compared to my other houses, was the size of former gate cottages: four rooms, one bath. It was bigger however than any of the others because it would have, already did have, qualities none of the others had. It would have God and it already faced such extravagant examples of God's handiwork.

I called it Green Pastures, the kind He maketh me to lie down in. All those months ago, when I'd lined up the pink pills, I'd thought it would be fine to lie down in green pastures and it was, and is, but there's no short cut, pills or otherwise.

By the time I'd lived in the house ten days the loss of Jim was shriveled to a flyspeck. The last shred of cord between us dropped away forever, amen, and again the process was one of substitution. As the need to respect myself had crowded out the need of men to admire me, the hurt of the failure of my marriage was crowded out. The law court had no part in this. The law deals with legal status; it has no power to stem the futile mulling of the rejected female. Too, the divorce mill chews too slowly to account for the Christian Liz learning to digest the pagan Liz's bitter brew.

The Lord God was what the Christian Liz was clinging to. Were it not for Him and the guts supplied by Him, today would find her in some swanky sanitarium, or dead or dead-drunk in some cocktail lounge with some trousered punk, either too young or too old.

If you choose to think it wasn't God, who do you choose to think it was? What other plus was there? If you choose to think it was a minus, a slowed-down age, that rescued me, you can't get around much! Go take a look. Go count the passé dames in bars and night clubs. Go take a quick glance at the records of de luxe nuthouses; behind every second door stands an erstwhile glamour puss, wringing her jeweled hands. Psychiatrists can tell you. Their couches are three deep in fading gals who got the heave-ho.

Axioms, adages, old saws happen to have survived for the reason that they happen to be true. It just happens that there is no fool like an old fool; that it is hard to teach the old dog new tricks. Habits are habits and the habit hardest to break, liquor included, is the habit of being married. It gets so it isn't who, but how. A few exceptionally courageous people have suggested that probably, having sowed my varied assortment of wild oats, God didn't have too hard a job to do, the inference being that by then my glands had stopped gasping. The trouble with this argument is that my glands never did gasp, poor dears.

No, the one factor that was new was God. God amputating the new Liz from the late Liz.

Ten days after buying the house a thing happened that erased even the flyspeck. I had left my private dune and was in the village looking for furniture, simple inexpensive things suitable to hold those who wished to sit and drink-in celestial landscaping instead of gin. When I drove home I found Pete, my son, waiting in the patio. Had the apostles leapt from their thrones to parade my flagstones they couldn't have been a more welcome sight though the apostles would most certainly have given me time to collect myself.

Pete did not. He kissed me and made only one unessential comment. "This is quite a slice of country you've got here," he said.

Then he said: "I think you ought to know Alan's alive. He's back in this country."

The jerk the words gave me was the jerk of a parachute opening. I appreciated fully that Pete's being here had to have a meaning of extraordinary import; he was at Divinity School 3,000 miles away and wouldn't have come without excellent cause yet I found myself wholly incapable of grasping the meaning of what he'd said.

He'd said: "Alan's back."

Staring stupidly, I felt a jumble of feelings, yet still unable to feel the significance of this statement. I was quite able to feel Alan, to transfer my thoughts to him. This was easy for actually I'd never once stopped feeling him and thinking of him any more than one stops feeling or thinking of any other continuous pain. But to dig up the pain, to hold it to the light, to be told that it might be operable, this I didn't seem capable of doing.

"Say—say that over," I said.

Now, several years later, I know how extremely troubled Pete was. I know that on the whole flight west he had searched for ways to break the news and now that the moment had come, all he could find to do was to blurt out the blunt fact.

"Mom, are you all right?" he was asking.

When I'd nodded he went on: "Well it's this way: I didn't know about the divorce, about you and Jim—you didn't write it—but somehow Dad heard and told me. Well, I knew how hard you'd prayed to fix up this marriage so I decided it was about time you had a break. And by now I was sure your faith could take it—take the good about Alan, and let the other go."

I said: "Let the other—*what* other?"

He crossed the patio and stood in front of me. He was eyeing me closely. "Look, Mom, I don't believe you got it. I don't think you understood what I said. Alan is *alive*, Mom! Good old Alan's back—get it?"

Suddenly I got it. Suddenly in one great swoop, the words had meaning. Suddenly, on one tremendous wave I was tossed from a state of grief to a state of thankfulness.

"Thank God—thank God," I whispered.

"Yes," Pete agreed.

"Oh—" I clutched his arm and pumped it. "Oh Pete, Pete, I always felt deep down—where—*where is he?*"

There was a short silence. Then reluctantly Pete said: "Well, here's the tough part. He's in New York, Mom. He's been there about a year—"

"A year—?" I echoed.

"Yes, he—but, think, Mom, Alan is alive! He's alive and well—at least his body is—no, no, he isn't psycho or anything. It's, well, you remember what being a war prisoner can do."

My throat closed. I did indeed remember. Remembered those jammed hospital wards. Remembered the snarling men, the animal noises that came out of them. Oh, Alan, Alan!

But prisoners, prisoners of war were kept track of; why wasn't Alan?

Reading my mind, Pete hurried on: "He escaped. He hid out back somewhere in the hills, he doesn't know exactly where, and then got to China. Over a year ago he worked his way back on a freighter—gosh, you should hear him tell it!"

I stared aghast. Yes, I really should hear him tell it, I thought. I, the one who cared the most, the last to hear. And then, only through the pity of a third party!

This was worse than before. This was like the house Jesus talked about; the one that was swept clean only to have fear and guilt and grief and self-pity and other "demons" return and be worse than before. To be told that pain might be operable and then told that no surgeon felt like doing it.

Pete was watching me. This time he misread my thoughts. Giving me the credit of believing that my silence stemmed solely from the anguish of Alan's having been a prisoner, he said: "Don't let yourself think of that. It's past. And anyway we've all been prisoners, in one form or another. Look at you, think how imprisoned you were! And look how free you are today. But Alan—well, he just isn't free. Not yet— Mom, are you okay?"

I was not okay. The exaltation and the compassion were ebbing. In their place was coming a dull resentment. It did seem such cruelty, such unnecessary cruelty. All those months, all those years of heartbreak! Alan's separation from me, his mother, had been devastating enough, but then to fear that that separation had been made final by death, this was hell itself. And all—all the time he was alive. And for a year he'd been right in New York—!

I cried: "Has he no heart—oh, this is hard, Pete. Very hard."

"But you will forgive," Pete told me. "You will forgive."

Tormenting myself, I cried: "I don't know. I'm not so

sure—how long have you known? Have you seen him? Did you think to ask him if he had a heart?"

"I didn't have to; I knew," was Pete's answer. "I know Alan's misery and so do you. Yes, we've seen each other several times. You know how Alan always respected Dad, well, when he got back he called Dad and made him promise not to tell. Just before you came to California—"

"You mean you knew before I came out here?" I cried.

"But, Mom, I had to promise too. That was the only way Alan would let Dad tell me. And I was willing to because you don't need Alan as much as Alan needs people to trust— you have God to trust!"

"But, Pete, Pete—didn't you tell him about the change in me? *Didn't* you? Oh, if he would see me, he'd know he could trust me too. I *must* see him—oh, won't Alan *ever* forgive me?"

It was then for the first time that I had a preview of the man of God Pete was going to be. His voice deepened. "I want you to listen carefully. This is beyond personal relationships; you should have the knowledge to understand that. You know God and you know His Son. You know the Son came here to search out the sick, the lost in mind and soul and body; *you do know this.* But does your knowing it, mean that Alan knows it? Of course not, and he doesn't know it. Alan calls it a lot of bushwa. He neither believes in God nor in your belief in God. Naturally this can change. The change can come any time. Either in this life or the one to follow, but that is not your business, it is the Father's! The Father had to wait for you and me and He will wait for Alan. Our part in this, yours and mine, is to love and go right on loving —the rest is personal pride. Alan's need is to come to God, not to you, at least not unless he believes that you can help him, that you have found something great enough to help him. If Alan wants help, he will seek it, and if he seeks, he will find; no one on earth should know this better than you."

324

Spoken with extraordinary sweetness, the words were devoid of judgment, of smugness, of self-righteousness. It was merely that Pete had had a choice to make and had made it. He had chosen between my filled cup and Alan's empty one. Faced with the rightness of his choice, my self-pitying resentment shivered and dropped away. I was ashamed and said so.

The rest of the day, however, and that night, after Peter had gone, I was a battleground. Alternate emotions of God's mercy and my own pain tore at me. My heart was a teeter-totter; Alan was alive; Alan would not see me.

It is said that to begin again is to be born again. Throughout that December night, through the silent glory of the desert moonlight to the golden glory of the desert sunrise, I began again. Over and over I examined Alan's speech to me the day he found I was leaving Silas: "The rest of your whole lifelong you can be sure that your son, Alan, isn't your son at all—he's dead."

Gradually I began to see that what he had said was true though not in the way he had meant it. Alan, my son, was indeed dead to me and must stay dead in the sense that not I, not any human being, can be permitted to manipulate the life of another. This was pride. It was trespassing. Alan was not my son, he was the son of the Father. I had been static on the Father's air waves and now must be silent, as silent as the waning night around me. I must release Alan and in so doing, would find myself released from the pain of him.

To release Alan, in *all* ways, might be my hardest test. The agony of allowing a loved one to suffer, to make decisions that are known to be wrong, and not be able to advise or even assuage whatever hurt comes; these are painful birth pangs. Yet as the Father Almighty had kept watch for me, little by little I would receive the strength to keep watch for Alan.

Gradually I began to feel Alan's misery, to exchange his

325

for mine. His very bitterness, his defiance, the wish to hurt, to tear down, were proof of his inner struggle. Alan was like me, God help him! A learner by the hardest way. A willfulness that was like a long sickness, like a siege with t.b.—but what, what if this were Alan's last struggle? His last t.b. spot? An infected area that hung on and on, seeming to say: No, not me. I'll not be healed. Living or dead, I'll accept help from no one!

Someday, who knew when, would come the burning-out of that last plague spot, for if Alan would not be healed by God's mercy, then he, like me, would have to be healed by God's might. So be it. Few there were like Pete, few who could cross the stream at its narrowest part.

The picture of these two sons together was the story of the Prodigal Son reversed. The one who stayed home, selfless, generous, welcoming; the one who had been lost, bitter, fearful, unfeeling. But wait—who did I think I was! The Bible story was one of returning to the *Heavenly* Parent, for only in finding Him does anyone ever come home. Of these two sons of mine, only one had found the Father and so only one had truly come home. As ever, it was a matter of heart, not geography.

Slowly, very slowly, my battle was fought out until at last the wonder of God's mercy was allowed to overcome my selfishness. My job was to be grateful and to love. I would stay quiet. I would sit here and watch the silent desert and the mountains.

But curious are the ways of the Maker of views. He leads you to a place you are now strong enough to take. He graduates you in weeks from gentle beauty to stern beauty, from closed gardens with hummingbirds and velvet roses, to the open austerity of sand and rock etched against a burning sky. But does He leave you to sit and look at these? He does not.

326

He nudged me to the local Alcoholics Anonymous and being me, bossy and humble rolled into one, by Christmastime I had moved their weekly meeting from cramped quarters to my large avocado-colored living room. He sent me to the tiny churchless Episcopal group and being me, by Christmas time, I had seen to it that the services which had been held in uncertain quarters were now conducted in my large avocado-colored living room. Because that room was no longer mine but a place where God could best be served. And being me, of course I talked—when didn't I?—and as my story got around, the trek to the pink house started. A trek of the lame in courage, the halt in faith, the blind in self-knowledge. I was in business, the Father's Business.

Christmas Day, my second Christ-mass, was like all desert Christmases. Standing by myself in the patio in the hot bright sun, I compared this place to the place of Jesus' birth. They must have been much alike; the branched Joshua trees, the network of trails seemingly going nowhere, the great circling buzzards, waiting, waiting. And the tremendous calm. And the little town five hundred feet below me.

I thought of all but His last birthday; why had I thought they were named Christ-mass? Why did I think we gave gifts and received them, the nicest we could find? Had I never heard of frankincense and myrrh? Early this morning at the town's one church I'd listened to children singing: "Happy Birthday, dear Jesus," which had made it very near and personal. So now, back in the coolness of my avocado-colored living room, I opened my own gifts, lovely ones in the loveliest of wrappings, and as I did I sang: "Happy Birthday, dear Jesus." I was glad I'd chosen to spend the day alone. Nowadays with the increasing trek of people, I was seldom alone.

Christmas night was like all Christmas nights. Clear enough to find a certain star to follow and to follow it. I ate some odds and ends from cans, recalling those other Christmases; all the goodies scarcely touched; Liz drinking her Christmas dinner. After the odds and ends I read. Then I went to bed and in great tranquillity I thanked Our Lord for His great graciousness in being born of Mary and for His great graciousness in being born in me. As I went to sleep my heart and house were filled with Him Whose birthday it was.

Along toward dawn, still half asleep, I was made aware that the fingers of my right hand were tugging at my shoulder strap. Under the left arm the lace had twisted and was caught uncomfortably. The fingers kept on tugging when all at once they found a lump.

There was a hard lump in the left breast, under the lace shoulder strap. The fingers froze. Releasing the lace, they froze around the lump, and in that instant I was more afraid than I have ever been.

I think every woman is afraid of cancer. I know I'd always been. Not afraid that I myself would get it, no, not that, for no one in my family had ever had it. The fear was of the thing itself just as one can fear a submarine without ever having stepped inside one. This fear had been a sword swaying high, high above my head and now it wasn't high above my head. It swayed so close my scalp prickled.

Since meeting the Father I had tried to face this old fear in the light of His healing power. Knowing that all sickness was the result of breaking His laws, consequences brought on ourselves by ourselves in a world of broken laws, knowing, accepting this, I still had looked at or heard of people who had cancer and thought, *what if it were me?*

And now—

Desert nights are cold. Under the electric blanket I'd been warm and toasty. Now I wasn't. Now I broke into a cold pagan sweat that trickled down my arms and back and legs.

This is it, I thought.

This is it. And I cannot take it. I have cancer and you die of cancer. Or worse. Either you die, snuffed out at the very time you are just beginning to know what life is about, or you live—if it could be called living! You live and you wait and the thing grows and spreads till it isn't you that lives but the spreading thing inside you.

Pain you can take. And death. But this—this *corruption*.

Shaking like a teacup in an earthquake, soaked in sweat, I clicked on a light. I could not bear the darkness. Sitting bolt upright, I stared into the faint first promise of dawn outside the window, my insides knotting.

But wait. Suppose—suppose it was benign? Stop! I told myself. *Stop*—here is the old pagan wishful thinking.

But, no—*fear* was pagan! Fear, the cold sweat, the shaking body, these were pagan—Oh God, God the Father!

In total panic I pushed back the blanket and slid to my knees beside the bed. Through teeth that chattered I cried aloud:

"Father, Father, my faith does not cover such as this—if it is what I think it is, it is too much for me. Take it— take all of it. Oh, Father, heal me of cancer or heal me of fear—just please, *please do not let me let You down!*"

He did not let me let Him down. From that exact instant fear left me.

Throughout the days and nights that followed, the examinations, the X-rays, the consultations, the wondering, the being wheeled into the operating room, I was as calm, as peaceful as a baby lamb. Through the period of returning consciousness when I realized that it had not been benign, I was somehow sustained as the air sustains the bird. For that awful moment in the dawn I had been the lamb that was lost and now was corralled.

CHAPTER TWENTY-FOUR

There came another awful moment; the moment I totaled the medical bills. Here was not fear, here was a matter of arithmetic; one thousand and one thousand made two thousand. Sitting in the pink house, fingering the bills, I glanced at the telephone. All at once I knew what I was going to do; I was going to contact Silas Addams. I had neither heard from him nor talked to him in years and years but now I would. All my life it had been a cinch for me to give—why not?—but only recently was I learning how to accept. Pride was at half mast.

The circuits were busy. The operator would call me. Waiting, I pondered on what a heck of a position Sam's well-heeled daughter had gotten herself into. With true alcoholic immoderation I had given away too much. I'd left nothing for emergencies.

The phone rang. I could have New York now; Mr. Addams was on the line.

I gulped once or twice. "Si? Si, this is Liz," I said.

Except for the humming of the wires, there was silence. "Si? This is—"

"Yes," Si's voice answered. "I heard—how are you, Liz?"

The voice was kind; it was also restrained and very impersonal. The voice had met me somewhere yet couldn't remember exactly where.

I swallowed hard. What—what was I *doing?* What on earth!

Then suddenly it was all right.

"I'm just fine," I said, "and you?"

"The same as ever," he told me.

That was it, yes, that was what made it all right; *Si was the same as ever.* This you could count on. While you could be quite certain that at this very second, in his plush office, his lower lip would be protruding like a child's, you could also be quite certain that he would never fail you. There are people who never fail anyone and Si Addams was one of these. Even if you had slit his throat as throats have seldom been slit, if you truly needed him, he'd be there.

Thinking back, thinking how I'd humiliated him, my eyes filled. "Si, I need you," I said.

It took a little time for this to sink in and then he said: "You need—*me?*"

"Si, I had an operation and—"

"Operation? What for, Liz? What was it?"

"Cancer and I'm fine but—"

"Cancer!" He was horrified. "My God, Liz, how horrible!"

How could I make him believe it wasn't horrible? That what I'd been freed of was far, far worse? He'd think I was crazy if I chirped: "Oh no, sweetie, fear is much worse than cancer—"

To theorize long distance, to pronounce at a buck a minute that it is Fear that gnaws at the world, that everybody has fear of some sort whereas nowhere near everybody has cancer, and that fear always breeds fear, would sound feeble-minded. And so darn goody, so blankety-blank heroic.

"No, I'm fine," I said. "It's the exchequer—"

This too was going to sound pretty silly. After you'd been wading in gold it was a touch stupid not to hold out on God at least the price of an operation. To Si Addams, top man on the brokerage totem pole, charity kept a foot in its own door; it didn't catapult you to the Poor Farm. Si believed in God but I wasn't too sure he believed in giving no thought for day after tomorrow.

I started over. "Look, Si, I'm not expecting St. Francis to move over but just the same I have given away all but a small income, which leaves me in a bind. I need help with the medical bills—I guess I ought to feel embarrassed but I don't seem to because I believe it's God's will that we share. If you don't feel this way, I'll understand perfectly. The operation was duck soup, but the bills—oh, I'm such a fool, Si!"

I heard him clear his throat. "If you're a fool, you're a courageous one," he said. "You—"

While he kept on saying how courageous I was, I lit a cigarette and squirmed. I was about as courageous as a run-away horse stopped by a barbed-wire fence. I'd run and run and cut myself to shreds and it was the Father Who'd taken over. Whatever I was that was better was the Father, not Liz. Being courageous included being loving, forgetful of self. The love that casts out fear. Nobody knew better than Silas Addams how fear-ridden I'd been and how little I ever forgot myself. Had I done so, truly done it, there wouldn't have been room for fear and God wouldn't have needed to free me of it.

"Liz, are they positive they got all of it?" Si was asking.

All of what? All my gold? I'd just explained—"All what?" I asked.

"All the—all the cancer?" he said.

"Oh sure," I told him. "You see, it was very little. God pointed it out when it was no bigger than a peanut."

"Why, Liz, that's a miracle!" Si exclaimed.

No, it wasn't a miracle. A miracle is just something we can't explain and haven't yet gotten used to. But what was the sense in mounting another soapbox? And anyway it was just more theorizing to say: "If finding cancer early is a miracle, what do you think water is? Or air? Or orange juice?"

Bit by bit, as I grew up a little, as I understood more, there were fewer "miracles" because whatever I understood had always been there waiting to be understood just as the atom was always there waiting to be split. It seemed to me to be this: Jesus had promised to return and I was finding that He did, more and more each day.

Theory or no theory, I decided to have a crack at it. I said: "If you want miracles, Si—you know me and fear, remember?—well, that's what I was healed of! It was Christmas night; Christ's Christmas gift. You know, quite often it's the greatest gift to take away something you don't want; the mortgage off the house, for instance. Or the seven-year itch."

Si laughed. "How much did it cost to get rid of the seven-year itch? How much do you need? And, oh yes, does Pete know?"

"No, and don't tell him," I said. "Pete's busy."

Even if he were told, Pete would know I was okay. Pete expected God to heal. Pete would see that being healed of an emotion was more important than having the body healed. At my flossiest I'd never been arrogant enough to dream of lugging this body, this tired kimona, into the next world. So, in remembering Jesus' words, "My Kingdom is not of this world," I could see why He'd be most interested in the part that is *eternal*; the mind, the heart, the soul. Here was where fear was so God could heal these nicely for these were "not of this world." Pete would get that.

But how about my other son, *how about Alan?* Ah, here was the perfect chance to get through to Alan! If I asked it,

Si would most certainly appeal to Alan! And might not Alan relent? Might he not forgive and come running? No—no! The nasty thought was so repulsive that I almost cried out: "You get behind me." This was cheating. It was self-pity at its most revolting. To use compassion as a whip could bring nothing but evil—oh, would that dead Liz never die!

Hurriedly I said: "No, Si, don't tell Pete or anyone."

"Very well," he said. "Then keep in touch with me. Write, Liz. And put the bills out of your mind. The money is practically there."

I thanked him and I thanked the Father for him. This experience was going to bring something splendid to Si too, and about time. It would bring about the final healing of the humiliation I had given him. In all the years I'd known Si this was the first time I'd ever unqualifiedly turned to him for help and no one can resent a person he is helping. The two can't co-exist. If you plant grapefruit, how can you get Scotch thistles? It is a law, and its results are what Jesus calls "fruits."

It was the same law that was working for me, its fruits evidenced by the increase in the trek to the pink house. In no way was this a personal tribute; those who came were thirsty and had heard of my years of drought and of my having found a Well. Sometimes those who came decided they weren't thirsty after all, and I would be discouraged only to have them return a week, a month, later. Sometimes those who came never did drink and sometimes I myself jostled the cup, wasting the precious liquid. Sometimes people dropped in my lap, pure chance. Or was it chance? Sometimes I'd take along a thermos of the precious liquid and drive somewhere and get stuck and God would tow me out.

One day that spring, my first in the desert, I headed for a certain section where, they told me, I would find mile on mile of desert flowers. I found them and sat in wonder. Their beauty was in such contrast that it stunned the senses. Up and down the dunes and beside the road ran the proverbial carpet, its background a vivid heliotrope, patterned in deep yellow and bright vermilion.

So it is true; the desert can rejoice and blossom as the rose!

One can absorb just so much beauty and so, in a dazed, grateful state of mind, I start the motor, back the car carelessly, and, plunk, I am into sand over my hubcaps. Having respect for tires, I cut the motor, cursing myself as accurately as God allows. As far as can be seen is space and magnificence and one small house, half a mile away.

I roll down my blue jeans and strap my boots. Half a mile in deep sand is no joke. Puffing and plowing, I reach the house. It is an old adobe. I go to the front door and knock and a strapping red-haired man comes. Beside him is a handsome little boy and behind is a young woman holding a Mongolian baby. The man's eyes are angry; the woman's are red-rimmed.

"Hello, I'm stuck," I say. "Can we tow her out?"

We can and do. But do I leave it there? No, not me, for, as St. Paul said, I am a fool for Christ. Thanking them I add: "You know that Our Lord could heal your baby if the world would let Him."

Well, the world, you and I, has not let Him heal their baby but it is completely wonderful how Nan and Pinky, these two, have let Him heal their hearts.

It was a house divided against itself; their love threatened by the age-old conflict. Nan unable to endure sending the baby away to be cared for and Pinky unable to endure keeping the baby in the home because of what he sees happening to the little boy.

My statement leads us back to the adobe house and to fresh strong coffee. I listen to both their sides. Pinky is more outspoken, he talks and talks. He is full of I's: "I think this, I say that—"

Nan is more gentle but she too is full of I's: "I say this—"

At last I say: "What does God say?"

There is silence. Finally when I ask if they believe in Him and they nod their heads, I tell my story. God, I told them, does not send trouble. His part is to help us wring good out of whatever trouble comes. I said that if they had the faintest notion that the Father had one thing to do with their baby's not being perfect, they'd better forget it. The Father is perfect and fashions only what is perfect.

"Then how can He allow it?" Nan cries. "How could—?"

"He doesn't," I answer. "We, the people, allow it."

I'm on my favorite topic now; I let go. Man chooses to do wrong, I say, more often than he chooses to do right, until wrong choice mounts and mounts, causing sickness and malformation and drunkenness and war and death. As the monstrous wave mounts, the innocent, like their baby, are dragged down in its undertow. God does not *allow* it; it's we ourselves who *cause* it!

"Look," I say. "Man was told that sin has consequences, that it is visited upon those who have not sinned. It's a law, the law of cause and result. Would you call it unjust of God to let a child be burned to death in a house where I'd dropped a lighted cigarette? Not by a darn sight—the child is dead as the result of my neglect!"

"But I can't—I can't give up my baby—I love my baby!" Nan weeps.

"Yes, Nan, except that there is no such thing as one-sided love. Love does what is best for all; blesses all. Sometimes love protects, sometimes it frees. If Alan, my son, were to return to me, I'll have to find the kind of love that sends him away again, free of me, to build his own life."

I take the baby in my arms. "I know it will be tough," I tell Nan. "But you have four to think of, not one, and acting with courage is often the greatest love. God will help. He'll find

336

someone to care wisely for your baby and still not encroach upon the love you owe Pinky and the little boy and others still to come."

I grin at Pinky. "You need more tenderness, big guy. Pool your courage with Nan's tenderness and God will take it from there. Just put it up to Him. If you two do, it's amazing how He will advise you what is best for everyone." It is indeed amazing how He has continued to advise these two!

Then there is another, one of the many who drop in my lap; a teen-aged drunk, the nephew of my laundress. As God will have it, he drops by one summer afternoon and he, as well as the day, is fried. I do not mention that his aunt has left. Instead I say: "Hi, come in. And don't bother to hold your breath, I love beer. Sure wish I could take it but I can't—have some iced tea? You're Vivian, aren't you? Gosh, what an awful name!"

He exhales gingerly. "I hate it. It stinks. It was my father's name."

I nod. "It sure does stink—secondhand beer stinks too. And since when did two stinks make a rose—want lemon and sugar?"

It was four when he came and nine when he left and that was some years ago and if he's had one can of beer since I haven't heard of it and I would have because we're both in A.A. and, brother, does that grapevine have long antennae! Vivian is Mike now. Mike Henessey.

Mike's mother and Mike's aunt think Mike's old man is buried at Forest Lawn but they couldn't be more mistaken. His old man was finally laid to rest that summer afternoon right outside my patio. Once the young man got it into his head how dumb it was to go on rebelling against an old man who was dead, the jug took care of itself. I don't believe Mike ever really liked liquor anyway. He just felt he ought to because his old man said he couldn't.

Then there are the ones I fail with, and they are many. But I plug on about His Business, a humble plugger. Not always humble before man but invariably humble before God. No man can say with truth that I am good and, on the other hand, no man can say with truth that I'm a stinker. I do get tired. As the months and the years of Our Lord go by, I often resent the traffic to Green Pastures. At times I agree with Tony Webb who says that the name of my house should be changed to The Gas Station because people drive up, fill up, and drive off, leaving me hanging on the ropes.

The type who leaves me hanging on the ropes is, say, the woman who thinks she wants to quit drinking; who would quit —yes, indeed—if she weren't so put upon. Who uses me for a sounding board and little else; who's too proud to give up to God and too proud to go to A.A. yet not too proud to fall down drunk in public.

For every one like her however there is the young minister retransfused in faith. A minister who was losing Christ in the minutiae of paying Christ's bills, bogged down in administrative business to the point that his faith too was bogging down. But who now has been revitalized, whose renewed faith has given him the courage to face his congregation with the unreasonable demands made of all ministers and to insist that others share these necessary burdens.

For every one like her there is the boy who was in love with his brother's wife but who now has a wife of his own and the four of them are fast friends.

There is the girl who at fourteen knew more of life than any person should ever know but who now is learning to serve God and is back with her family and back in school. The girl who gave me the epitaph I'd like on my tombstone. She said: "Why, didn't you know? Every kid on the desert says, 'If you get in trouble, go see Liz Hatch'?"

Sure, I get tired. But when this happens something else happens to counteract it. When I'm pretty tired something pretty nice happens and when I'm terribly tired something glorious happens. For example, the Reverend Peter Addams comes as he did a few months ago and takes the service in our new small church and I am a woman born anew like that woman years ago at All Angels Hospital.

It is a Holy Communion Sunday. The little church is filled, for anyone who has heard of me has heard of Peter. Other Sundays I sit in the first row but today I sit in back because this is my son and I am somewhat nervous.

There is no need to be. From his opening sentence, Pete's voice is clear and strong, his manner direct and simple. I can relax and listen, thinking, this is my son, one of my beloved sons.

The sermon isn't long, it never is on Communion Sundays. It is followed by a period of stillness. Outside the church are the ancient hills and then, inside the church, a voice repeats the ancient words:

> " 'Almighty God, unto whom all hearts
> are open, all desires known, and
> from whom no secrets are hid—' "

The voice goes on and at last people rise from their knees and file two by two up to the altar rail. I remain kneeling for everyone is ahead of me. Over and over come the words addressed to each person at the altar rail:

> " 'The Body of our Lord Jesus Christ
> Which was given for thee—' "

And then:

> " 'The Blood of our Lord Jesus Christ
> Which was shed for thee—' "

Above and beyond the joy of hearing my son repeat these words, the words themselves hold the same splendor, the same truth and beauty, as that first Sunday in Gordon Rogers'

Church. In no way have they become abstract, impersonal; the Body was still given for me, the Blood was still shed for me. The Crucifixion and the Resurrection were for me, Liz, just as they were for Simon, called Peter, and now for this Peter.

I do not lift my head till those in the row in front of me stand and then I stand and walk with them to the altar. There are only five of us, the remnant as yet unserved. We kneel together, bowing our heads, cupping our right hands, waiting to receive the bread.

As I receive the bread, I do not look up but now I do; again the coarse white robe is coming close. I raise my eyes; I see the firm blunt fingers around the Cup; I see the bent head, the steady eyes, the thick cropped hair. My heart overflows. *This is my son.*

Then all at once I know that this is not my son—*this is the Father's son!* Peter is the son of the Father as I, Liz, am the daughter of the Father! I know this utterly and am moved to the depths of my being. Tears of wonder come. I cover my face with my hands and my heart rejoices. Now I know what Jesus meant: "Who is my mother?" The meaning is: no human relationship can be compared to this relationship, to being children of the One Almighty Father. It was this and this alone for which mankind was fashioned. To seek, to know, to serve Him, is man's destiny, just as the destiny of the peach tree is to bear peaches.

In surrendering my son, my thoughts recall the little boy who said: "Whatever you do is okay with me—you know that, Mom." So now the circle had been completed; the trust, the love, were where they belonged, centered on What they had come from, the Source of trust and love. This son who was not mine is closer than he has ever been but not because of him or me; because we are joint heirs of Christ.

Unhappily it is not possible to stay forever on the crest of emotional splendor. Not even the saints did that, not even

Jesus. Pete leaves the desert and returns to New England to take over his first church and, little by little, I come down to earth. As the months pass sometimes I descend into craggy valleys which are dark and narrow and I grow tired of plugging on and on.

There are days when I get sick of people. I cry: "No, Father! Not *another*," when our desert doctors and ministers and bartenders send be-fuzzed humans in need of the precious liquid the Father measures out for me. Days when I regret the nonchalance with which I depleted Sam's stocks and bonds till there's barely sufficient to meet necessities.

Often I'm such a badly clogged pipeline. Critical, impatient, self-willed, far too quick to speak, far too quick to judge, far too weary. Weary of my own haste, of giving people hell when there is heaven to give; weary of being on call. But I am on call. And I do go and I do try to exchange the hell I have given for the heaven there is to give.

Though weary and badly clogged, I am on call. You do not say to a woman: "Postpone your suicide. Come back tomorrow. I'm exhausted." You do not say: "Too bad your baby's sick but I happen to be low on dough."

No, you cannot say these things. All you can do is pray for wisdom to separate the needy from the greedy for you have come to know that time and energy and money are gifts and must be wisely spent. It is of yourself that you give unstintingly. You hoist your spiritual breeches and, lo, the strength is given.

You thank the Lord God for Love and Truth and Beauty and Forgiveness and for Answer to Prayer. You thank the Lord God that you have enough but not too much so that no longer can you be accused of being Lady Bountiful since now your bounty has been shared with others. You thank the Lord God for those alterations you have let Him make in you, for being used in place of using. You thank the Lord God for allowing

341

you time and opportunity to tell your story for this is what He said to do; He said to go and tell.

This is my life today and I would not have it otherwise only more so. I know freedom from stuff in bottles, from guilt and fear and resentment and material possessions, from the judgment of human beings, myself included. My days are filled with challenge and almost too much drama, but, above all, I am at peace with myself. The only Judge I have to make a hit with is the Judge of judges and I must be doing better for last week I was awarded the most beautiful of gifts.

Last week at dusk my doorbell rang. It had been a crowded day and I thought, Oh no, Lord, not again! I did not want to answer but I had to, I always have to, and when I went and saw who stood there, my very soul trembled. Eight years of love, the Father's love for us, had brought a visitor.

It was Alan.

(2)